About Pearson

Pearson is the world's learning company, with presence across 70 countries worldwide. Our unique insights and world-class expertise come from a long history of working closely with renowned teachers, authors and thought leaders, as a result of which, we have emerged as the preferred choice for millions of teachers and learners across the world.

We believe learning opens up opportunities, creates fulfilling careers and hence better lives. We hence collaborate with the best of minds to deliver you class-leading products, spread across the Higher Education and Test Preparation spectrum.

Superior learning experience and improved outcomes are at the heart of everything we do. This product is the result of one such effort.

Your feedback plays a critical role in the evolution of our products and you can contact us at reachus@pearson.com. *We look forward to it.*

CLASS

8

Trishna's

PEARSON FOUNDATION

Biology

Seventh Edition

CLASS

8

Trishna's

PEARSON FOUNDATION

Biology

Seventh Edition

2025

Pearson

Photo Credits

Chapter 1 Opener: Andrii Vodolazhskyi / Shutterstock
Chapter 2 Opener: Choksawatdikorn / Shutterstock
Chapter 3 Opener: HotFlash / Shutterstock
Chapter 4 Opener: Kazakov Maksim / Shutterstock
Chapter 5 Opener: natalyla / 123RF
Chapter 6 Opener: Curioso.Photography / Shutterstock
Chapter 7 Opener: Dusan Petkovic / Shutterstock

ISBN 978-93-615-9511-0

First Impression

Published by Pearson India Education Services Pvt. Ltd, CIN: U72200TN2005PTC057128.

Head Office: 1st Floor, Berger Tower, Plot No. C-001A/2, Sector 16B, Noida - 201 301, Uttar Pradesh, India.
Registered Office: Featherlite, 'The Address' 5th Floor, Survey No 203/10B, 200 Ft MMRD Road, Zamin Pallavaram, Chennai - 600044
Phone: 044-66540100
Website: in.pearson.com, Email: companysecretary.india@pearson.com

Compositor: Satish Kumar Shrivastava
Printed in India at Rajkamal Electric Press, Kundli, Haryana-131 028.

Brief Contents

Brief Contents

Contents

Preface

"If you have a great ambition, take as big a step as possible in the direction of fulfilling it. The step may only be a tiny one, but trust that it may be the largest one possible for now."

Mildred McAfee

Pearson Foundation Biology Series has been created keeping in mind the learner's ambition to excel in a competitive examination like NEET and other Biology Olympiads. The series can be used in addition to the books studied in school to attain that extra edge required to strengthen the concepts and prepare well for future endeavours.

Why Start Early with Pearson Foundation Series

Classes VI to X are the base years of a learner's academic life. In these years learner explore their interests and determine the goals they wish to attain. *Pearson Foundation Biology* series is filled with interactive learning that not only nurtures a learner's interest in science and mathematics but also strengthens their concepts.

The series uses real-life examples and application-based problems to teach theoretical concepts. The objective of this series is to help learners cultivate an analytical mind.

Most of the lessons to be learnt are introduced to the learners in the books for class VI. As they get promoted to higher classes, new topics are added to these lessons. This additive method helps the learners' span their learning over four standards, from VI-X. Thus, learners are not overwhelmed by the introduction of completely new lessons every time they are promoted to a new class.

While their learning is being spanned across five years, so is their ability to resolve doubts for further conceptual clarity. For instance, they can use concepts learnt in class VI to solve questions in class VII. If, in case, they get stuck while answering a question, the learners can infer for themselves that they might be lacking in conceptual clarity. They can then approach their teachers, requesting them to explain the concept once again. This helps the learner to clarify their concepts while revising the lessons previously learnt.

Since classes VI-X are deemed to be a student's formative years, we, at Pearson, aim to provide a foundation level course which serves more than just a standard curriculum.

Here is how it makes a difference to a learner's overall learning ...

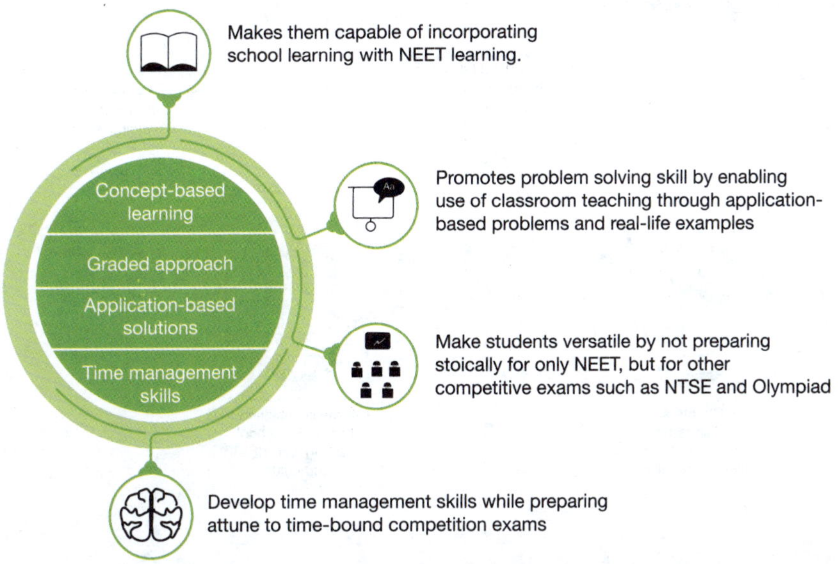

Other Uses of the Series

Instead of limiting themselves to NEET, a learner can also use this series to prepare for several other competitive examinations such as NSTSE, National and International Olympiads, BITSAT, etc. This series offers a level of concept learning that empowers learners to handle the challenging nature of questions posed in these examinations. Moreover, this will also allow the learners to have an early insight into their key strengths as well as improvement areas and help them work on them selves.

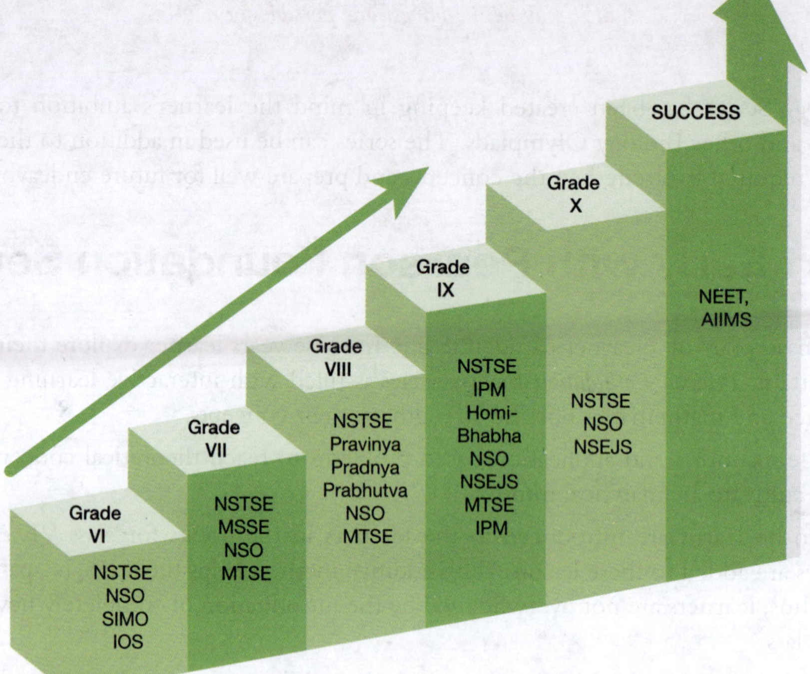

[IMO: International Mathematics Olympiad; NSO: National Science Olympiad, IOS: International Olympiad of Science, NSTSE: National Level Science Talent Search Examination, MTSE: Maharashtra Talent Search Examination, RMO: Regional Mathematical Olympiad, PPP: Pravinya Pradnya Prabhutva, NSEJS: National Standard Examination in Junior Science, IIT: Indian Institute of Technology, IISc: Indian Institute of Science, NIT: National Institute of Technology.]

Highlights of the Series

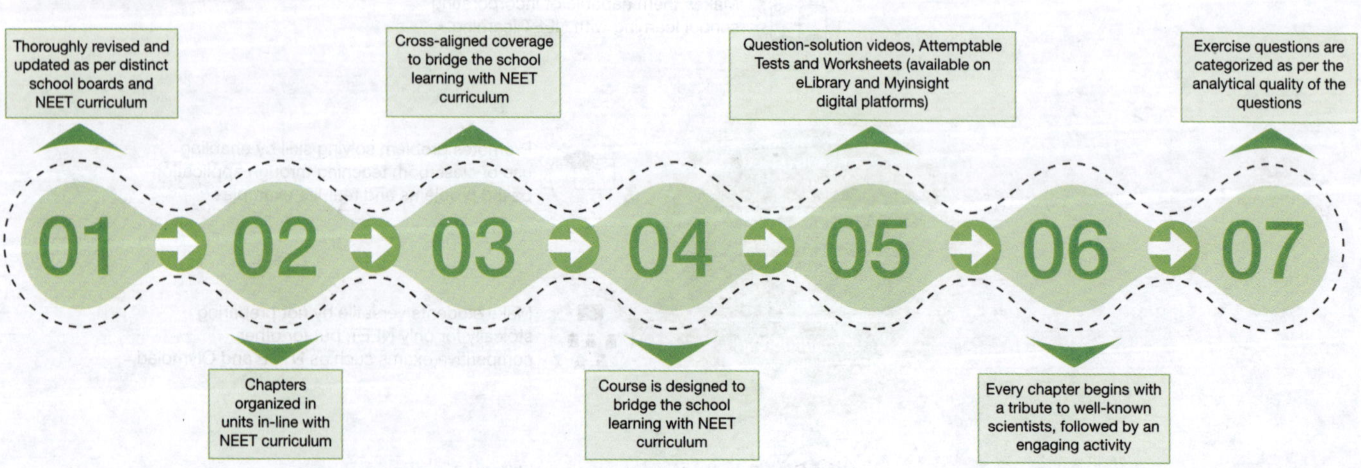

Pearson Foundation Biology series provides a perfect blend of learning through theory and practice questions with a fusion of school and NEET curriculum. It is imperative to note that this series would be as profound as you want it to be. Therefore, to get maximum benefit from this book, we recommend following the given study plan.

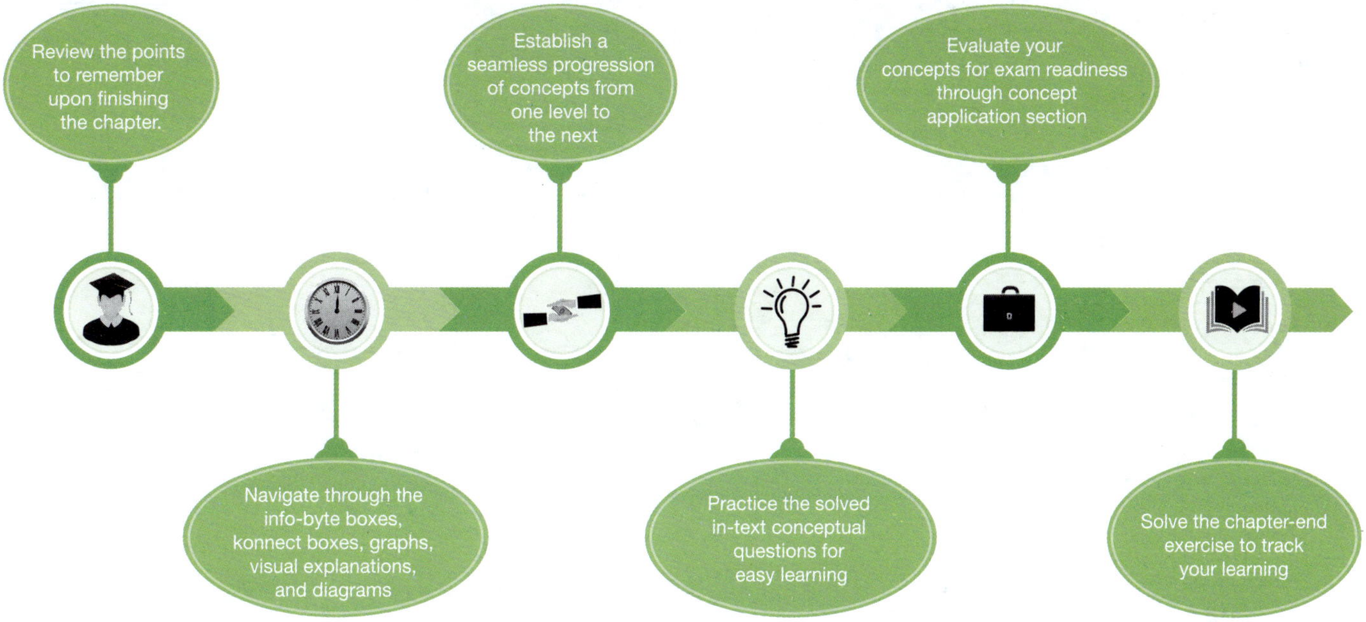

To provide a graded learning approach, the exercise part of each chapter is categorized by using four icons for question tagging. The question categorization helps the learners assess their own problem-solving and analytical skills and motivates them to improve to reach their objectives.

The following icons are used to categorize the questions with specific meanings:

Real-life situations question: 

Analytical questions: 

Conceptual questions: 

Value-based questions: 

With this refined and well-tuned course from Pearson, students will become more confident when they enter the competitive world for actual NEET preparation. The effort put in today will transform into a valuable asset, contributing to success in future competitive examinations.

Chapter Insights

Remember

Before beginning this chapter, you should be able to:

- Recall the cellular organization in humans
- Remember important cell organelles and

Remember section will help them to memorize and review the previous learning on a particular topic

Key points will help the students to identify the essential points in a chapter

Key Ideas

After completing this chapter, you should be able to:

- Understand the role of cell in maintaining life
- Identify the different cell organelles and

Scientific Crypt

A Tribute to Robert Brown (1773-1858)

Robert Brown (1773–1858), a well-known Scottish botanist, is well-known for his seminal contributions to cell biology, most notably determining the existence of the cell nucleus in 1831. This monumental discovery revealed the nucleus' critical role in cell function, propelling advances in Cell Theory and biology. His profound observations and meticulous research have significantly shaped our understanding of the fundamental structures of life, serving as a foundation for modern biological sciences. Brown's in-depth investigation also introduced the phenomenon of Brownian motion, which elucidated the erratic and random movement of particles suspended in a fluid and provided critical insights into molecular kinetics and particle theory.

Beyond Cellular Biology, his extensive research on plant species has provided the scientific community with a wealth of information on plant anatomy and classification. His unwavering pursuit of knowledge in the various domains of botany resulted in the identification and classification of numerous plant species, improving our understanding of plant life and its various forms.

Scientific Crypt provides information about well known scientists related to the chapter. The engaging activity is also given in the form of a crossword to keep the learners interested

INTRODUCTION

In the previous chapter, we have studied that cell is the basic structural and functional unit of life. All living organisms are made up of cells, and the living world comprises both unicellular and multicellular organisms. In unicellular organisms, a single cell performs all functions or activities needed for the survival and in multicellular organisms, the work is divided among group of cells, i.e., there is a division of labour. Tissue can be defined as a group of cells either similar or dissimilar that perform a specific function, for example, muscular tissue in humans is involved in movement or locomotion, and blood connective tissue helps in transport of respiratory gases and nutrients.

Introduction section helps to lay the foundation of the following chapter and leads the way for further learning

Wildlife and its Conservation

Traditionally, **wildlife** refers to undomesticated animal and plant species that occur in their natural habitat or are in a state of life in wild. Wildlife resources form an important link in the survival of human species and maintenance of the ecological balance of nature. It is also an area of much curiosity, research and interest among naturalists all over the world. Most of the wildlife habitats are under severe pressure and a large number of wildlife species have become extinct or are on the verge of extinction, due to the deleterious activities of humans. So finding and implementing effective

Concepts are explained in a well-structured and lucid manner

Konnect

Acid rain is caused by emissions of sulphur dioxide and nitrogen oxide. These gases react with water in the atmosphere and produce acids, such as sulphuric acid and nitric acid, resulting in acid rain.

Konnect boxes are some add-on information of related topic

Info bytes are interesting trivia and facts that engage young minds and keep the grey cells ticking!

Info Bytes!

Chlorella (a green alga) is taken as a food supplement.

Quick Recap

✔ **How are microorganisms classified?**

Microorganisms are typically classified into five major groups: bacteria, fungi, protozoa, algae, and viruses. For instance, while *Escherichia coli* is a bacterium, *Penicillium* is a fungus.

✔ **Why can't viruses perform metabolic activities outside a host?**

Viruses cannot perform metabolic activities on their own because they lack the necessary cellular machinery. They need to infect a host cell to replicate and perform life processes, which is why they're often considered at the boundary between living and non-living entities.

✔ **What role does yeast play in bread-making?**

In bread-making, yeast undergoes fermentation to produce carbon dioxide. This carbon dioxide causes the bread to rise, making it fluffy. Thus, yeast is a key ingredient in many bread recipes.

✔ **How do vaccines help in building immunity?**

When a vaccine is introduced into the body, it stimulates the immune system to produce specific antibodies against a particular microorganism without causing the disease. This "memory" allows the immune system to quickly recognize and combat the microorganism if encountered again in the future.

Quick Recap section will help to review all important concepts, discussed in that particular chapter

Each section contains detailed diagrams, images, real life microscopic views for better understanding and conceptual clarity.

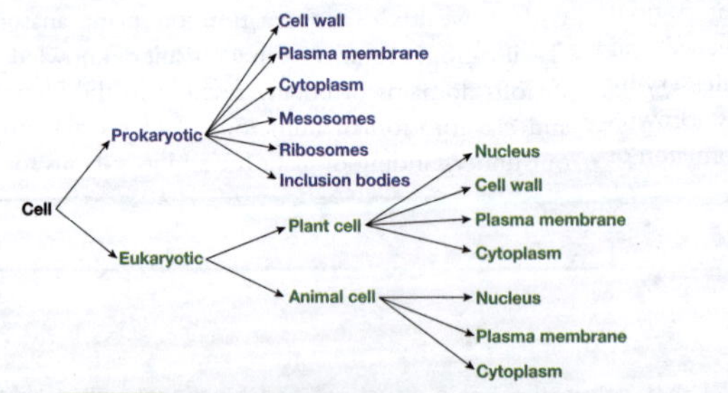

Figure 1.12 Cellular organization in prokaryotes and eukaryotes

POINTS TO REMEMBER

✔ The organisms which are too small to be seen by naked eye and are visible only through microscopes are called microorganisms.

✔ The study of microorganisms is termed as microbiology.

✔ Microorganisms are widely used for the production of curd, bread, alcohol, antibiotics, etc.

✔ Microorganisms can also be harmful and cause

✔ The coordinated response of the immune system towards any foreign particles is known as an immune response.

✔ Diseases that can spread from one person to another are called communicable diseases, example common cold.

✔ Diseases that do not spread from one person to another are called non-communicable diseases, for example, diabetes.

Points to remember summarises the concepts and topics presented in each chapter

PRACTICE QUESTIONS CLASSROOM WING

Very Short Answer Type Questions

Directions for questions from 1 to 5:
Fill in the blanks in each question.

1. Curd contains bacteria called __________ that convert milk into curd.
2. A __________ is a biological preparation that consists of either dead or weakened microbes.
3. Leguminous plants are of interest in agriculture as they can fix free nitrogen due to the microbe __________.
4. ___ is a substance that can initiate an immune response, often a bacterium, fungus, or toxin.

10. What plays a critical role in distinguishing 'self' from 'non-self' in the human immune system?
    (a) Lymph nodes
    (b) Bone marrow
    (c) Molecules like proteins on the surface of cells
    (d) Red blood cells
11. Identify the wrong statement.
    A. A vaccine is a biological preparation that contains active or weakend microbe.
    B. Polio is an infectious disease caused by bacteria.
    A.

Short Answer Type Questions

18. Explain the role of microorganisms in improving soil fertility.
19. Explain the importance of Sir Alexander Fleming's discovery in relation to microorganisms.

Essay Type Questions

41. Discuss the major threats to biodiversity and the importance of its conservation.
42. (a) What are the various control methods for soil pollution?
    (b) How deforestation causes species extinction?

Different typologies of questions have been included in the *Classroom Wing* which help students to develop the problem-solving skill

Competition Wing has been integrated chapter-wise in the exercise part to prepare students for various competitive examinations.

Graded as per complexity level: Level 1; Level 2; Level 3

PRACTICE QUESTIONS COMPETITION WING

Level 1: Apply your Concepts

Directions for questions from 1 to 5:
Fill in the blanks in each question.

1. An organism that breaks down decaying matter and simultaneously improves soil fertility is _______.
2. _______ is the science that studies the relationship of li...
3. ...
4. Deforestation, apart from being caused by mining and infrastructure, is also accelerated due to the creation of ________ plantations.
5. Among air, water, and soil pollution, the contamination that results from the excessive use and mismanagement of chemical fertilizers and pesticides primarily ffects the

Level 2: Review your Concepts

10. The temperature inside the scrotum is two degrees less than the normal human body temperature. What could be the possible reason for this?
11. A single ejaculation of semen contains around 300 million sperms, whereas fertilization involves fusion of

Level 3: Assess Your Concepts

10. Aakanksha was shown two slides of plant tissues; parenchyma and sclerenchyma. How did she identify sclerenchyma?
11. Generally shrubs and herbs are grown in open places and are exposed to strong winds. But they do not break. Why?

Level 2: Review your Concepts

7. Ravi decides to make notes on a group of 20 different living organisms which he observes on a daily basis. How can the knowledge of taxonomy be helpful in this exercise?
8. Dogs and cats are different from each other. At the levels of hierarchy, are they grouped under any common taxon?
9. Tiger and lion have scientific names, *Panthera tigris* and *Panthera leo*, respectively. What similarities could be identified?
10. Bryopsida is called amphibian of the plants. What can be inferred about this plant?

Level 3: Assess Your Concepts

11. Plant body in higher plants is well-developed. Roots are the organs used for absorbing water and minerals. What is the equivalent of roots in the less developed lower plants?
12. Whittaker's five-kingdom classification was a more logical method of classification as compared to two-kingdom classification. Justify the statement.

AT

The icons are used for categorization of the questions in Classroom Wing and Competition Wing

PRACTICE QUESTIONS NEET SPECIAL WING

Multiple-Answer Type Questions

Questions number 1 to 5 are multiple-choice questions. Each question has FOUR options (a), (b), (c), and (d). ONE OR MORE THAN ONE of these four option(s) is/are the correct answer(s).

1. Fungi are:
   (a) Eukaryotes
   (b) Prokaryotes
   (c) Have cell wall
   (d) Mostly multicellular

(a) Porifera
(b) Ctenophora
(c) Cnidaria

Comprehension-Based Questions

A. Read the paragraph given below and answer the questions number 6 to 11:

An American ecologist Robert Whittaker in the year 1969 gave the five-kingdom classification of organisms. There were five major criteria based on which he classified the organisms which include-cell structure, body organisation, body organisation, mode of nutrition and phyloge-

NEET Special Wing is curated specifically for targeted preparation of NEET examination

Hints and Explanations

CLASSROOM WING

Short Answer Type Questions

36. Protista includes single-celled eukaryotes which are mostly aquatic. They can have a cell wall in some members, possess a nuclear membrane, have a cellular level of body organization, and can be either autotrophic or heterotrophic.

37. Bryophytes are considered the amphibians of the plant kingdom because they are terrestrial but require water to complete their life cycle.

38. Monera consists of prokaryotic cells with no nuclear membrane, whereas Protista consists of eukaryotic cells with a defined nuclear membrane.

39. Joint legs in Arthropoda provide these organisms with enhanced mobility and agility. This adaptation has played a significant role in their success, as evidenced

Essay Type Questions

44. The five-kingdom classification provides a comprehensive method for differentiating organisms based on a variety of characteristics. This kingdom, which begins with Monera, includes prokaryotic organisms, primarily bacteria, that lack a nuclear membrane. They have a cell wall and are primarily unicellular (Nutrition mode: autotrophic or heterotrophic).

    Protista are eukaryotic unicellular organisms that may or may not have a cell wall. They have a nuclear membrane, unlike Monera, and can be autotrophic or heterotrophic.

    Fungi are eukaryotic organisms that can be unicellular or multicellular. They have a distinct chitin cell wall and are purely heterotrophic, feeding on either saprophytic or parasitic means.

Hints and Explanation for key questions of classroom wing, competition wing and NEET special wing along with highlights on the common mistakes that students usually make in the examinations

COMPETITION WING

Level 2: Review your Concepts

6. The tissue responsible for the regeneration of parts eaten by grazing herbivores is intercalary meristem. It is a kind of meristematic tissue that has the ability to divide. Intercalary meristem is seen between mature tissues, on either side of the nodes and is also responsible for the increase in length of internodes.

7. The apical meristem, meristematic tissue responsible for the increase in length of a plant body (or here in this case root) is located at the root tip. Removal of root tip causes the removal of apical meristem and thus the growth of root stops.

8. (a) A – Humerus B – Radius

synthesis. Whereas, animals are dependent on plants and other animals for food and have to travel to fulfill this requirement.

NEET SPECIAL WING

Multiple-Answer Type Questions

Questions number 1 to 5 are multiple-choice questions. Each question has FOUR options (a), (b), (c), and (d). ONE OR MORE THAN ONE of these four option(s) is/are the correct answer(s).

1. Fungi are eukaryotic in nature and they possess cell wall which is made up of chitin. Most of the fungi are multicellular organisms but unicellular fungi are also found such as yeast.

2. Kingdom Monera includes prokaryotic organisms (bacteria), that is, both archaebacteria and eubacteria. They have cell wall, nucleus is absent. They can have both autotrophic and heterotrophic mode of nutrition.

3. Among the options given, aquatic organisms are found

11. Match the following:

    Lions and tigers belong to the same genus Panth and they are a group of related species.
    (i) d

    A group of related families constitutes an order.
    (ii) a

    Phyla that have common characters are grouped i various kingdoms.
    (iii) b

    A new three kingdom classification was develo by a German biologist Ernst Haeckel in 1886. T three kingdoms according to Haeckel were: Kingd Plantae, Kingdom Animalia and Kingdom Protista
    (iv) c

    Carolus Linnaeus classified all organisms into t kingdoms on the basis of nutrition and locomot

DW

WORKSHEET

CHAPTER 1: CELL—THE BASIC UNIT OF LIFE

Directions for questions from 1 to 5.
Select the correct alternative from the given options.

1. _____plastids store carbohydrates in them.
   (a) Aleuroplasts (b) Elainoplasts
   (c) Amyloplast (d) Chloroplast
2. ____is the place where ribosomes are synthesized in the cell.
   (a) Nucleolus
   (b) Nucleus
   (c) Endoplasmic reticulum
   (d) Mitochondria
5. Components of Golgi complex in plant cells are called _____.
   (a) Plastids (b) Lysosomes
   (c) Dictyosomes (d) Mitochondria

Directions for questions from 6 to 10.
Answer the following questions.

6. Differentiate between mitosis and meiosis.
7. Write the significance of cell division.
8. Both plants and bacteria contain cell wall but former cannot survive in harsh conditions. Explain.

DW: *Downloadable worksheets* supplementing textual exercises for hand-on learning

AT

AI Assessments

1. _________________ is where parents are selected carefully to produce young ones having desired characters.

- Artificial breeding
- Selective breeding
- Artificial hybridization
- DNA cloning

Question 1 of 4 Next

AT: Attemptable Tests for assessing understanding of concepts and getting a clear picture of your exam readiness

66. In the following line diagram showing taxonomic hierarchy of plants, identify the missing taxonomic unit.

Division ⟶ Class ⟶ Family

(a) Order (b) Family
(c) Species (d) Phylum

Video icon: Audio and visual learning to difficult questions for effective learning and retention

[illegible] components of [illegible]

[illegible]

2. Write the [illegible]

[illegible]

[illegible] identify the [illegible]

[illegible] Family

[illegible]

SCOPE OF SCIENCE

Introduction

From the time humans came on earth, they were fascinated and curious about the natural phenomena happening in the world (like the formation of a rainbow, birth of a child, changes in the weather, etc.). People since time immemorial had been attempting to understand and explain the world around them with all its processes and mechanisms. So, to cater to all these queries and curiosity of mankind a specific branch of study developed called science. Science was an approach to understand and explain the immediate world around us.

Science

The English term 'science' has been derived from the Latin term 'scientia' meaning 'knowledge'. It involves the study of natural world and how it works, by observing and experimenting. It is a tool for searching and exploring the nature.

Branches of Science

Science is divided into many branches according to the area of study such as:

- **Natural science:** Study of natural phenomenon (biological science, physical science, etc.)
- **Social science:** Study of human behaviour and societies
- **Applied science:** Applies scientific knowledge to develop technologies (e.g., engineering, medicine, etc.)
- **Formal science:** Concerned with logic, mathematics, etc.

How do Scientists Work?

A person engaged in observing and experimenting to gain knowledge about nature is called scientist. Scientists follow a specific way for their innovations and this is called scientific method. Scientific method involves a series of techniques such as:

- Observation
- Asking questions
- Making hypotheses
- Experimentation
- Data analysis and making conclusions
- Communicating the results

Observation

Observation involves receiving knowledge about a natural phenomenon through our senses and recording the questions that we would like to answer.

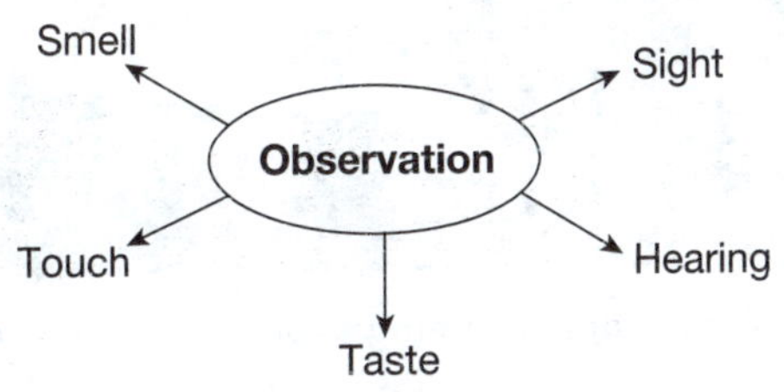

Fig. S.1 Means through which observations can be made

Asking Questions

After making an interesting observation, a scientific mind will be more curious to know about it. And this curiosity would lead to asking questions, like what, why, how, when and where?

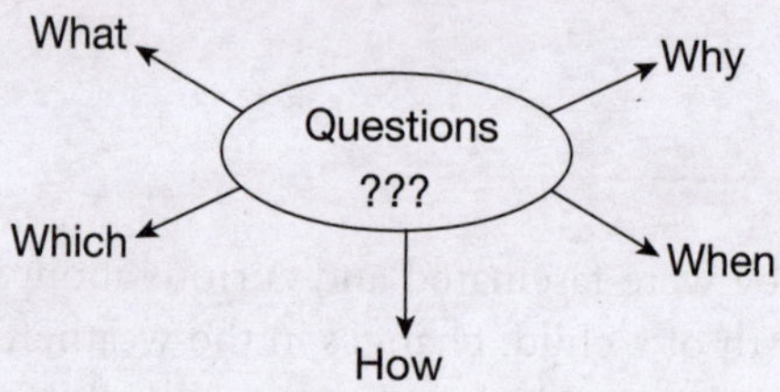

Fig. S.2 Types of questions asked after making an observation

Hypothesis

A hypothesis is a proposed explanation (guess) about a phenomenon on the basis of evidences as a starting for further investigation. It is provisionally accepted and provides guidance for further investigations, to find out the possible solutions for the problem you observed.

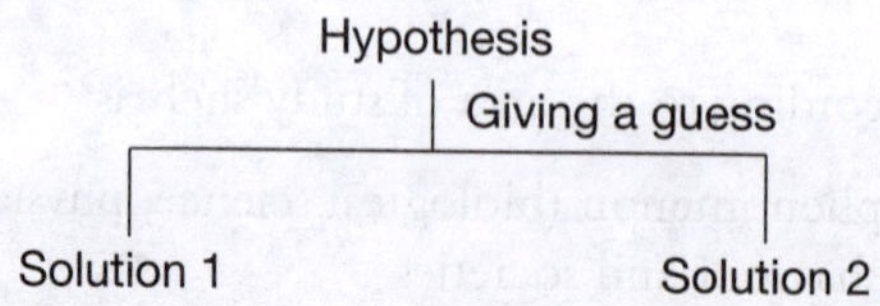

Fig. S.3 Possible explanations for a hypothesis

Experimentation

To conduct experiments is one of the most important steps in the scientific method. It involves testing of hypotheses made on the basis of observations. Experiments help in proving whether hypothesis is right or wrong and also to formulate scientific theories.

Fig. S.4 A student performing experiment in chemistry lab

Data Analysis and Conclusion

Results or data obtained after several trials of experiment are analyzed thoroughly. With this, we come to a conclusion to know whether the hypothesis is right or wrong. If the experiment results prove hypothesis, then the original question is answered otherwise the research continues, forming new hypothesis and then conducting an experiment to test it.

Communicate Results

This step involves reporting the results of experiments to let others know about it. The results could be presented as written reports or oral reports. Communicating the results among peers may lead to a new question which may in turn lead to another investigation.

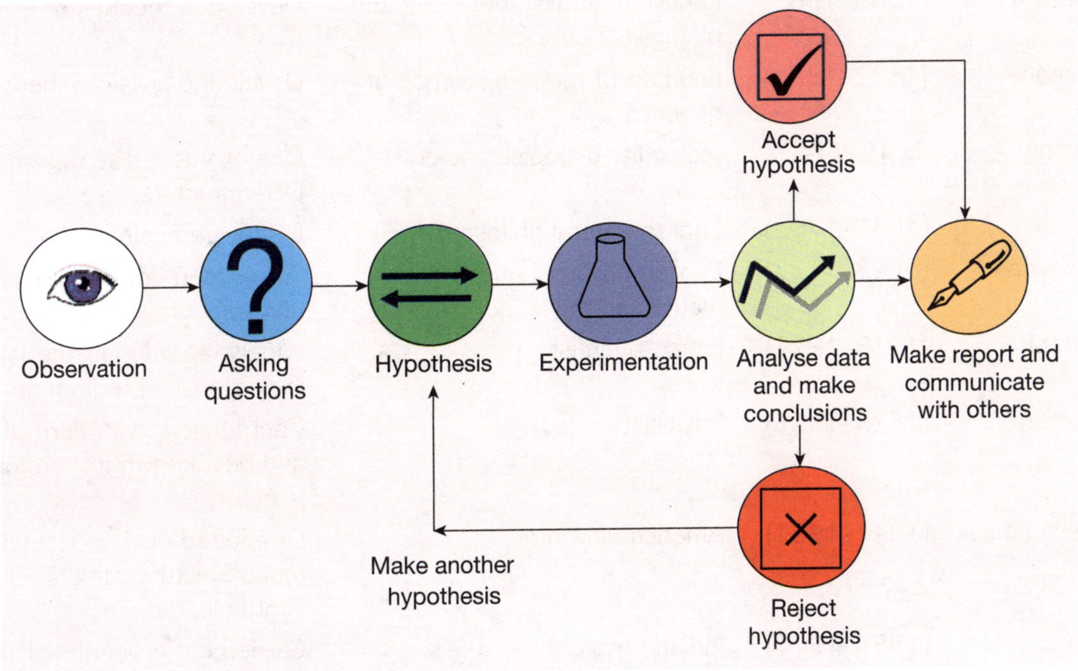

Fig. S.5 Series of techniques followed in a scientific method

Work of a Scientist: An Example

The methodology followed by scientists while working on any hypothesis is explained in the following steps.

- When you place a plant near a window, after a few days, you can observe that the plant bends towards the window.
  - This phenomenon makes you curious and you start asking questions like:
    - Why did the plant bend?
    - What is this phenomenon?
- Based on the observation, you make a hypothesis about the possible reasons for this, such as:
  - Plant bends to get enough air.

    or
  - Plant bends to get sunlight
- Experiments were conducted to prove this, by placing the plants in different surroundings and it was observed that in all the experiments, plant was bending towards the light source.
- You analysed your data and came to a conclusion that it was sunlight that made the plant to bend towards the window. And also, you found that all plants show these kinds of movements in which they bend towards the light source.
- After getting a proper conclusion you then make a report and present it, so that others will get to know about it.

Famous Scientists and their Contributions

The world has witnessed some very great scientists since the historic times who have made a huge impact on our understanding and reasoning of scientific phenomena. A few of these great scientists are mentioned in this section along with their contributions.

Table S.1 Some famous scientists and their important contributions

Name	Year	Country	Contribution
Aristotle	(384–322 BC)	Ancient Greek philosopher and scientist	One of the earliest scientists to classify living organisms
Charles Darwin	(1809–1882)	English naturalist, geologist and biologist	Developed theories of evolution
Gregor Mendel	(1822–1884)	Founder of modern science of genetics	Developed laws of inheritance
James Watson	(b. 1928)	Molecular biologist, zoologist	One of the codiscoverers of the DNA structure.
Robert Hooke	(1635–1703)	English natural philosopher	Discovered cell
Sir Isaac Newton	(1643–1727)	English physicist and mathematician	Formulated laws of motion and universal gravitation
Vikram Sarabhai	(1919–1971)	Indian scientist	Widely regarded as the father of India's space programme.
Albert Einstein	(1879–1955)	Physicist	Contribution to modern physics and best known for the formula E = mc2
Thomas Alva Edison	(1847–1931)	American inventor	Developed devices including motion picture camera, electric light bulb, etc.
CV Raman	(1888–1970)	Indian physicist	Carried out groundbreaking work in the field of light scattering
Dmitri Ivanovich Mendeleev	(1834–1907)	Russian chemist	Formulated periodic law and created periodic table of elements.
Srinivasa Ramanujan	(1887–1920)	Indian mathematician	Made substantial contributions to mathematical analysis number theory, infinite series

Science in Everyday Life

Almost everything that makes our life easy is the outcome of science and scientific studies. It is impossible to lead a life without science and its innovations. Science has gifted us with innovations such as:

- **It makes communication easy:** Science has made the communication possible and easy even if we are far away. Major inventions in this field include mobile phones, internet, etc.
- **Helps us to find cure for many diseases:** Through science and its innovations, we have found cure for millions of diseases. It has also become possible to prevent some diseases through methods like vaccinations. Doctors are able to view inside the body with the help of various techniques, such as x-rays, MRI scans, etc., and all of

Info Bytes!

The first ever email was sent in 1971.

The Internet took four years to reach its first 50 Million Users.

these are a result of science and innovations.

- **Helps us to reduce the work load:** Most of the work in everyday life can be done using machines. Starting from using a calculator for simple calculations to a washing machine for washing, everything is a product of science.
- **Makes our transportation easy:** With the inventions of vehicles, it made our transportation easy. After the invention of aeroplanes, it became possible for us to travel around the world in less time.

Science for Human Welfare

The ultimate aim of science is human welfare. It has made our life comfortable. It has provided us with many amenities of life. Science has made our life better than what it was in the past.

Table S.2 List of agricultural revolutions

Type of revolution	Goal
Green Revolution	Food grain production
White Revolution	Milk Production
Black Revolution	Petroleum Production
Blue Revolution	Fish Production
Silver Revolution	Egg/Poultry Production

- Now we are able to produce more food to meet the requirements of world through developments in agriculture, such as green revolution, blue revolution, white revolution, etc.
- We are able to travel across the world by land, air and water.
- It is possible for us to dress better than our forefathers.
- We live in a better, safe place than in the past. Our houses, villages, town everything has improved through science.
- Science has also increased the lifespan of individuals through inventions in the medical field.
- Science has made us capable of surviving natural calamities to a great extent.
- In fact all the basic requirements of life are now fulfilled by science and its innovations.

Info Bytes!

Dr. Norman Borlaug is known as the 'Father of Green Revolution' and Dr. M.S.Swaminathan is the 'Father of Indian Green Revolution'.

Future of Science

Researches in science are going on to explore the hidden truths about the world. New technologies and tools provide new ways to discoveries. The main goal of all these studies is to make the life comfortable on earth. Even research is going on to find out whether life is possible in other planets, such as mars. Through science we aim for a better future, keeping in mind the studies should not harm the environment we live in and also it should not cause harm to the human race and other life forms.

Quick Recap

✔ **What is science? What are the main branches?**

Science involves the study of natural world and how it works. It is a tool for searching and exploring the nature by observing and experimenting. The various branches according to the area of study are:

- **Natural science:** Study of natural phenomenon (biological science, physical science, etc.)
- **Social science:** Study of human behaviour and societies
- **Applied science:** Applies scientific knowledge to develop technologies (e.g., engineering, medicine, etc.)
- **Formal science:** Concerned with logics, mathematics, etc.

✔ **What does it mean by a hypothesis?**

A hypothesis is a proposed explanation (guess) about a phenomenon on the basis of evidences. It is the initial stage of investigation. It is provisionally accepted and provides guidance for further investigations, to find out the possible solutions of the problems you observed.

POINTS TO REMEMBER

✔ Science involves the study of the natural world through observation and experimentation.

✔ A scientific method involves a series of techniques to create an innovation.

✔ The world has seen many great scientists, like Darwin and Newton whose discoveries have made a huge contribution in improving the life on this planet.

✔ Science have made our life much easy by its many inventions, like mobile phones, MRI scans, trains, etc.

✔ Still further researches are going on to make our lives better by more advanced technologies.

PRACTICE QUESTIONS CLASSROOM WING

Directions for questions 1 to 5:
Fill in the blanks in each question.

1. The scientist who introduced the formula $E = mc^2$ is ________.
2. Cell was discovered by ________.
3. The proposed explanation or guess for the possible solution for a problem observed is ________.
4. The first step in a scientific study is ________.
5. Study of human behaviour and societies comes under ________ branch of science.

Directions for questions 6 to 11:
For each of the following questions, four choices have been provided. Select the correct alternative.

6. The branch of science related to developing technologies is
   (a) Formal science (b) Natural science
   (c) Social science (d) Applied science
7. Observation involves
   (a) Observing a natural phenomenon
   (b) Recording the questions to be solved.
   (c) Asking questions about the observed phenomenon
   (d) Both (a) and (b)
8. Match the following

A	Gregor Mendel	i	Laws of motion
B	Mendeleev	ii	Indian physicist
C	CV Raman	iii	Laws of inheritance
D	Sir Isaac Newton	iv	Periodic table

	A	B	C	D
(a)	iv	i	ii	iii
(b)	iii	ii	i	iv
(c)	iv	iii	ii	i
(d)	iii	iv	ii	i

9. Which one of the following is a wrong statement?
   (a) Science has made our communication easy.
   (b) Green revolution and blue revolution are revolutions that have happened in IT industry.
   (c) Thomas Alva Edison invented electric bulb.
   (d) Vikram Sarabhai is considered as a father of Indian space programme.
10. Indian mathematician who contributed to number theory is
    (a) Vikram Sarabhai
    (b) CV Raman
    (c) Gregor Mendel
    (d) Srinivasa Ramanujan
11. Complete the table with the name of scientist or his contribution accordingly.

Scientist	Contribution
____________	Motion picture camera
Dimitri Ivanovich Mendeleev	____________
____________	Infinite series
Albert Einstein	____________
____________	Universal gravitation
Charles Darwin	____________
____________	DNA structure

PRACTICE QUESTIONS COMPETITION WING

1. Write a note on various advantages of science in everyday life.

2. Which is the last step in a scientific method?

3. Name any three scientists from India and their contributions.

4. Explain how scientists work with one suitable example.

ANSWER KEYS

Classroom Wing

1. Albert Einstein
2. Robert Hooke
3. Hypothesis
4. Observation
5. Social science
6. (d)
7. (d)
8. (d)
9. (b)
10. (d)
11.

Scientist	Contribution
Thomas Alva Edison	Motion picture camera
Dmitri Ivanovich Mendeleev	Periodic table and periodic law
Srinivasa Ramanujan	Infinite series
Albert Einstein	$E = mc^2$
Sir Isaac Newton	Universal gravitation
Charles Darwin	Theories of evolution
James Watson	DNA structure

Competition Wing

1. Science plays a major role in everyday life. It has made our communication easy, even if we are at far away places. It has also made our transportation easy and comfortable. Through science, it is now possible to treat millions of diseases, thereby increasing the lifespan of people.

2. Communicating the results obtained after data analysis to let others know about it is the last step in a scientific method. The results can be presented as written or oral reports. Communicating the results to peers may lead to new questions every time which may in turn lead to another investigation.

3. **Vikram Sarabhai:** Father of India's space programme.

   Srinivasa Ramanujan: Indian mathematician who made major contributions to number theory, infinite series, etc.

   CV Raman: Indian physicist who carried out major work in the field of light scattering.

4. Scientists follow a specific pathway for their innovations, which is known as a scientific method. It involves a series of techniques such as:
   - Observation
   - Asking questions
   - Making hypothesis
   - Experimentation
   - Data analysis and making conclusions
   - Communicating the results to others

   Example:
   - Ram tried to germinate pea seed in water. He observed that pea seed did not germinate.
   - He made hypothesis for the possible reasons behind this.
     - Hypothesis I—pea seeds do not require water for germination
     - Hypothesis II—pea seeds require air for germination
     - Hypothesis III—pea seeds require adequate amount of both water and air for germination.
   - He conducted experiments to prove his hypotheses. He tried to germinate pea seeds in three different conditions.
     - Exp I—placing pea seeds completely in water without air for germination.
     - Exp II—placing pea seeds in a plate without water and provided only air for germination.
     - Exp III—pea seeds are provided with both water and air in sufficient amount.
   - The result obtained were
     - Exp I—no seed germination
     - Exp II—no seed germination
     - Exp III—Seed germinated
   - He analyzed the experiment results and made conclusion that pea seeds require both air and water for germination.

CHAPTER

1

Cell—The Basic Unit of Life

Remember

Before beginning this chapter, you should be able to:

- Recall the cellular organization in humans
- Remember important cell organelles and their functions

Key Ideas

After completing this chapter, you should be able to:

- Understand the role of cell in maintaining life
- Identify the different cell organelles and their functions
- Differentiate between mitosis and meiosis

A Tribute to Robert Brown (1773-1858)

Robert Brown (1773–1858), a well-known Scottish botanist, is well-known for his seminal contributions to cell biology, most notably determining the existence of the cell nucleus in 1831. This monumental discovery revealed the nucleus' critical role in cell function, propelling advances in Cell Theory and biology. His profound observations and meticulous research have significantly shaped our understanding of the fundamental structures of life, serving as a foundation for modern biological sciences. Brown's in-depth investigation also introduced the phenomenon of Brownian motion, which elucidated the erratic and random movement of particles suspended in a fluid and provided critical insights into molecular kinetics and particle theory.

Beyond Cellular Biology, his extensive research on plant species has provided the scientific community with a wealth of information on plant anatomy and classification. His unwavering pursuit of knowledge in the various domains of botany resulted in the identification and classification of numerous plant species, improving our understanding of plant life and its various forms.

FUN TIME

CROSSWORD

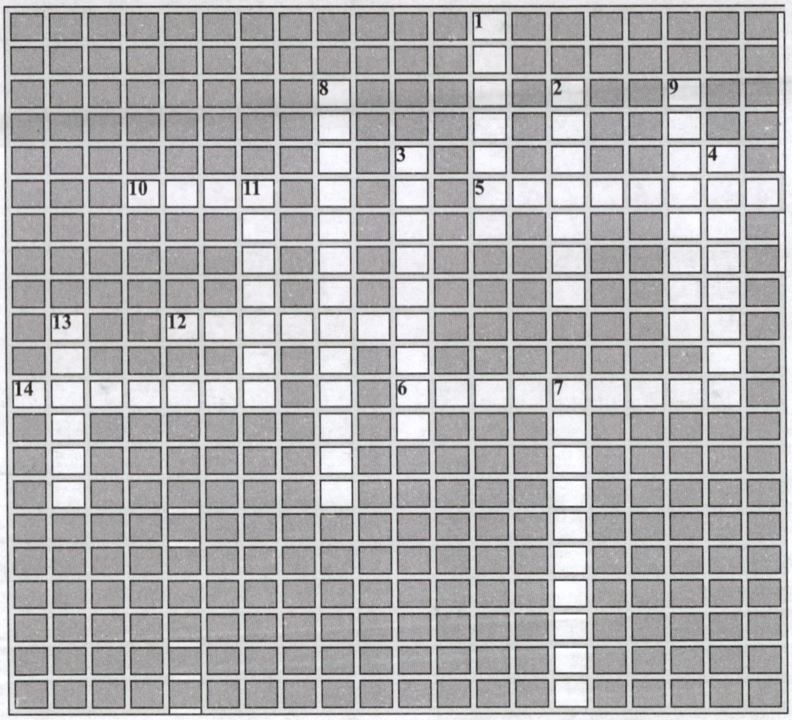

Across

5. The region where genetic material is found in a prokaryotic cell
6. Matthias Jakob ____, a co-proposer of the Cell Theory in 1838
10. Christian ____ developed a staining method to classify bacteria
12. Denatures the proteins and imparts a negative charge to it
14. This type of cell division is associated with sexual reproduction and gamete formation

Down

1. Theodor ____, who, along with Schleiden, proposed the Cell Theory in 1839
2. Rudolf ____, who stated that new cells arise from existing cells
3. The fluid substance inside the cell containing organelles, except in prokaryotic cells where there is no nucleus
4. The process by which a cell splits into two daughter cells
7. Cells with a true nucleus and membrane-bound organelles, like those in plant cells
8. This substance makes up the cell wall and is composed of carbohydrates
9. The sites of protein synthesis associated with the plasma membrane but not enclosed by any membrane system
11. A type of cell division resulting in genetically identical daughter cells
13. What is the concept proposed by Schleiden and Schwann regarding cells is referred to as?

INTRODUCTION

Things around us can be classified as living or non-living. Both living things and non-living things are composed of certain basic chemical elements, such as Carbon, Hydrogen, Oxygen and Nitrogen. These chemical elements are found in an organized manner in the form of cells in living beings, which distinguishes them from non-living. Cells are the basic structural and functional units of life. A cell is the smallest individual unit of matter capable of performing all essential life processes by itself.

Cell—The Basic Unit of Life

The term 'cell' is derived from Latin word *cellula*, meaning 'little room'. The term cell was coined by Robert Hooke in 1665. A **cell** is the smallest building block of life. It is defined as the basic structural and functional unit of a living organism. Cells in various organisms depict the variation in cell size, shape and number. A cell is capable of performing all vital functions to sustain life.

Info Bytes!

- There are more bacterial cells in human body than human cells!
- Bacteria are so tiny that you would need about 5 million of them lined up to stretch across just 1 centimetre.

Discovery of Cell

In 1665, Robert Hooke observed thin slices of cork under a microscope. He noticed several small compartment-like structures that resembled the structure of a honeycomb.

Figure 1.1 Microscope used by Robert Hooke to make his observations of cells

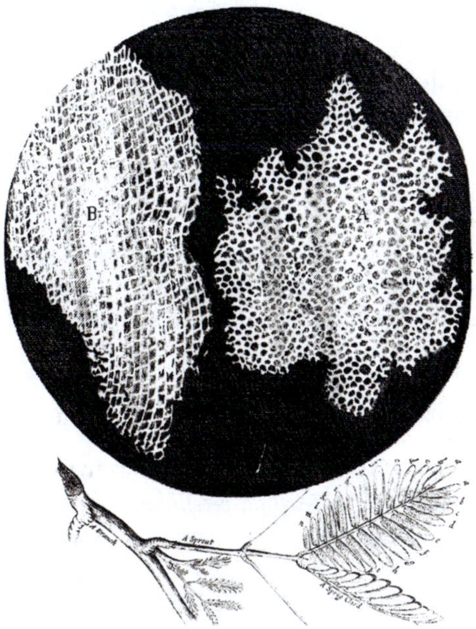

Figure 1.2 Robert Hooke's observations of cellular structure of cork

Unicellular and Multicellular Organisms

All living organisms are made up of cells. In one case, a single cell may constitute an organism (unicellular) and in other case, an organism may consist of many cells (multicellular). According to this, organisms can be divided into two types:

Info Bytes!

In 1674, Antonie Van Leeuwenhoek observed free-living cells in pond water.

1. **Unicellular organisms:** Organisms with only one cell, for example, *Amoeba*, *Chlamydomonas*, *Paramoecium*, bacteria, etc.

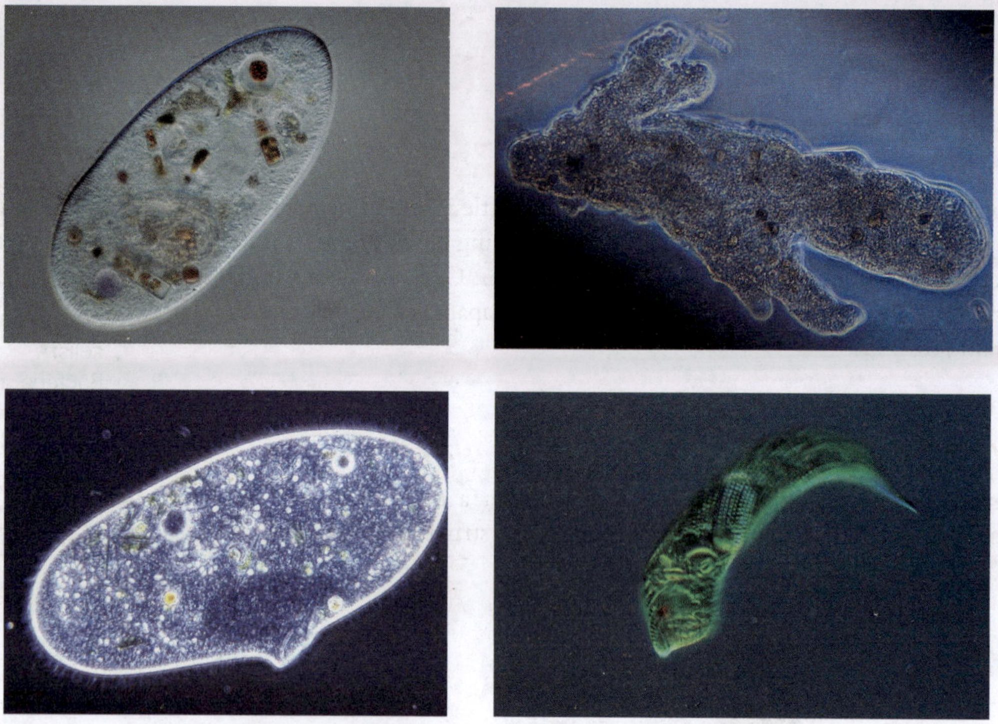

Figure 1.3 Some common unicellular organisms

2. **Multicellular organisms:** Organisms which are composed of many cells and can perform various functions are multicellular organisms, for example, plants and animals, are multicellular organisms.

Cell Theory

Cell theory was proposed by Matthias Jakob Schleiden (1838) and Theodor Schwann (1839) and was later modified by Rudolf Virchow. The two main postulates are:

Info Bytes!

The number and type of cells in a given tissue is called cellularity.

1. All organisms are made up of cells.
2. Cell is the basic structural and functional unit of life.

An important addition to the Cell Theory was made by Rudolf Virchow in 1868. He stated that new cells arise from pre-existing cells (in Latin: *omnis-cellula-e-cellula*).

Table 1.1 Some famous scientists and their contribution to the field of cell biology

Scientist	Contribution
Robert Hooke	Discovered cell
Antonie van Leeuwenhoek	Observed first living cell
Robert Brown	Discovered cell nucleus
Purkinje	Coined the term 'protoplasm'
Schleiden, Schwann, Virchow	Cell theory
Camillo Golgi	First described Golgi apparatus

Size of Cell

Most cells are minute and are visible only under the microscope. They are only a few micrometres in diameter. The cells range in size from micrometers to as long as 1 m. There are some cells which are big enough to be seen with naked eye. For example, egg of an ostrich is about 15-cm long and 13-cm wide.

Info Bytes!

Size and mass of a typical cell are 10 micrometre and 1 nanogram, respectively

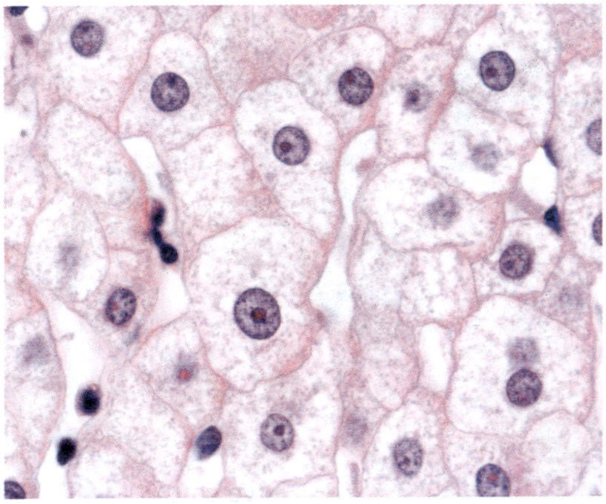

Figure 1.4 (a) Microscopic view of cells that are not visible to naked eye (**b**) Ostrich eggs in in nest, Kalahari desert (Africa)

Shape of Cell

The shape of the cells varies according to their function. They may be disc-like, polygonal, columnar, cuboid or thread-like. Nerve cells have an elongated structure and this helps them in conducting impulses quickly. Similarly, there are cells that have flexible shape, for example, *Amoeba* and some blood cells. The flexibility in *Amoeba's* shape helps it to perform various activities, such as movement, feeding, etc. The change in shape of *Amoeba* is due to the formation of pseudopodia that are projections on its body.

Info Bytes!

Smallest cell: Mycoplasma
Largest cell: Ostrich's egg
Longest cell: Neuron (in humans)

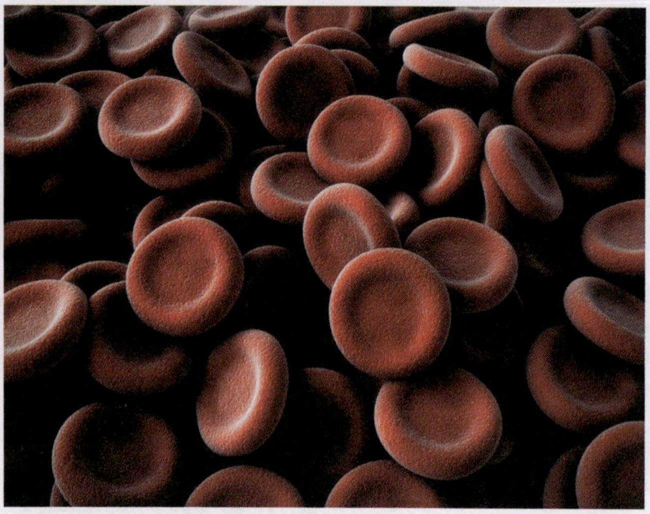

Red blood cells
(round and biconcave)

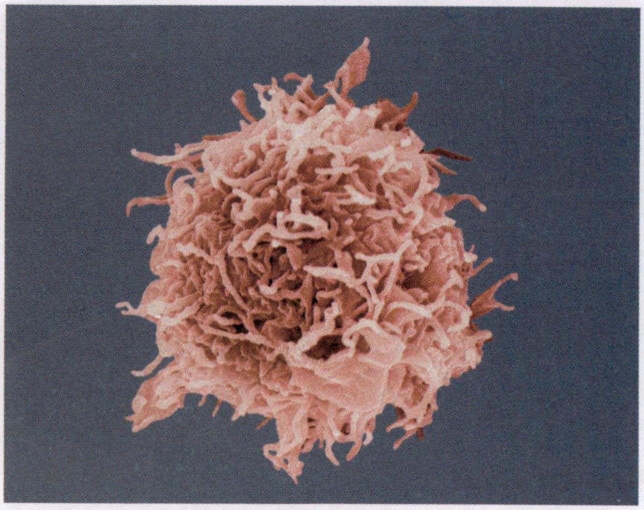

White blood cells
(amoeboid)

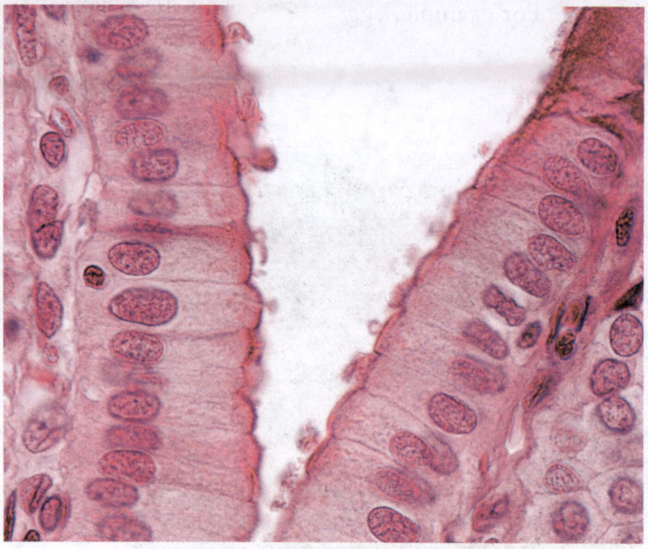

Columnar epithelial cells
(long and narrow)

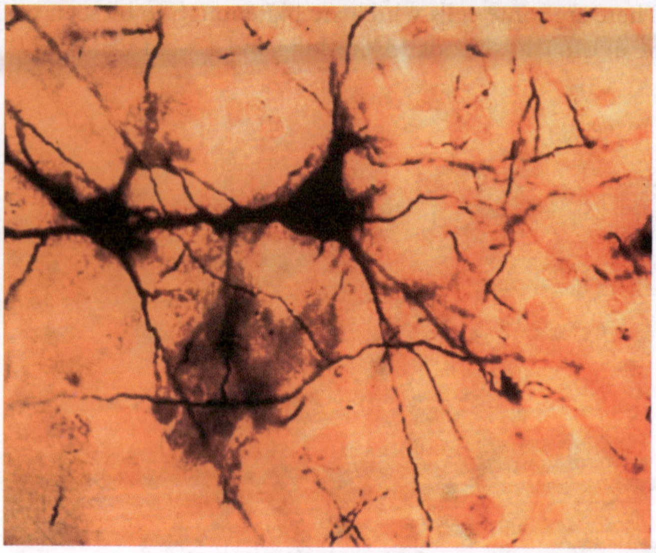

Nerve cells
(branched and long)

Figure 1.5 Different types of cells showing different shapes

Types of Cells

The cells can be divided into two types: prokaryotic and eukaryotic, according to the differences in their cellular organization. The cells which possess a true nucleus along with membrane-bound organelles are called **eukaryotic cells**, for example, plant cell and animal cell. The cells which do not possess a well-defined nucleus as well as membrane-bound organelles are called **prokaryotic cells**, for example, bacterial cell.

Prokaryotic Cells

Prokaryotic cells are primitive and lack a true nucleus. Their genetic material is not surrounded by a nuclear membrane and is confined to a particular region known as **nucleoid**.

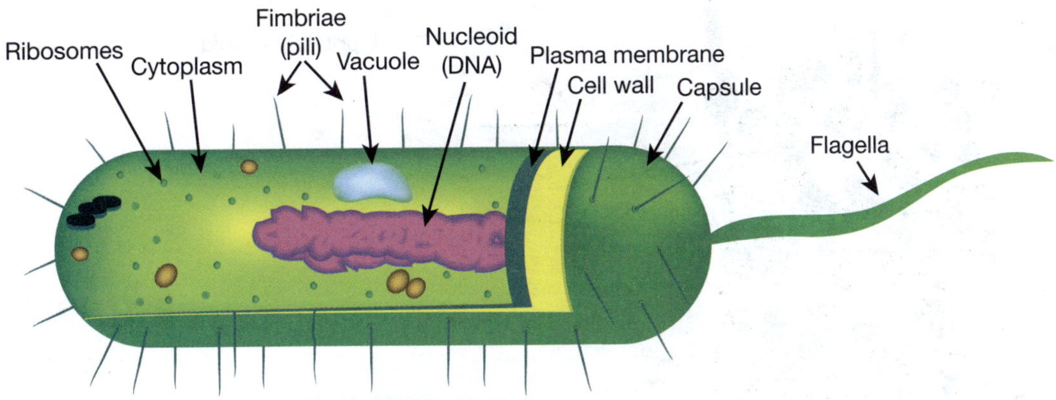

Figure 1.6 A prokaryotic cell

Prokaryotic cells are generally smaller than eukaryotic cells. There are four basic shapes for prokaryotes (bacteria) listed as follows:

1. Coccus
2. Bacillus
3. Vibrio
4. Spirillum

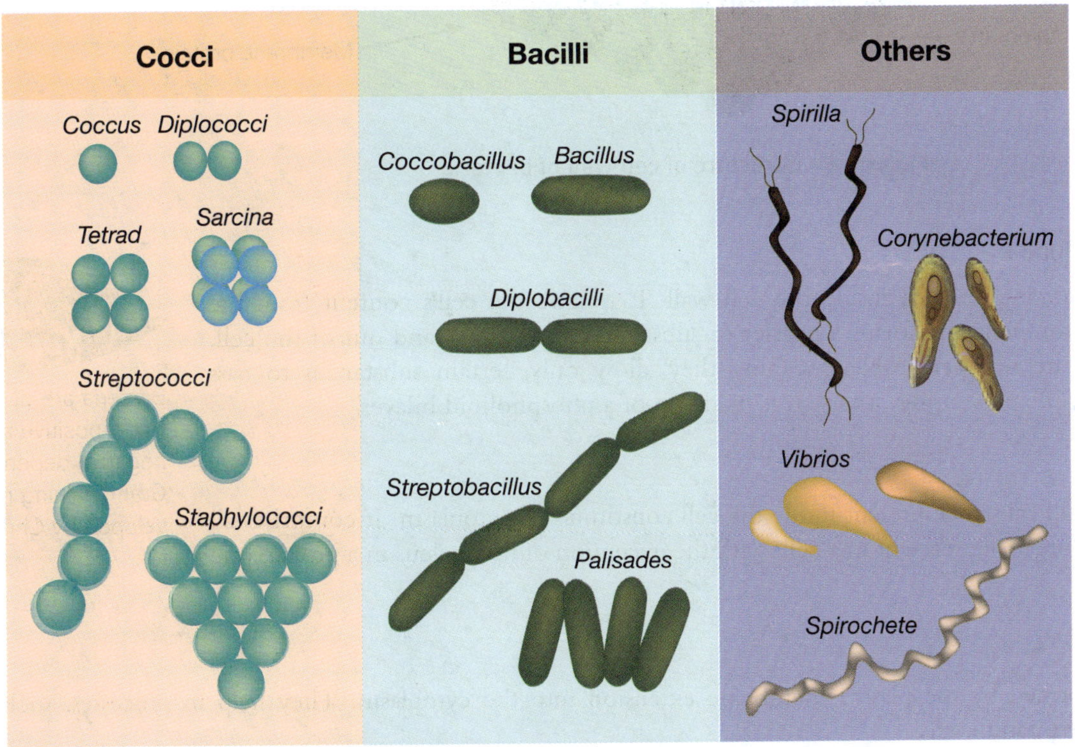

Figure 1.7 Different types of bacterial shapes

Though their shapes and sizes vary, all cells possess a common structure. All prokaryotic cells have major components that are discussed here:

Cell Wall

Cell Wall forms the outermost layer of the cell. It provides integrity to the cell. It is made up of peptidoglycan, which in turn is made up of carbohydrates. It is absent in *Mycoplasma*.

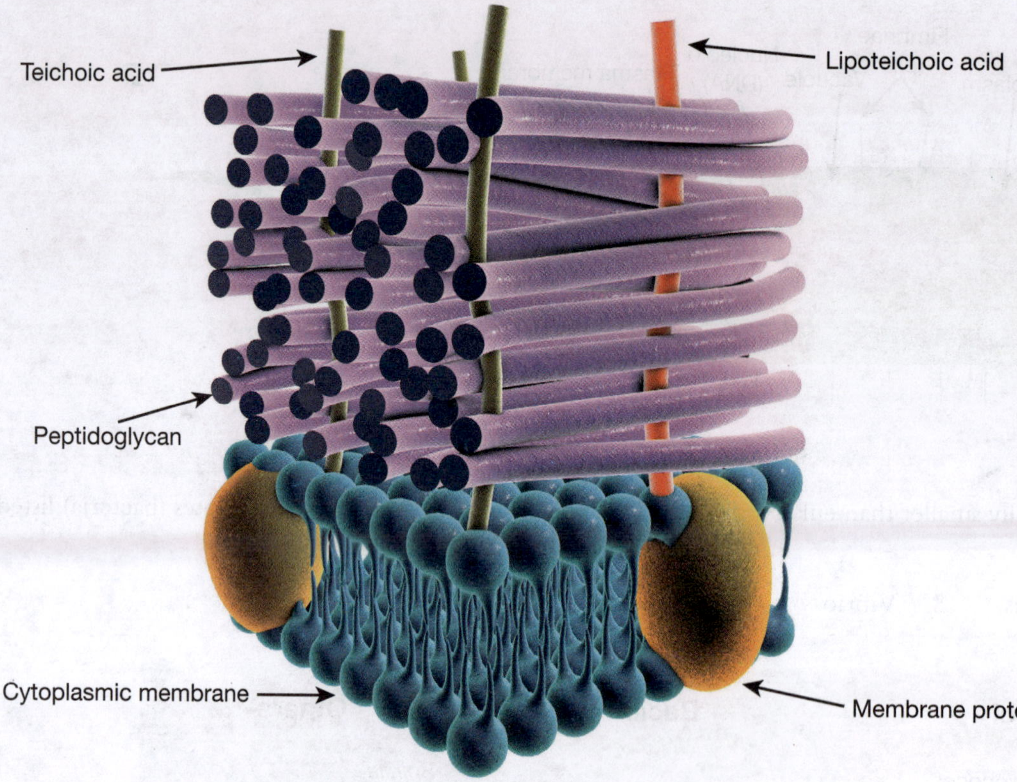

Figure 1.8 Structure of cell wall of bacteria

Info Bytes!

In 1665, Robert Hooke made the first observation and named the plant cell wall.

Plasma Membrane

Plasma Membrane lies just inside the cell wall. It isolates the cell's content from the outside environment and forms a barrier to substances entering in and out of the cell. Membranes are semipermeable, meaning they allow only certain substances to pass through it while preventing others. It is made up of a phospholipid bilayer.

Konnect

Bacteria are divided into Gram-positive and Gram-negative depending upon Gram staining method developed by Christian Gram.

Cytoplasm

All of the fluid substance present inside the cell constitutes its cytoplasm. It comprises all kinds of cell organelles present in a cell, with the exception of no nucleus in a prokaryotic cell.

Mesosomes

These are formed by the plasma membrane extension into the cytoplasm. They help in processes, such as cell wall formation, respiration, etc.

Ribosomes

These are the sites of protein synthesis. Ribosomes are found to be associated with plasma membrane. They are not bound by any membrane system.

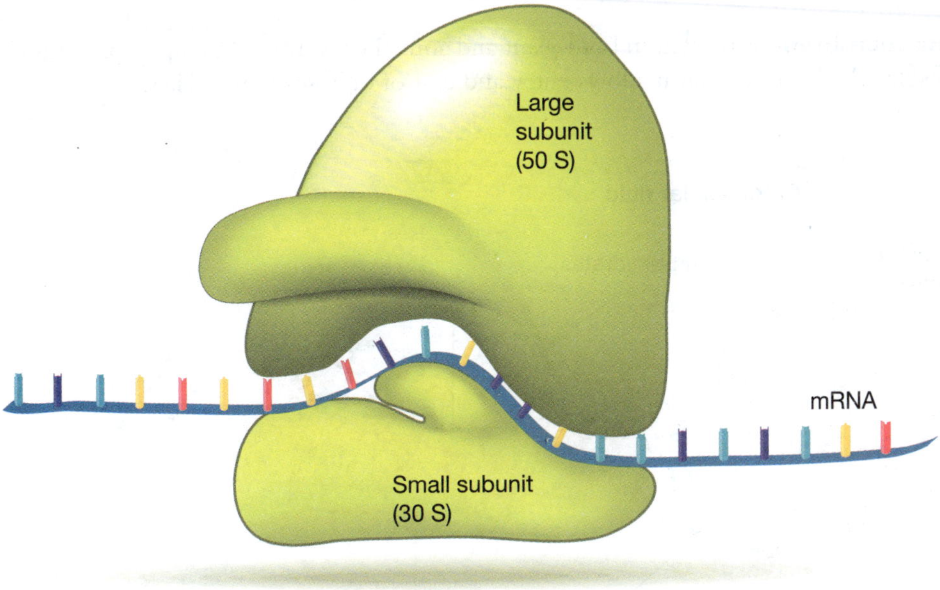

Figure 1.9 Diagram showing ribosome structure

Info Bytes!

The RNA known as ribonucleic acid (RNA) is what gives ribosomes their "rib"—the instructions needed to make proteins.

Cytoplasmic Inclusions

Inclusion bodies lie free in the cytoplasm. They help in storage of reserve materials, for example, phosphate granules.

Eukaryotic Cells

All eukaryotic cells possess a true nucleus, that is, their genetic material is surrounded by a nuclear envelope. All protists, fungi, plants and animals are eukaryotes. They possess membrane-bound organelles, such as endoplasmic reticulum, mitochondria, Golgi bodies, etc.

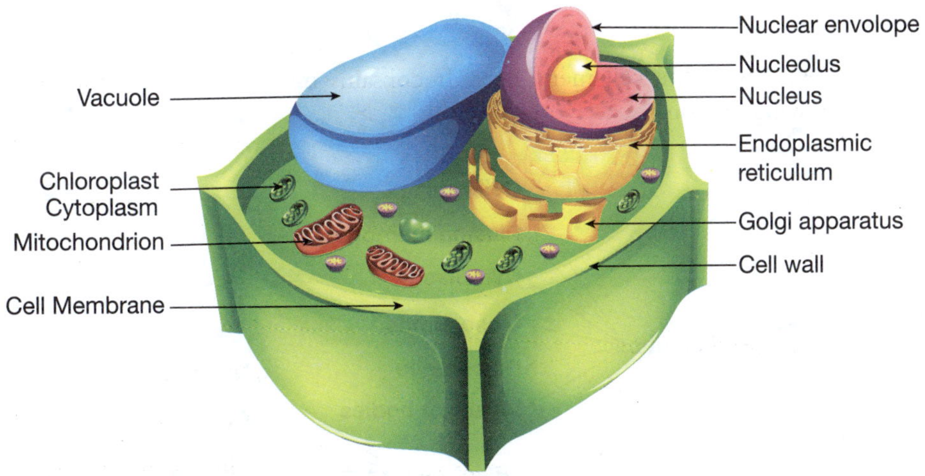

Figure 1.10 A typical plant (eukaryotic) cell

All eukaryotic cells typically have:

Cell Wall

Plant cells are surrounded by a non-living, rigid, permeable outer layer known as **cell wall**. Cell wall is a typical feature of plant cell. It provides structural integrity and protection to the cell. It is made up of cellulose. Cell walls of adjacent cells are joined together by a jelly-like substance called **middle lamella**.

Konnect

Cell wall is a characteristic of plant cell, fungi, bacteria and few protists. A cell without cell wall is called protoplast.

Cell Membrane

Cell membrane also known as **plasma membrane** is present in both plant and animal cells. It is made up of proteins and lipids. Cell membrane is semi-permeable which means that it allows entry and exit of only some materials.

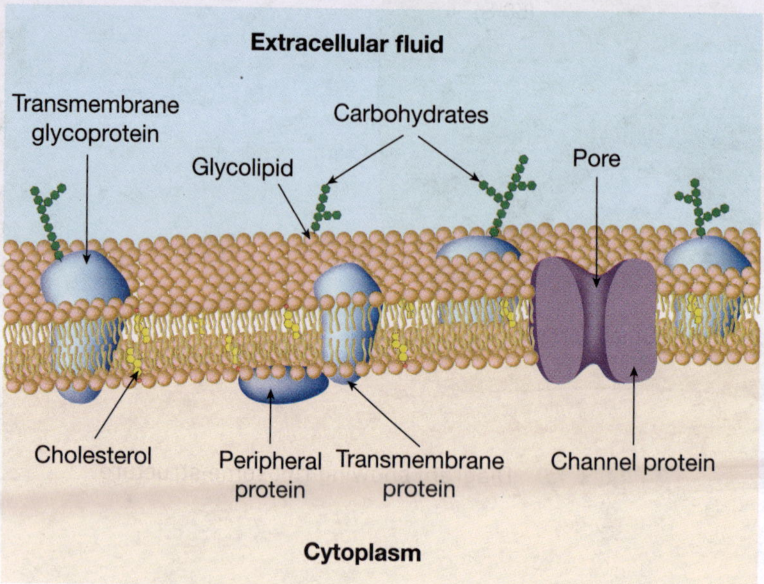

Figure 1.11 Structure of plasma membrane

Protoplasm

The living material comprising cytoplasm, nucleus and other organelles is called protoplasm.

Cytoplasm

Cytoplasm is the fluid content inside the cell membrane. It contains many membrane-bound organelles. These are discussed in detail in the following section.

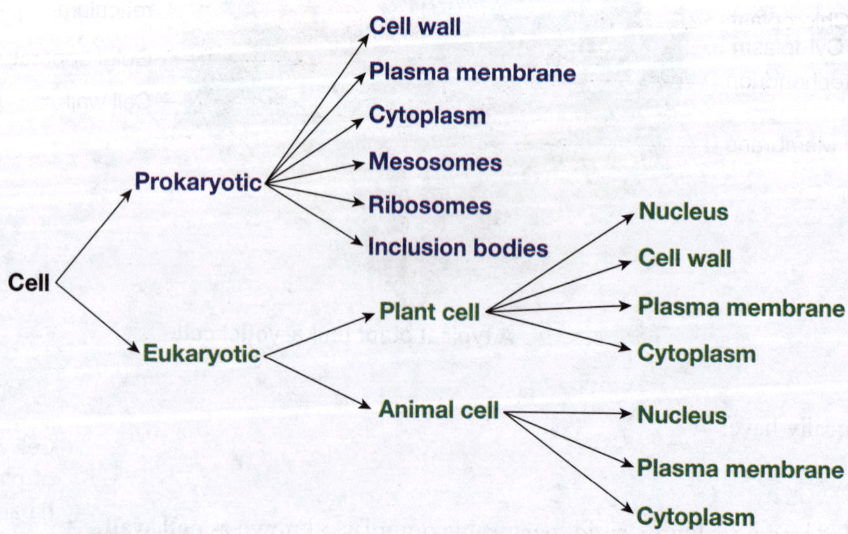

Figure 1.12 Cellular organization in prokaryotes and eukaryotes

Table 1.2 Difference between Prokaryotes and Eukaryotes

Parameter	Prokaryotes	Eukaryotes
1. Size	The size is generally small (1-10μm).	The size is generally large (5-100μm).
2. Nucleus	The true nucleus is absent.	Nucleus is present.
3. Membrane bound Organelles	Membrane-bound cell organelles absent, such as endoplasmic reticulum, Golgi complex, etc.	Membrane-bound cell organelles present.
4. Number of chromosomes	It has single chromosome.	It has more than one chromosome.

Cell Organelles

An organelle is a unit inside the cell that performs a special function. The various functions performed by a cell are actually divided among the organelles, that is, there is a division of labour inside the cell in eukaryotic cells. This division of labour is absent in prokaryotic cells. For example, energy production is performed by mitochondria, photosynthesis by plastids, etc. The various cytoplasmic organelles are given below:

Endoplasmic Reticulum

Endoplasmic Reticulum is a large network or reticulum of membrane-bound tiny tubular structures that start at the nuclear membrane and extend into the cytoplasm. The structure of endoplasmic reticulum is sac like. They are mainly involved with the synthesis, folding, modification and transport of proteins.

Endoplasmic reticulum is of two types:

1. **Rough Endoplasmic Reticulum (RER):** It possesses ribosomes on its surface and hence got the name. It helps in protein synthesis. It also plays a vital role in protein folding and protein sorting.
2. **Smooth Endoplasmic Reticulum (SER):** It lacks ribosomes on its surface. They are a major site for lipid synthesis and responsible for the metabolism of carbohydrates. They are also involved in the detoxification of poisons.

Figure 1.13 Rough ER and Smooth ER

Ribosomes

Ribosomes consists of dense and spherical particles which are present in both prokaryotic and eukaryotic cells. Ribosomes are made up of proteins and ribonucleic acid. 80S Ribosomes are found in eukaryotic cells, which include cells of plants, animals, fungi, and protists. The "S" in 80S stands for "Svedberg unit". It has two sections called units - the large subunit (50 S) and the smaller subunit (40 S). These are the sites of protein manufacture. They are found either free in cytoplasm or attached with RER. These are not bound by any membrane and are complex of ribonucleic acid (RNA) and proteins.

Figure 1.14 Golgi Apparatus

Golgi Apparatus

Golgi Apparatus was first described by Camillo Golgi in 1898. It consists of a system of many, flat disc-shaped sacs called cisternae, which are arranged parallel to each other. Its functions include packaging, storing and dispatching of various products received from endoplasmic reticulum.

It remains in close association with endoplasmic reticulum. It is involved in synthesis of complex sugars and lysosome.

Lysosomes

These are composed of tiny spherical structures surrounded by a single membrane. They contain many digestive enzymes that are manufactured in RER. Lysosomes are known as waste disposal system of the cell as they help in cleaning the cell by removing the worn out or damaged cellular organelles. They are also called suicide bags of cells as they can digest their own cell, if anything happens to the cell structure or if the cell gets damaged.

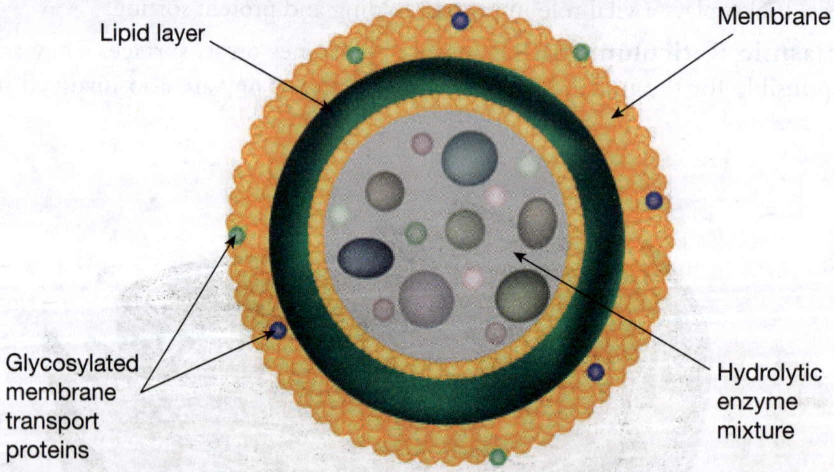

Figure 1.15 Structure of lysosome

Mitochondria

They are referred to as the powerhouses of the cell. They are the main sites for energy production. They produce energy in the form of adenosine triphosphate (ATP). ATP is known as energy currency of the cell. Number of mitochondria per cell vary according to the physiological activity of the cell.

Structure of a typical mitochondrion is characterized by the following features.

- It is surrounded by a double-membrane covering.
- Its outer membrane is porous and inner membrane is deeply folded.
- The foldings of inner membrane are called cristae which increase the surface area.

- The compartment enclosed by inner membrane is called matrix.
- Mitochondrion possesses its own DNA (single circular DNA) and ribosomes.

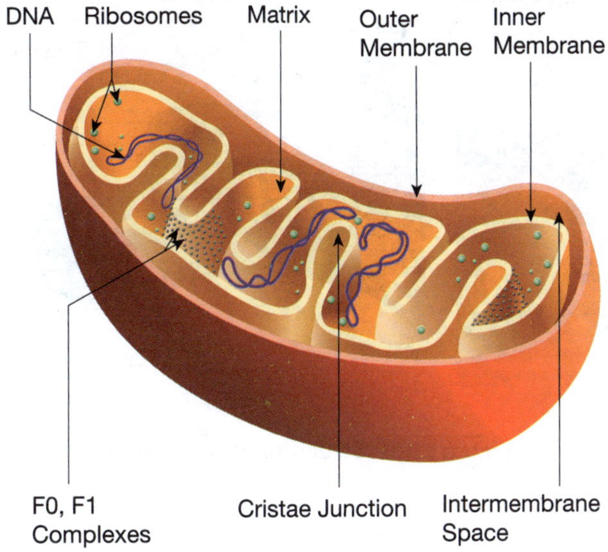

Figure 1.16 Structure of mitochondria

Plastids

Plastids are present in most plant cells and are absent in animal cells. Like mitochondria, plastids contain their own DNA and ribosomes. Plastids are of three types as detailed below:

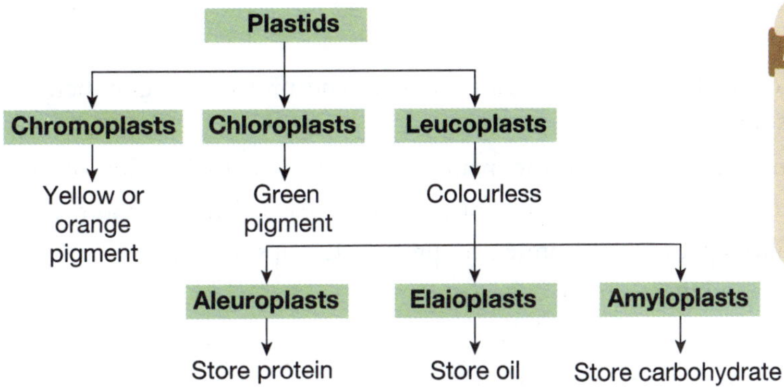

Figure 1.17 Division of plastids on the basis of presence or absence of pigments

> **Info Bytes!**
>
> Green chilly is converted into red chilly due to conversion of chloroplast into chromoplast.

1. **Chromoplasts**: Coloured plastids in which chlorophyll is absent and contain yellow or orange pigment. They are found in fruits, flowers, etc.
2. **Chloroplasts:** Consist of a green pigment called chlorophyll and its main function is **photosynthesis**. Chloroplast is also known as kitchen of the cell.
3. **Leucoplasts:** They are white or colourless and its main function is storage. Depending upon the storing material, leucoplasts are of three types: Aleuroplast (stores protein), elaioplast (stores oil), amyloplast (stores carbohydrate).

Structure of Chloroplasts

It is surrounded by a double-membrane covering. It consists of many membrane-bound flat discs called **thylakoids** which have chlorophyll. Thylakoids are arranged in stacks called **grana**. The matrix found inside the chloroplast is called stroma. Thylakoids of different grana are connected by stromal lamellae.

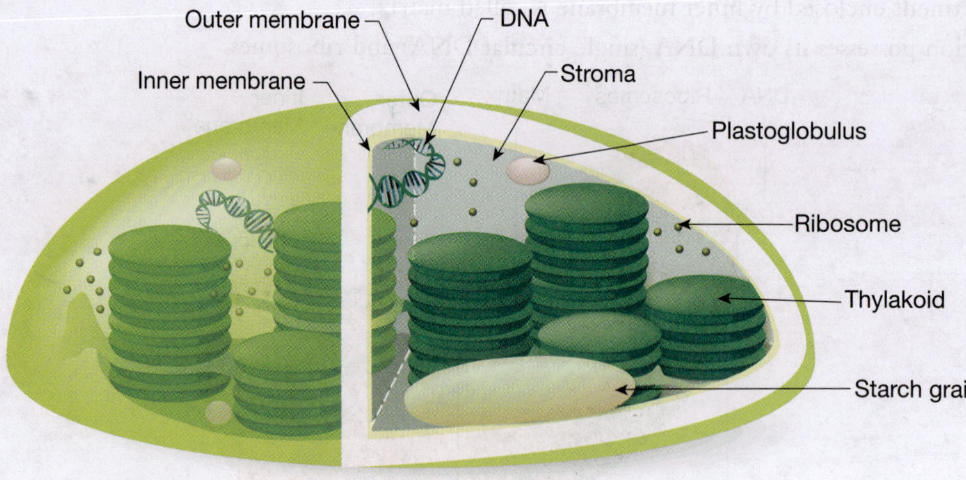

Figure 1.18 Structure of choloroplast

Vacuoles

These are membrane-bound spaces seen in the cytoplasm of mainly plant and fungal cells. These are the storage sacs that store proteins, amino acids, water and other nutrients. They can occupy up to 90% of the cell volume in plant cells. In animal cells, vacuoles are either very small or absent. A vacuole is surrounded by a single membrane called tonoplast. The substance present inside the vacuole is called cell sap. It provides turgidity and rigidity to the plant cell.

Microbodies

Microbodies are a kind of organelles present in plants, animals and protozoa. They include peroxisomes, glyoxysomes, glycosomes and hydrogenosomes.

1. **Peroxisomes:** Present in cytoplasm and the main function is the detoxification of toxic substances.
2. **Glyoxysomes:** Specialized peroxisomes in plants. These are used in the breakdown and conversion of fatty acids.
3. **Glycosomes:** Specialized peroxisomes present in protists. It helps in glycolysis and oxidation of fatty acids.
4. **Hydrogenosomes:** Found in anaerobic eukaryotes.

Centrosomes

They are only found in animal cells. They are not bounded by a membrane and consist of two centrioles. Centrosomes help in cell division.

Nucleus

It was first described by Robert Brown in the year 1831. It is a large, spherical, centrally placed organelle found in eukaryotic cells which is the central controlling unit of all the activities of a cell.

Structure of nucleus

It is surrounded by a double membrane called nuclear envelope or nuclear membrane. Nuclear envelope contains many pores called nuclear pores. Nuclear pores allow transport of materials across nucleus, that is, from nucleus to cytoplasm and from cytoplasm to nucleus. Liquid substance present inside the nucleus is called nucleoplasm. It contains nucleolus and chromatin material.

Nucleolus is the place where ribosomes are synthesized, it is rich in protein and RNA molecules. Chromatin material consists of thin, thread-like, entangled structure composed of deoxy-ribonucleic acid (DNA) and proteins. At the time of cell division, chromatin condenses to form rod-shaped chromosomes.

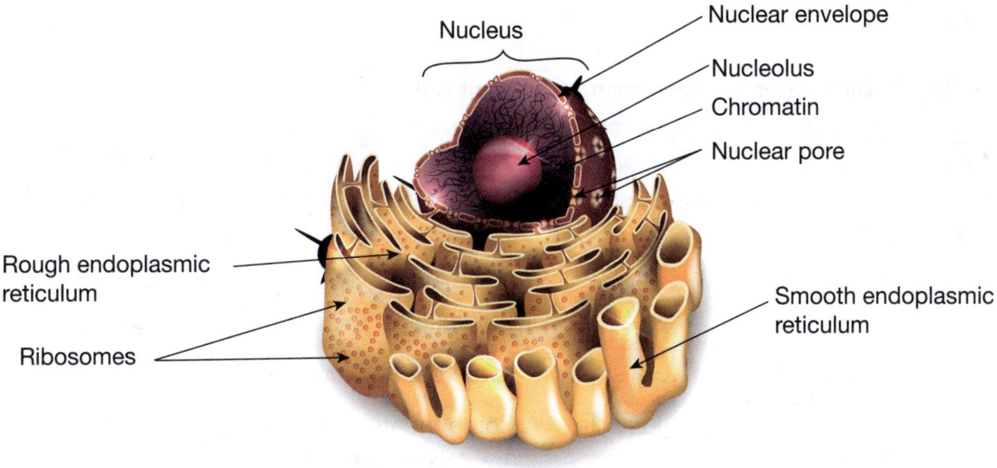

Figure 1.19 Anatomy of the nucleus and endoplasmic reticulum

DNA stores information necessary for the inheritance of characters from parents to offspring. Functional segments of DNA are called genes.

Nucleus is the control centre of the cell as it controls the metabolic activities of the cell. Usually there is only one nucleus per cell, but there are exceptions where more than one nucleus is present, for example, *Paramoecium*. Some mature cells even lack nucleus, for example, RBCs.

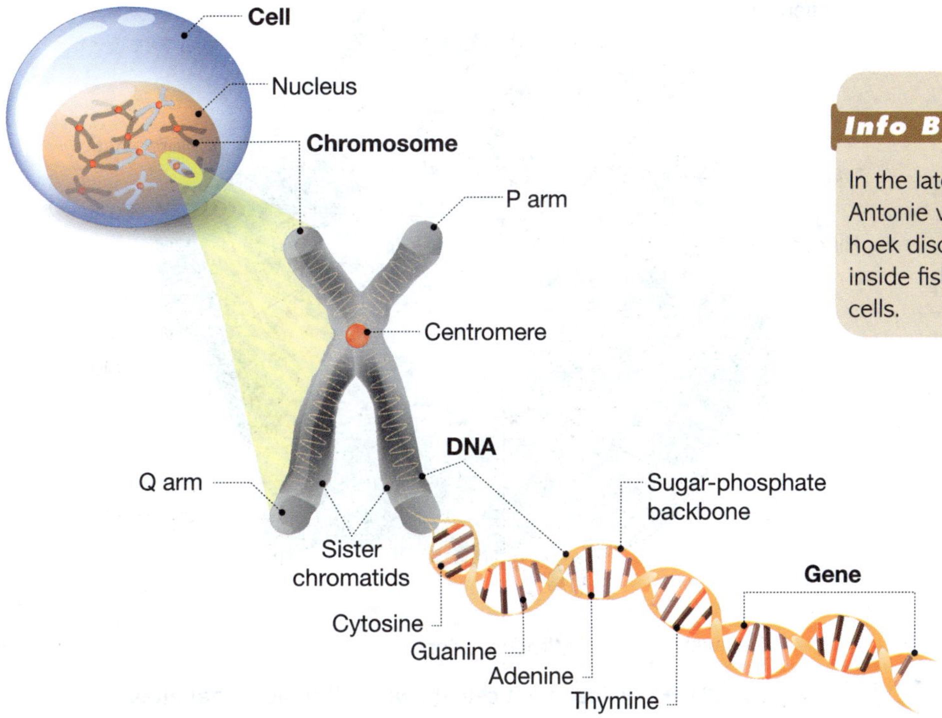

Figure 1.20 Organization and compaction of DNA inside nucleus

Info Bytes!

In the late 1600s, Antonie van Leeuwenhoek discovered DNA inside fish blood skin cells.

Comparative Study of Animal and Plant Cells

Animal and plant cells show considerable variations in their structure. Plant cells are surrounded by an outer cell wall, whereas cell wall is absent in animal cells. Similarly, plastids and large central vacuoles are present in plant cells but are absent in animal cells.

Table 1.3 Differences between animal and plant cell

Animal cell	Plant cell
Usually smaller in size and oval in shape.	Comparatively larger in size and rectangular in shape.
Cell wall is absent.	Cell wall is present and is made up of cellulose.
Vacuoles are either absent or very small.	Large central vacuole.
Golgi complex is well developed and is present near the nucleus.	Components of Golgi complex in plant cells are called dictyosomes.
Centrosome and centrioles are present.	Centrosomes and Centrioles are absent.
Plastids are absent.	Plastids are present.
Reserve food is stored in the form of glycogen.	Stored in the form of starch or oil.

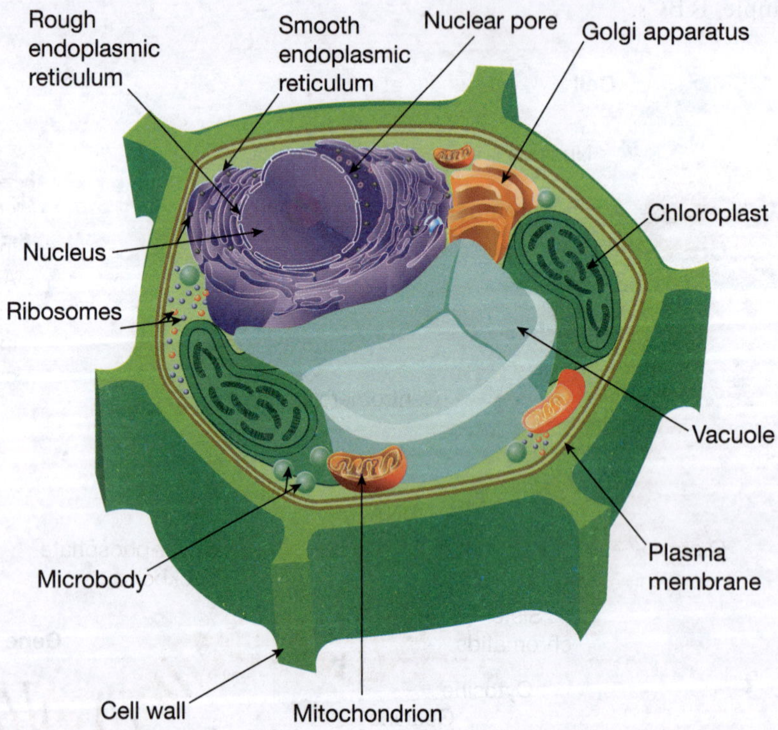

Figure 1.21 A typical plant cell showing all major organelles

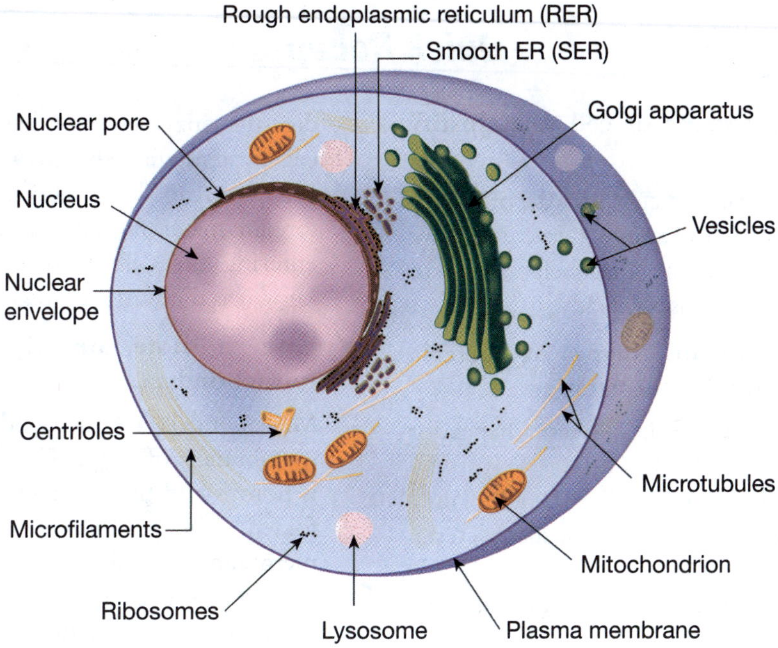

Figure 1.22 A typical animal cell showing all major organelles

Various Organelles and their Role in Cell

Functions of all the cell organelles are collaborated in the table below:

Table 1.4 Functions of different organelles in a cell

Organelles	Functions
Endoplasmic reticulum	Protein and lipid synthesis
Ribosome	Protein manufacture
Golgi complex	Packaging, storing and dispatching of materials received from the endoplasmic reticulum
Lysosome	Waste disposal system of the cell
Vacuole	Storage sac, provides rigidity and turgidity to the plant cell
Mitochondria	Power house of the cell
Chloroplast	Photosynthesis
Centrosome	Cell division
Nucleus	Control centre of the cell, contains chromosomes

Quick Recap

✔ **The size and shape of cell vary. Justify the statement.**

The size and shape of cells vary according to their function. For example, nerve cells have an elongated structure that helps them to conduct nerve impulses quickly.

✔ **List out the various shapes of bacteria and give examples for each.**

There are basically four different shapes for bacteria:

(i) Rod-shaped or bacillus, *Lactobacillus*.

(ii) Spherical-shaped or coccus bacteria, *Staphylococcus*.

(iii) Spiral-shaped bacteria, for example, *Treponema*.

(iv) Comma-shaped bacteria, for example, *Vibrio cholerae.*

✔ **What are inclusion bodies?**

Inclusion bodies are structures that lie free in the cytoplasm and help in storage of reserve materials, for example, phosphate granules, glycogen granules, etc.

✔ **Differentiate between rough and smooth endoplasmic reticulum.**

Rough endoplasmic reticulum	Smooth endoplasmic reticulum
Looks rough under the microscope	Looks smooth under the microscope
Ribosomes are present on the surface	Ribosomes are absent
Involved in protein synthesis	Major site for lipid synthesis and is also involved in the detoxification of poisons

✔ **Which organelle is the waste disposal system of the cell and why is it called so?**

Lysosome is known as the waste disposal system of the cell. Lysosome encloses many digestive enzymes and it helps in cleaning the cell by removing the worn out or damaged cellular organelles. It also helps in destroying foreign materials such as bacteria and virus entering the cell. Hence, lysosome is also known as the waste disposal system of the cell.

✔ **Give a note on the structure of mitochondria.**

Mitochondria are surrounded by a double-membrane covering. The outer membrane is porous and the inner membrane is deeply folded. The folding seen inside the inner membrane is called crista and it helps in increasing the surface area. The compartment enclosed by inner membrane is called matrix. Mitochondria possess their own DNA (single circular DNA) and ribosomes.

✔ **Why do nerve cells have extensions?**

Nerve cells, or neurons, have extensions called axons and dendrites. These structures help neurons receive and transmit electrical signals efficiently across long distances within the body, allowing for rapid communication between different parts of the body.

✔ **Can bacteria be multi-shaped within a single species?**

While most bacterial species tend to have a consistent shape, some species can exhibit different shapes depending on environmental conditions, a phenomenon known as pleomorphism. For example, some bacteria might transition between a *coccus* and rod shape under specific circumstances.

✔ **What role do glycogen granules play in a cell?**

Glycogen granules are storage units for glycogen, a polysaccharide. Cells store glycogen as an energy reserve. When the cell requires energy, glycogen is broken down into glucose, which can be used in cellular respiration to produce ATP, the cell's main energy currency.

Cell Division

The process in which a cell divides into two daughter cells is called cell division. In single-celled organisms, one cell division results in the formation of two new organisms, for example, *Amoeba*, bacteria, etc. Cell division in prokaryotes is much simpler as compared to that in eukaryotes.

Cell Division in Prokaryotes

The common type of cell division seen in prokaryotes is binary fission. The fully grown parent divides into two halves resulting in two new cells.

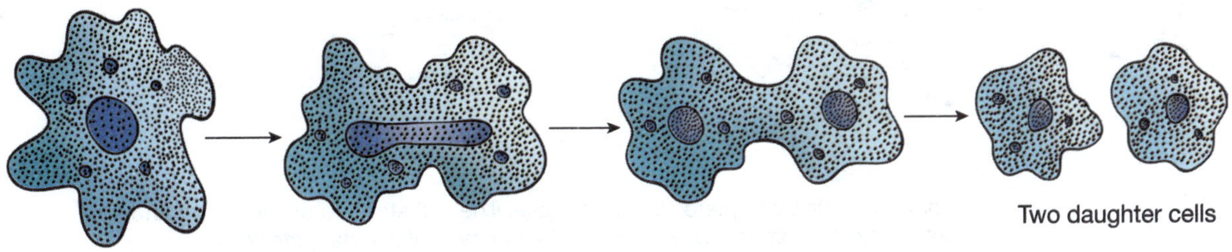

Figure 1.23 Binary fission in *Amoeba*

Significance of Cell Division

Reproduction: A cell must divide in order to reproduce. Hence, cell division is responsible for continuity of life.

Replacement of cells: All cells have a limited lifespan. They die after completing their lifetime. New cells are needed to replenish this loss. Hence, cell division helps in replacement of dead cells by producing new cells.

Growth: We observe that an infant grows into an adult, a small seed grows into a big tree, etc. These changes are possible only when the number of cell increases in order to increase the size of the organism. Hence, cell division enables the living organisms to grow.

Cell Division in Eukaryotes

Cell division in eukaryotes is more complex than in prokaryotes and involves two processes:

1. **Karyokinesis**: Division of nucleus
2. **Cytokinesis**: Division of cytoplasm

There are two different types of cell division:

1. Mitosis
2. Meiosis

Mitosis

In this type of cell division, there is formation of daughter cells that are genetically identical to the parent cell. Daughter cells produced by mitosis possess the same number of chromosomes as that of parent cell. Mitosis helps to replace the worn-out cells and also helps in the growth. Mitosis can be divided into four stages:

1. Prophase
2. Metaphase
3. Anaphase
4. Telophase

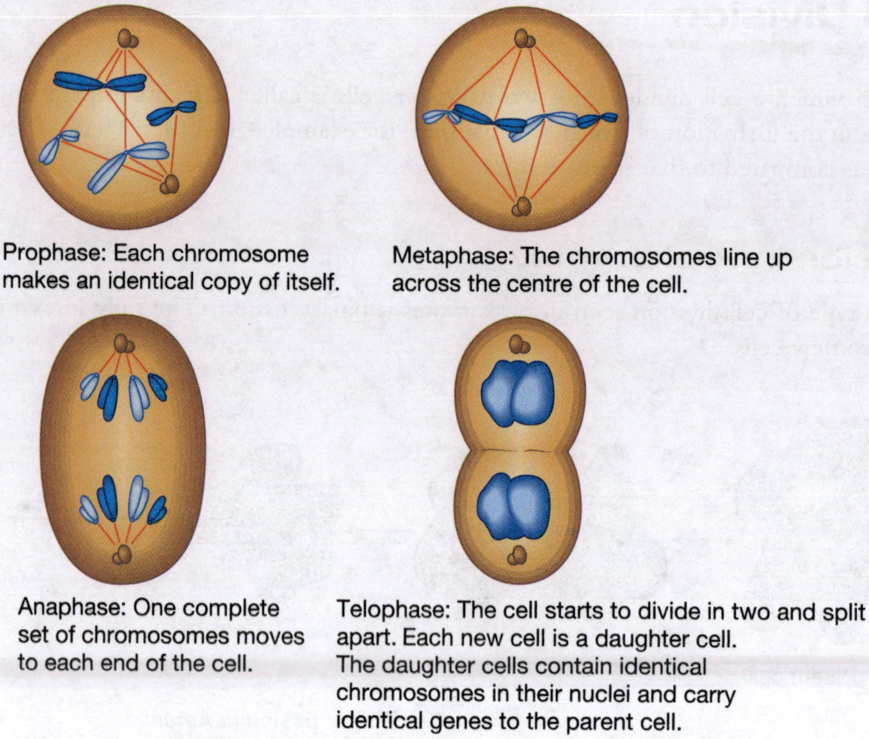

Figure 1.24 Phases of mitosis

In animals, mitosis occur generally only in diploid somatic cells, whereas in some lower plants, mitosis can occur in haploid cells also. A cell that contains two sets of chromosomes (two copies of the same chromosome) is called diploid cell, whereas a cell with only one set of chromosome is called haploid cell. Mitosis occurs as a part of normal cell growth and to replace worn out cells.

> **Info Bytes!**
> A somatic cell is any cell other than reproductive cells or germ cells.

Meiosis

Meiotic cell division occurs during sexual reproduction leading to gamete formation. The daughter cells formed possess half the number of chromosomes than the parent cell. Meiosis involves two sequential cycles of divisions:

1. Meiosis I
2. Meiosis II

Both meiosis I and II can be again subdivided into four stages as given below.

Stages of Meiosis I	Stages of Meiosis II
a. Prophase I	a. Prophase II
b. Metaphase I	b. Metaphase II
c. Anaphase I	c. Anaphase II
d. Telophase I	d. Telophase II

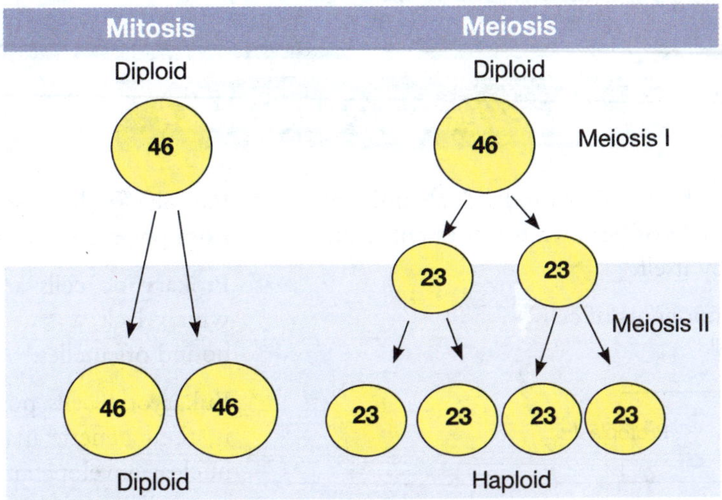

Figure 1.25 Diagrammatic representation of Mitosis and Meiosis

Main differences between mitosis and meiosis are given in the table below.

Table 1.5 Differences between Mitosis and Meiosis

Mitosis	Meiosis
Occurs generally in somatic cells	Occurs in germ cells
During normal growth of cell	During gamete formation
Chromosome number remains the same	Chromosome number reduces to half
Two daughter cells are formed	Four daughter cells are formed

Quick Recap

✔ **Give a brief note on the differences between unicellular and multicellular organisms.**

Unicellular organisms	Multicellular organisms
Composed of only one cell	Contain many cells
Single cell performs the entire functions	Various functions are performed by many cells
For example, *Amoeba* and bacteria	For example, plants and animals

✔ **Describe the process of cytokinesis.**

Cytokinesis is the phase in cell division where the cytoplasm divides, leading to the separation of two daughter cells. Following mitosis, the cell's cytoplasm and its components get distributed between the two forming cells, ensuring both cells have the necessary components to function effectively.

✔ **What is meiosis and why is it crucial for sexual reproduction?**

Meiosis is a type of cell division resulting in four daughter cells, each with half the number of chromosomes of the parent cell. It is vital for sexual reproduction as it produces haploid gametes, ensuring offspring inherit a combination of genetic material from both parents.

✔ **Explain the term "centromere" and its role during cell division.**

The centromere is the region of a chromosome where the two sister chromatids are most tightly connected. During cell division, spindle fibres attach to the centromere, ensuring that each daughter cell receives an identical set of chromosomes.

✔ **Give a note on diploid cell and haploid cell with an example.**

A cell that contains two sets of chromosomes, that is, two copies of the same chromosome, one from each parent is called diploid cell. Haploid cell contains only one set of chromosomes, for example in human diploid cells (any cell other than gametes), there are 46 chromosomes whereas human gamete is haploid with 23 chromosomes.

POINTS TO REMEMBER

- ✔ A cell is the smallest individual unit of matter capable of performing all essential life processes by itself.
- ✔ Major components of cells

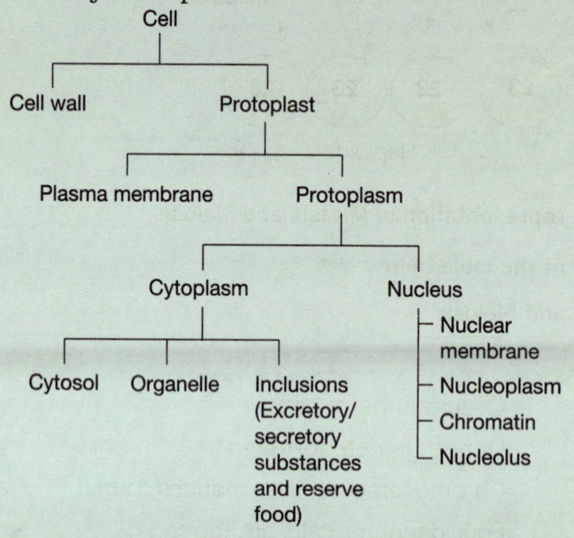

- ✔ Cell theory was proposed by Matthias Jakob Schleiden (1838) and Theodor Schwann (1839).
- ✔ Rudolf Virchow stated that new cells arise from pre-existing cells.
- ✔ Prokaryotic cells are primitive type of cells which lack a true nucleus and membrane bound organelles.
- ✔ Eukaryotic cells possess a true nucleus, that is, their genetic material is surrounded by a nuclear envelope and have membrane-bound organelles, example, plant cell.
- ✔ The process in which a cell divides into two daughter cells is called cell division.
- ✔ Cell division is required for growth, reproduction and repair.
- ✔ Mitosis is that type of cell division which results in the formation of daughter cells that are genetically identical to the parent cell.
- ✔ Meiosis is that type of cell division which occurs during sexual reproduction leading to gamete formation.

PRACTICE QUESTIONS CLASSROOM WING

Very Short Answer Type Questions

Directions for questions from 1 to 15:
Fill in the blanks in each question.

1. The smallest cell is ________.
2. The largest cell is ________.
3. *Lactobacillus* is ________ shaped.
4. *Mycoplasma* lacks ________.
5. Phosphate granules are examples for ________.
6. The term 'cell' is derived from the Latin word '*cellula*', meaning 'little room.' The term was coined by ______________ in 1665.
7. According to the Cell Theory, all organisms are made up of cells, and the cell is the basic ____________ unit of life.
8. All eukaryotic cells possess a true nucleus, and their genetic material is surrounded by a ____________.
9. In plant cells, the cell wall is made up of ____________.
10. Golgi complex components in plant cells are called ____________.
11. Specialized peroxisomes in plants are called ________.
12. Thin thread-like structure present inside the nucleus is called ________.
13. The membrane surrounding vacuole is called ________.
14. In plant, reserve food is stored in the form of________.
15. Plant cell wall is made up of ________.

Directions for questions from 16 to 25:
For each of the following questions, four choices have been provided. Select the correct alternatives.

16. Which of the following scientists made an important addition to the Cell Theory, stating that new cells arise from pre-existing cells?
    (a) Robert Hooke
    (b) Matthias Jakob Schleiden
    (c) Rudolf Virchow
    (d) Theodor Schwann
17. What is the function of Teichoic Acid in the structure of the bacterial cell wall?
    (a) Cell wall integrity
    (b) Protein synthesis
    (c) Storage of reserve materials
    (d) Respiration
18. What is the main function of peroxisomes?
    (a) Photosynthesis
    (b) Detoxification of toxic substances
    (c) Synthesis of proteins
    (d) Storage of carbohydrates
19. Which organelle is referred to as the "powerhouse of the cell"?
    (a) Endoplasmic Reticulum
    (b) Lysosomes
    (c) Mitochondria
    (d) Golgi Apparatus
20. What is the primary function of the Rough Endoplasmic Reticulum (RER)?
    (a) Lipid synthesis
    (b) Protein synthesis
    (c) Carbohydrate metabolism
    (d) Detoxification
21. Match the following

A. Inclusion bodies	(i) Eukaryotic
B. Mesosome	(ii) Protein manufacture
C. Ribosome	(iii) Cell wall formation
D. Golgi complex	(iv) Nutrient reservoir

	A	B	C	D
(a)	(iii)	(ii)	(i)	(iv)
(b)	(iv)	(iii)	(i)	(ii)
(c)	(iii)	(i)	(iv)	(ii)
(d)	(iv)	(iii)	(ii)	(i)

22. Select the wrong statement.
    (a) Plant cells are surrounded by a living, rigid outer layer called cell wall.
    (b) Plant cell wall is made up of cellulose.
    (c) Bacterial cell wall is made up of peptidoglycan.
    (d) Both prokaryotic and eukaryotic plasma membranes are composed of lipids and proteins.

23. Adjacent plant cells are joined together by
(a) Middle lamella
(b) Plasmodesmata
(c) Mesosomes
(d) Plasma membrane

24. Which of the following is the correct statement?
(a) Endoplasmic reticulum is the site of protein manufacture in bacteria.
(b) The membrane-bound inclusion bodies help in the storage of nutrients in prokaryotes.
(c) The living material inside the cell is called protoplasm.
(d) Mesosome is the cell wall extension that helps in photosynthesis.

25. Which one of the following is/are included in protoplasm?
(i) Nucleus
(ii) Cytoplasm
(iii) Organelles
(iv) Nucleoplasm
(a) (i) and (ii)
(b) (i), (ii), (iii)
(c) (ii) only
(d) (i), (ii), (iii), (iv)

Short Answer Type Questions

26. Who postulated cell theory and what are the main postulates?
27. How does *Staphylococcus* differ from *Lactobacillus* in shape?
28. What are mesosomes and write their significance in the cells?
29. Explain the role of the nucleus in eukaryotic cell.
30. Discuss the significance of the endoplasmic reticulum in cellular functions.
31. Why plasma cell membranes are said to be semipermeable in nature?
32. Make a comparison between the three types of leucoplasts.
33. Differentiate between nucleolus and nucleoid.
34. Which organelles are known as semi-autonomous organelles and why are they called so?
35. Differentiate between animal cell and plant cell based on structure.

Essay Type Questions

36. Discuss the contributions of Robert Hooke, Matthias Jakob Schleiden, Theodor Schwann, and Rudolf Virchow in the development of the Cell Theory.
37. Explain the intricate relationship between the various organelles in a eukaryotic cell and how their specialization contributes to cellular functions.
38. Which organelle is known as 'power house' of the cell and why is it called so?
39. What are vacuoles and what is their role in a cell?
40. Explain the structure of cell nucleus.

PRACTICE QUESTIONS COMPETITION WING

Level 1: Apply your Concepts

Directions for questions from 1 to 5:
Fill in the blanks in each question.

1. The first living cell was discovered by ________
2. ________ is the basic structural and functional unit of life.
3. Take the odd one out.

   Amoeba, Bacteria, Plant, Honeybee.
4. The concept '*Omnis cellula e cellula*' was put forward by ________.
5. The term 'protoplasm' was coined by ________.
6. Complete the table given below:

	Structure	Features
(a)	________	Plasma membrane extension
(b)	Ribosome	Site of ________
(c)	________	Joins adjacent plant cells
(d)	Plasma membrane	Made up of ________ and ________
(e)	________	Living material inside the cell
(f)	________	Fluid content inside the cell membrane

Level 2: Review your Concepts

7. Why Golgi apparatus is seen associated with endoplasmic reticulum inside the cell?
8. Why lysosomes are also called 'suicide bags' of cells?
9. Animal cells differ from plant cells in a number of ways. What is one specific characteristic that makes their mode of nutrition significantly different?
10. Both bacteria and plants contain cell walls yet they are entirely different from each other. Justify.
11. A eukaryotic cell has mitochondria in their cytoplasm which are specially organized organelles that perform respiration. Whereas prokaryotic cells lack mitochondria yet they perform respiration. How?

Level 3: Assess Your Concepts

12. There are two substances, namely 'A' and 'B' which are present outside a cell. Substance 'A' is able to pass through the cell and 'B' is not able to do so. How can you justify this selective movement of substances in and out of a cell?
13. After one round of division, a cell receives half the number of chromosomes as in the parent cell. What can be inferred about the nature of the parent cell?

AT

PRACTICE QUESTIONS NEET SPECIAL WING

Multiple-Answer Type Questions

Questions number 1 to 5 are multiple-choice questions. Each question has FOUR options (a), (b), (c), and (d). ONE OR MORE THAN ONE of these four option(s) is/are the correct answer(s).

1. Which of the following are characteristics of prokaryotic cell wall?
   (a) Forms outermost boundary of animal cell
   (b) It is made up of peptidoglycan and carbohydrates
   (c) It is made up of cellulose and fatty acid
   (d) Forms outermost boundary and integrity of prokaryotes

2. Which of the following are not the functions of Lysosomes?
   (a) Waste disposal system of cells
   (b) Protein manufacturing machine
   (c) Detoxification of poisons
   (d) Suicide bags of the cell

3. Identify the colourless plastids among the following:
   (a) Chloroplast
   (b) Elaioplast
   (c) Amyloplast
   (d) Aleuroplast

4. Identify the functions of the microbodies from the following:
   (a) Detoxification of toxins
   (b) Breakdown of proteins
   (c) Breakdown and conversion of fatty acids
   (d) Glycolysis and oxidation of fatty acids

5. Events that take place in mitosis include:
   (a) Formation of two identical daughter cells
   (b) Chromosome number is retained
   (c) Event takes place during gamete formation
   (d) It takes place in the germ cells

Comprehension-Based Questions

A. Read the paragraph given below and answer the questions number 6 to 11:

Cell division is the process in which a mother cell divides to give rise to daughter cells. In prokaryotes the process of cell division is much simple in comparison to eukaryotes. Eukaryotic cell division is of two major types- mitosis and meiosis. Mitosis is the process which takes place to produce new body cells mainly for growth and healing. On the other hand, meiosis occurs to produce gametes or sex cells. Cells which are about to go through cell division undergo a series of well-timed events which include stages of growth, DNA duplication and ultimately division that produces genetically identical cells. The cyclical series of events which involve cell growth and cell division is called cell cycle. The cell cycle consist of two major events- Interphase and mitosis. Interphase consists of growth phases and DNA replication whereas in mitosis cellular division takes place. Mitosis further consists of two major divisions- i. Karyokinesis (nuclear division) and cytokinesis (cytoplasmic division). Karyokinesis is further divided into Prophase, Metaphase, Anaphase and Telophase.

6. Meiosis occurs in:
   (a) Somatic cells (b) Germ cells
   (c) Mitochondria (d) Chloroplast

7. Which stage of mitosis involves division of cytoplasm?
   (a) Cytokinesis (b) Karyokinesis
   (c) Anaphase (d) Telophase

8. Number of cells and gametes formed by mitosis and meiosis respectively are:
   (a) 2, 8 (b) 4, 8
   (c) 2, 4 (d) 4, 2

9. Cell division is required:
   (a) For reproduction, replacement and growth
   (b) For cell build up
   (c) For gaining power
   (d) For replacement

10. Cell division in prokaryotes occur by:
    (a) Mitosis
    (b) Meiosis
    (c) Binary fission
    (d) Both a and b

11. Match the following:

Characteristic	Male
(i) Karyokinesis	(a) Division of nucleus
(ii) Anaphase	(b) The cell starts to divide and split into two identical daughter nuclei
(iii) Telophase	(c) Chromosomes line up at the equator
(iv) Metaphase	(d) Division of cytoplasm
(v) Cytokinesis	(e) Chromosomes move towards the poles

B. Read the paragraph given below and answer the questions number 12 to 17:

Cell organelles are mini machines that have special functions in the cell. They perform various functions in the cell and show division of labour. Many organelles can be membranous or non-membranous. Organelles without membranes include cell wall, ribosomes, these organelles are found both in prokaryotic as well as eukaryotic cell. Vacuoles, lysosomes, golgi apparatus, endoplasmic reticulum have a single membrane and are found only in eukaryotic cells. Nucleus, mitochondria and chloroplast are double membrane structures present only in eukaryotic cells. Plasma membrane is selectively permeable and is formed of lipid bilayer and proteins. In plant cells an extra boundary of cell wall is present which is protective in nature. Cytoplasm is a jelly like ground material in which all the organelles are embedded inside. Nucleus is a control centre for all the cellular activities.

12. Which of the following organelles do not possess their own DNA?
(a) Mitochondria
(b) Nucleus
(c) Chloroplast
(d) Endoplasmic reticulum

13. The organelle/s which is/are absent in prokaryotic cells is / are
(a) Endoplasmic reticulum
(b) Nucleus
(c) None of the above
(d) All of the above

14. Which of the following is found in plant cell but absent in animal cell?
(a) Centrosome
(b) Nucleus
(c) Ribosomes
(d) Cell wall

15. Which of the following statement is true about golgi apparatus?
(a) Made up of flat disc like shaped sacs called cisternae
(b) Sites of protein manufacture
(c) Suicide bags of the cell
(d) Possess their own DNA and ribosomes.

16. Which among the following organelles are comparable to prokaryotic cell?
(a) Mitochondria
(b) Chloroplast
(c) Endoplasmic reticulum
(d) Both a and b

17. Match the following:

Column – A	Column – B
(i) Centrosome	(a) Energy production
(ii) Chloroplast	(b) Protein production
(iii) Mitochondria	(c) Digestive system of cell
(iv) Lysosome	(d) Present only in plant cell
(v) Ribosome	(e) Present only in animal cell

ANSWER KEYS

Crossword

Across

5. Nucleoid 6. Schleiden 10. Gram 12. SDS gel 14. Meiosis

Down

1. Schwann 2. Virchow 3. Cytoplasm 4. Division 7. Eukaryotic
8. Peptidoglycan 9. Ribosomes 11. Mitosis 13. Theory

Classroom Wing

Very Short Answer Type Questions

1. *Mycoplasma* 2. Ostrich egg 3. Rod 4. Cell wall 5. Inclusion bodies
6. Robert Hooke 7. Structural 8. Nuclear envelope 9. Cellulose 10. Dictyosomes
11. Glyoxysomes 12. Chromatin material 13. Tonoplast 14. Starch
15. Cellulose 16. (c) 17. (a) 18. (b) 19. (c) 20. (b)
21. (d) 22. (a) 23. (a) 24. (c) 25. (d)

Competition Wing

Level 1: Apply your Concepts

1. Anton Van Leeuwenhoek 2. Cell 3. Bacteria (all others are eukaryotes)
4. Rudolf Virchow 5. J.E. Purkinje

NEET Special Wing

Multiple-Answer Type Questions

1. (b, d) 2. (a, d) 3. (b, c, d) 4. (a, c, d) 5. (a, b)

Comprehension-Based Questions

6. (b) 7. (a) 8. (c) 9. (a) 10. (a)
11. (i) → (a); (ii) → (e); (iii) → (b); (iv) → (c); (v) → (d)
12. (d) 13. (b) 14. (d) 15. (a) 16. (d)
17. (i) → (e); (ii) → (d); (iii) → (a); (iv) → (c); (v) → (b)

Hints and Explanations

CLASSROOM WING

Short Answer Type Questions

26. Cell theory was proposed by Matthias Jakob Schleiden (1838) and Theodor Schwann (1839) and was later modified by Rudolf Virchow. The main postulates are:

- All organisms are made up of cells.
- Cell is the basic structural and functional unit of life.
- All cells arise from pre-existing cells only (*Omnis cellula e cellula*)

27. *Staphylococcus* is spherical in shape whereas *Lactobacillus* is rod shaped.

28. Mesosomes are the structures seen in prokaryotes, which are formed by the plasma membrane extension into the cell. Mesosomes help in cellular activities, such as cell wall formation, respiration, etc.

29. The nucleus is the central controlling unit of eukaryotic cell. It houses the genetic material, controls metabolic activities, and plays a vital role in cell division. The nucleolus within the nucleus is responsible for ribosome synthesis.

30. The endoplasmic reticulum is crucial for protein synthesis, folding, modification, and transport. The Rough ER, with ribosomes, is involved in protein synthesis, while the Smooth ER is essential for lipid synthesis, carbohydrate metabolism, and detoxification.

31. Plasma cell membranes are made up of proteins and lipids. They are said to be semi-permeable membranes, as they allow entry and exit of only some materials and prevent others.

32. Leucoplasts are colourless plastids that mainly function in storage. Leucoplasts are of three types, such as aleuroplasts, elaioplasts and amyloplasts. Aleuroplasts store protein, elaioplasts store oil, whereas amyloplasts store carbohydrates (starch).

33.

Nucleolus	Nucleoid
Present in eukaryotes	Present in prokaryotes
Region inside the nucleus that is rich in RNA and protein	Region in the cytoplasm where genetic material is present

34. Mitochondria and plastids are known as semiautonomous organelles as they contain their own DNA and ribosomes. Both of them can synthesize some of the proteins required for the function on their own.

35.

Animal cell	Plant cell
Usually smaller in size and oval in shape	Comparatively larger in size and rectangular in shape
Cell wall is absent	Present (cellulose)
Vacuoles are either absent or very small	Large central vacuole
Golgi complex are well developed and present near nucleus	Components of Golgi complex in plant cells are called dictyosomes
Centrosome and centrioles are present	Absent
Plastids are absent	Present

Essay Type Questions

36. Robert Hooke discovered cells in 1665, and Matthias Jakob Schleiden and Theodor Schwann proposed the Cell Theory in 1838 and 1839, respectively. Rudolf Virchow added the concept of cells arising from pre-existing cells in 1868. Together, their contributions formed the foundation of the Cell Theory, stating that all organisms are made up of cells, and the cell is the basic structural and functional unit of life.

37. In a eukaryotic cell, organelles collaborate to perform specialised functions. The endoplasmic reticulum synthesises and modifies proteins, which are then transported to the Golgi apparatus for packaging and dispatch. Lysosomes play a vital role in cellular cleaning, while mitochondria act as Energy Powerhouses producing ATP. Plastids, exclusive to plant cells, contribute to processes like photosynthesis. The nucleus, the control centre, regulates activities, and the vacuole provides structural support. This collaborative specialization ensures the cell's survival, growth, and functioning.

38. Mitochondria are known as powerhouses of the cell as they are the main sites for energy production. Mitochondria produce energy required for various chemical activities in the form of adenosine triphosphate (ATP). ATP is known as energy currency of the cell. The number of mitochondria per cell vary according to the physiological activity of the cell.

39. Vacuoles are membrane-bound spaces seen in the cytoplasm. They are the storage sacs that store proteins, amino acids, water and other nutrients. In plant cells, vacuoles can occupy up to 90% of the volume, whereas in animal cells, vacuoles are either very small or absent. Vacuoles are surrounded by a single membrane called tonoplast and the substance inside a vacuole is called cell sap. Vacuoles provide turgidity and rigidity to the plant cell.

40. Nucleus is the large, spherical, centrally placed organelle found in eukaryotic cells. It is surrounded by a double membrane called nuclear envelope. Nuclear envelope contains many pores called nuclear pores, which allow the transport of materials across the nucleus. The liquid substance present inside the nucleus is called nucleoplasm, which contains nucleolus and chromatin material. Nucleolus is the region, which is rich in RNA and protein and not enclosed by a membrane. Chromatin is the thread-like structure composed of DNA and proteins. DNA stores information necessary for the inheritance of characters from parents to offsprings.

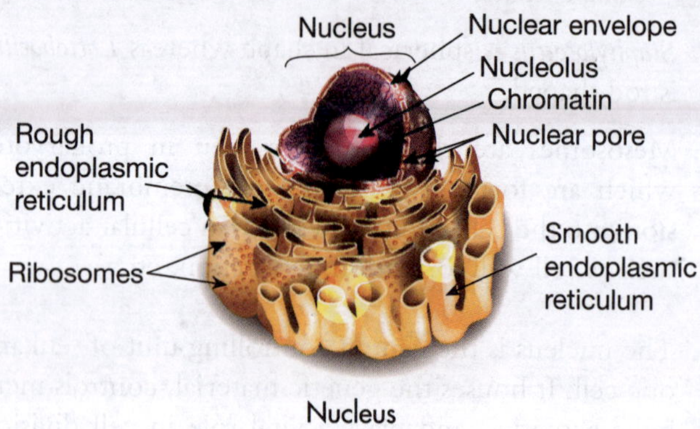

COMPETITION WING

Level 1: Apply your Concepts

6.

Structure	Features
Mesosome	Plasma membrane extension
Ribosome	Site of protein manufacture
Middle lamella	Joins adjacent plant cells
Plasma membrane	Made up of lipids and proteins
Protoplasm	Living material inside the cell
Cytoplasm	Fluid content surrounded by the cell membrane

Level 2: Review your Concepts

7. Main functions of Golgi apparatus include packaging, storing and dispatch of various products received from the endoplasmic reticulum. It modifies the proteins and lipids received from the endoplasmic reticulum and also directs these products to various targets. For this reason, Golgi apparatus remains in close association with the endoplasmic reticulum.

8. Lysosomes are tiny, spherical structures that contain many digestive enzymes. If any kind of disturbance is caused to the cell structure and its organization, lysosomes burst releasing their enzymes. These enzymes are capable of digesting their own cell. Therefore, lysosomes are also known as 'suicide bags' of cells.

9. Plant cells contain a specialized organelle, chloroplast which contains chlorophyll, while animal cells do not contain chloroplast. Plants are capable of synthesizing their own food with the help of chloroplast in the presence of sunlight and water, whereas animal cell is not able to do so. Hence, plants show autotrophic mode of nutrition and animals show heterotrophic mode of nutrition.

10. Bacterial cell walls are different from the cell walls of plants in terms of composition. Major component of bacterial cell wall is peptidoglycan while the major component of plant cell wall is cellulose.

11. The plasma membranes of prokaryotic cells (bacterial cells) have special ingrowths that are called mesosomes which are the sites for respiration. Therefore, a prokaryotic cell is able to carry out the process of respiration even without mitochondria.

Level 3: Assess Your Concepts

12. Cells are surrounded by a selectively permeable membrane called plasma membrane. This membrane is designed such that it allows certain specific molecules to pass through it while not allowing certain molecules to do so. Hence, this selective nature of plasma membrane guides the entry and exit of substances around the cell.

13. Since the number of chromosomes is reduced to half in the process of division, it can be inferred that the division is through meiosis. We know that meiosis occurs only in germ cells. Hence, the parent cell is a germ cell.

NEET SPECIAL WING

Multiple-Answer Type Questions

1. Cell wall forms the outermost layer of the prokaryotic cell. It provides integrity to the cell. It is made up of peptidoglycan, which in turn is made up of carbohydrates.

2. Lysosomes are known as waste disposal system of the cell as they help in cleaning the cell by removing the worn out or damaged cellular organelles. They are also called suicide bags of cells as they can digest their own cell, if anything happens to the cell structure or if the cell gets damaged.

3. Leucoplasts are white or colourless and its main function is storage. Depending upon the storing material, leucoplasts are of three types: Aleuroplast (stores protein), Elaioplast (stores oil), amyloplast (stores carbohydrate).

4. There are many different microbodies like peroxisomes, glyoxysomes, hydrogenosomes and glycosomes. Peroxisomes is responsible for the detoxification of toxic substances. Glyoxysomes are used in the breakdown and conversion of fatty acids. Glycosomes helps in glycolysis and oxidation of fatty acids.

5. In mitosis, there is formation of daughter cells that are genetically identical to the parent cell. Daughter cells produced by mitosis possess the same number of chromosomes as that of parent cell. Mitosis helps to replace the worn-out cells and also helps in the growth.

Comprehension-Based Questions

A.

6. Meiosis takes place in the germ cells and is responsible for the formation of gametes.

7. Division of cytoplasm and organelles happens in Cytokinesis

8. Mitosis involves formation of 2 daughter cells and Meiosis involves formation of four gametes from a single germ cell.

9. Mitosis is required for reproduction, replacement and growth which enables the living organisms to grow.

10. Prokaryotic cells have a simple system of cell division. They divide via binary fission.

11. Match the following:

    Karyokinesis is the division of nucleus which divides the nuclear material into two.

    (i) (a)

    In Anaphase the separated chromatids move towards the opposite poles.

    (ii) (e)

    In Telophase the cell starts to divide in two and split apart. Each new cell is a daughter cell. The daughter cells contain identical chromosomes in their nuclei and carry identical genes to the parent cell.

    (iii) (b)

    In Metaphase all the chromosomes align themselves at the equatorial plane.

    (iv) (c)

    Cytokinesis involves division of cytoplasm and its inclusions.

    (v) (d)

B.

12. Mitochondria and chloroplast have their DNA and are able to produce their own proteins, on the other hand endoplasmic reticulum do not have their proteins.

13. Prokaryotic cells do not have membrane bound organelles and hence both nucleus and endoplasmic reticulum is absent in prokaryotic cells.

14. Centrosome is only found in animal cells whereas nucleus and ribosomes are found in both the cells. Cell wall is the protective structure found only in plant cells.

15. Golgi apparatus consists of a system of many, flat disc-shaped sacs called cisternae, which are arranged parallel to each other. It remains in close association with endoplasmic reticulum and is involved in synthesis of complex sugars and lysosome.

16. Since both mitochondria and chloroplast have their own DNA present in them and are able to produce their own proteins, these organelles are comparable to a prokaryotic cell.

17. Match the following:

Centrosomes are only found in animal cells. They are not bounded by a membrane and consist of two centrioles. Centrosomes help in cell division.
(i) (e)

Chloroplast consist of a green pigment called chlorophyll and its main function is photosynthesis. Chloroplast is also known as kitchen of the cell.
(ii) (d)

Mitochondria are referred to as the powerhouses of the cell. They are the main sites for energy production. They produce energy in the form of adenosine triphosphate (ATP). ATP is known as energy currency of the cell.
(iii) (a)

Lysosomes are also called suicide bags of cells as they can digest their own cell, if anything happens to the cell structure or if the cell gets damaged.
(iv) (c)

Ribosomes are the sites of protein manufacture. They are found either free in cytoplasm or attached with RER. These are not bound by any membrane and are complex of ribonucleic acid (RNA) and proteins.
(v) (b)

CHAPTER

2

Tissues and Body Movements

Remember

Before beginning this chapter, you should be able to:

- Recall the basic structure of a cell
- Recall the basic characteristics of a cell
- Remember the meaning and organization of tissue
- Differentiate between mitosis and meiosis

Key Ideas

After completing this chapter, you should be able to:

- Understand different types and functions of plant tissues
- Understand different types and functions of animal tissues
- Understand the body movements of unicellular organisms
- Describe human skeletal system

A Tribute to Anton Van Leeuwenhoek (1632-1723)

Anton Van Leeuwenhoek (1632–1723) is widely regarded as the first virtuoso of microscopy, illuminating the enigmatic realm of the microscopic world. He was a self-taught scientist who created superior microscopes that allowed him to investigate unseen ecosystems teeming with "animalcules"—his term for microorganisms. Leeuwenhoek painstakingly revealed the existence of bacteria, protozoa, sperm cells, and intricate tissue structures, fostering a deep understanding of biological entities and body movements.

His insatiable curiosity and keen observations provided profound insights into cellular life and tissue complexity, catalysing advances in cellular biology and medicine. Leeuwenhoek's discoveries were so pioneering that he was awarded honorary membership in the prestigious Royal Society of London for his contributions to scientific knowledge and microbiological exploration.

His revolutionary explorations underpin modern microbiology and have left indelible imprints on the realms of science related to tissues and body movements, ensuring his enduring recognition in the annals of scientific discovery.

FUN TIME

CROSSWORD

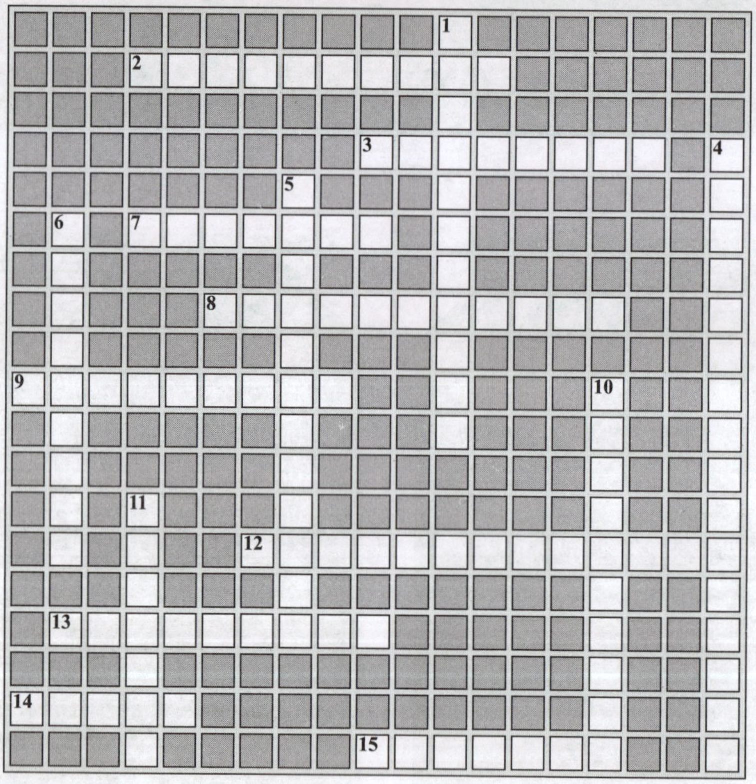

Across

2. The cells which constitute the fat storage tissue in our body
3. The appendages having whip-like appearance
7. Waxy coating on the leaves which reduces rate of transpiration
8. Temporary projections of plasma membrane in eukaryotes
9. Short branches arising from the cell body of a neuron
12. Type of joints which include knee joint
13. The tissue which makes up the ear lobes
14. Name of thigh bone
15. The tissues which connect muscles to bones

Down

1. The bones of a palm
4. The layer of tissue which forms lining for internal organs in animals
5. Dead permanent tissue in plants
6. Single continuous layer of tissue generally present on the surface of plant parts
10. Cells which constitute bones
11. Flat bone found in the centre of chest

INTRODUCTION

In the previous chapter, we have studied that cell is the basic structural and functional unit of life. All living organisms are made up of cells, and the living world comprises both unicellular and multicellular organisms. In unicellular organisms, a single cell performs all functions or activities needed for the survival and in multicellular organisms, the work is divided among group of cells, i.e., there is a division of labour. Tissue can be defined as a group of cells either similar or dissimilar that perform a specific function, for example, muscular tissue in humans is involved in movement or locomotion, and blood connective tissue helps in transport of respiratory gases and nutrients.

Plant Tissue

Plant body is composed of different types of tissues, like meristematic tissues, vascular tissues, etc. Unlike animals, plant body is abundant in dead supportive tissues. Plants are adapted for a sedentary existence as they do not move. Because of this reason, the main requirement is structural support which can be provided by dead tissues with least maintenance.

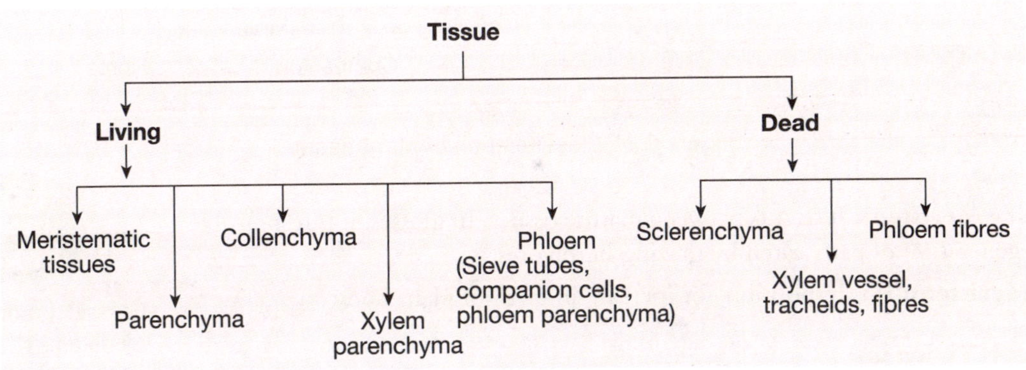

Figure 2.1 General classification of plant tissue

In plant body, the growth is not uniform, that is, their growth is confined to particular regions. Plant tissues according to their dividing abilities can be divided into two:

1. Meristematic tissue
2. Permanent tissue

Meristematic Tissue

The plant tissue that can be divided throughout its life is called meristematic tissue. Meristematic tissues can be again divided according to their position as:

1. **Apical meristem:** Seen at the growing tips of roots and shoots, and helps in increasing length of root and stem.

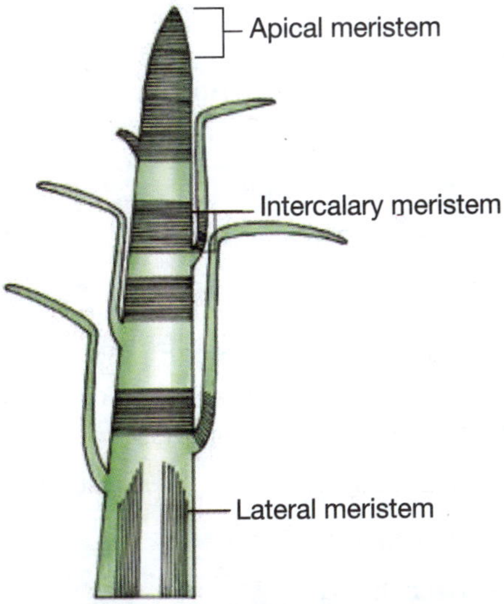

Figure 2.2 Location of different types of meristem on a plant

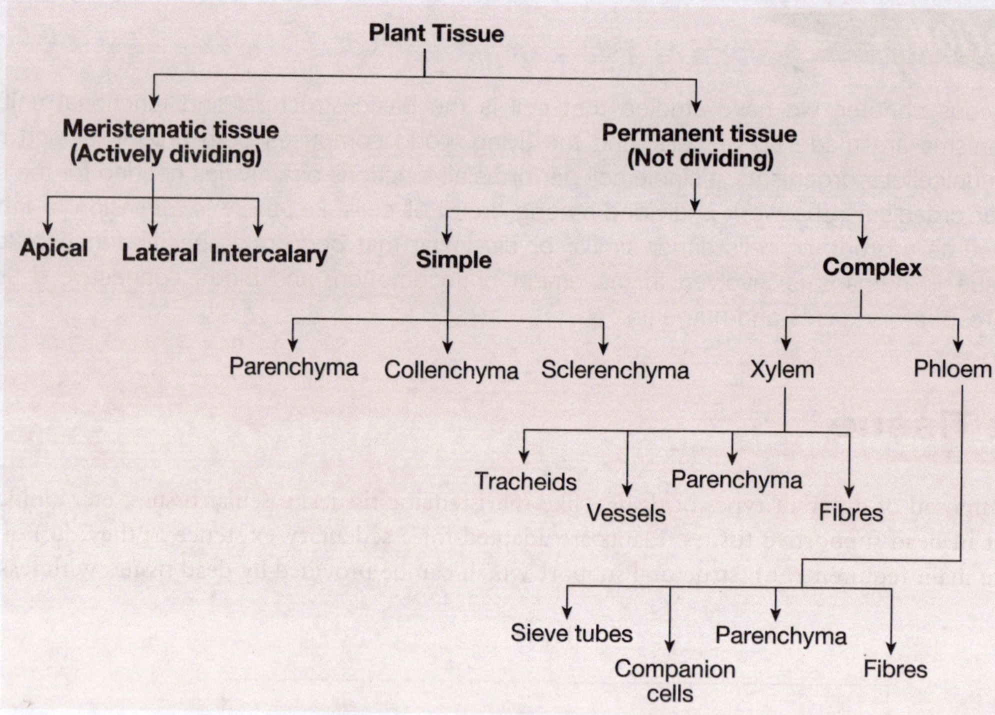

Figure 2.3 Classification of plant tissue

2. **Intercalary Meristem:** It occurs between mature tissues. In grasses, it is responsible for the regeneration of parts eaten by grazing herbivores.
3. **Lateral Meristem:** It is responsible for increase in girth of plant body.

Permanent Tissue

The tissues that do not undergo division are called permanent tissues. Meristematic tissue loses its ability to divide and takes up a permanent shape, size and function. This process is called **differentiation**. Thus, meristematic tissue undergoes differentiation to form permanent tissue.

Depending on whether they are made of one type of cell or different types of cells, permanent tissues can be divided into two:

1. Simple permanent tissue
2. Complex permanent tissue

Simple Permanent Tissue

Simple permanent tissue is made up of only one type of cell. Simple permanent tissues are of different types listed as follows:

1. Parenchyma
2. Collenchyma
3. Sclerenchyma

Konnect

Grasses do not have apical meristem. They grow by intercalary meristem and therefore pruning or cutting from tips cause no effect to their growth.
Moving or rolling on grass in lawns stimulate intercalary meristem to grow.

Info Bytes!

The term 'meristem' is derived from a Greek word 'meritos' meaning 'divided'.

Parenchyma

They are living tissues. The cells of parenchyma can be spherical, oval, polygonal or elongated. Parenchymatous cells have a thin cell wall and dense cytoplasm. They are involved in a variety of functions, like photosynthesis, gaseous exchange, food storage and other specialized functions. Parenchymal cells which contains chlorophyll and perform photosynthesis in the plants are called **chlorenchyma**.

Modified parenchyma, where the cells are arranged with regular air spaces or air chambers to facilitate diffusion of gases in aquatic plants is called **aerenchyma**. It is found in many aquatic plants such as lotus and water hyacinth.

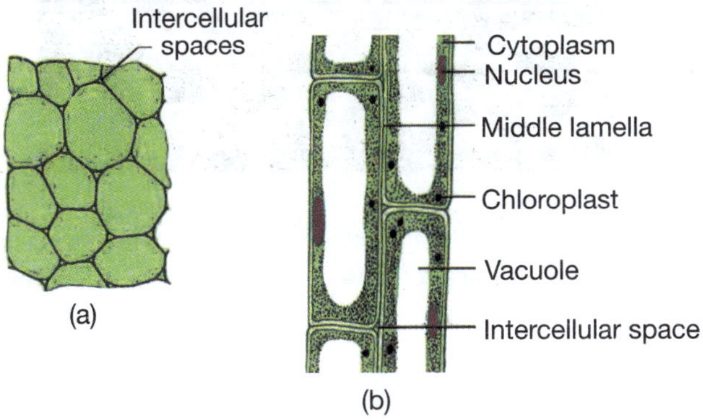

Figure 2.4 (a) Transverse section and (b) Longitudinal section **of parenchyma**

Figure 2.5 Longitudinal section of parenchyma tissue in pumpkin (cucurbits) stem

Collenchyma

Collenchyma tissue consists of living cells. Their cell wall is irregularly thickened at the corners. Their cells can be oval, spherical or polygonal. They give mechanical support and flexibility to the plants. They allow the plant to bend without breaking by providing elasticity.

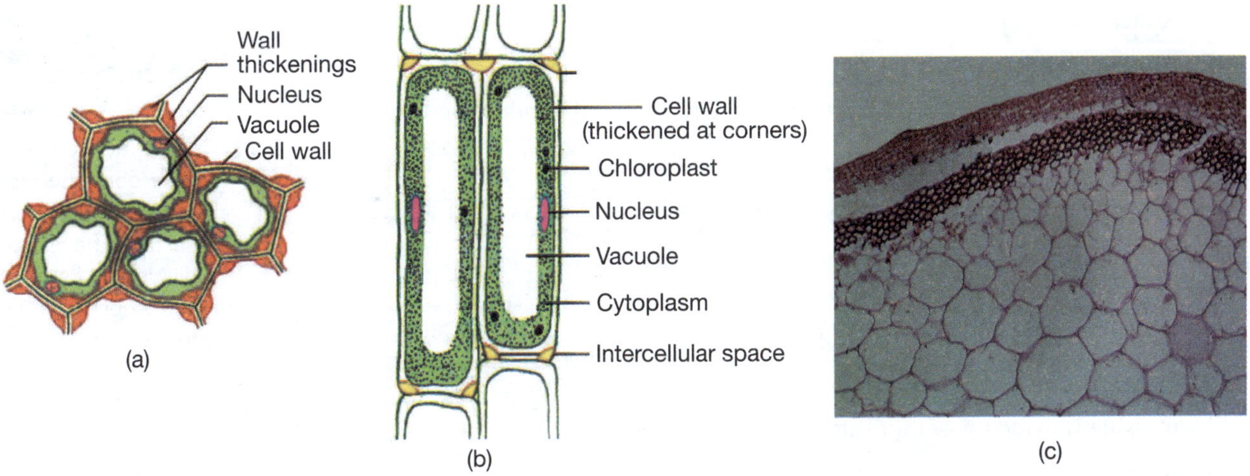

Figure 2.6 (a) Transverse section, (b) Longitudinal section of collenchyma and (c) Light microscopic cross-section of stem collenchyma

Sclerenchyma

Sclerenchyma are dead tissues. Their cells are long with narrow lumen. Their wall is thick due to lignin deposition. Sclerenchyma provides mechanical support to the organs. It is in the fruit walls of nuts, seed coats of legume, etc., for example, in coconut husk.

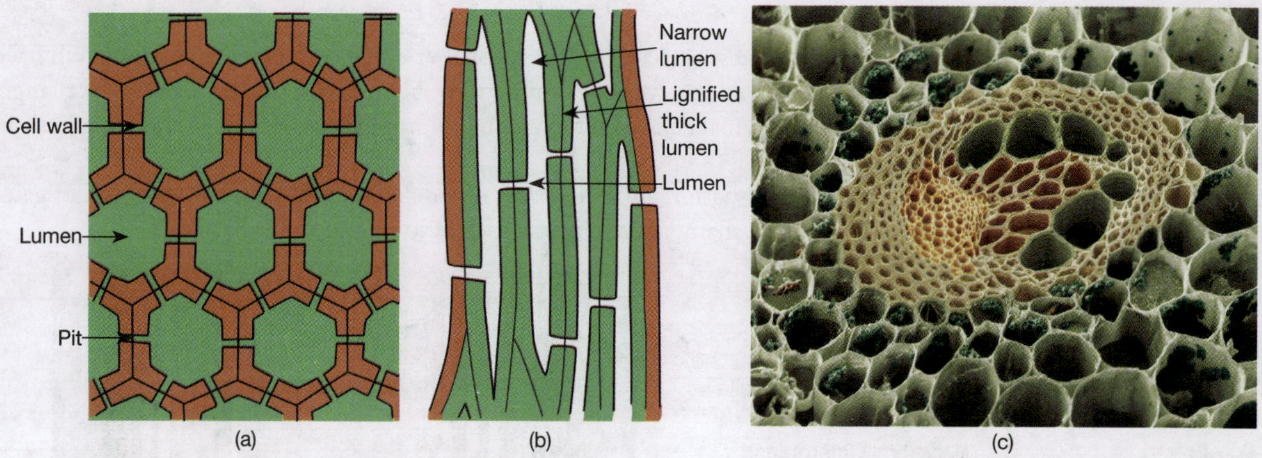

Figure 2.7 (a) Transverse section, (b) Longitudinal section of sclerenchyma and (c) Electron micrograph of cross-section of a stem of a Buttercup, showing vascular bundle embedded in parenchyma cells (yellow). At the outer edge of the vascular bundle is sclerenchyma tissue

Complex Permanent Tissues

Permanent tissue that is made up of more than one type of cell is called complex permanent tissue. There are two different types of complex permanent tissues: xylem and phloem.

Xylem

Xylem is involved in the transport of water and mineral nutrients that are absorbed through roots from the soil. It also provides mechanical support to the plant. Xylem is composed of four different elements as listed below.

1. Xylem tracheids } Main conducting elements
2. Xylem vessels }
3. Xylem parenchyma (Storage tissue and helps in lateral conduction of water)
4. Xylem fibres (Support)

Among the xylem elements, except xylem parenchyma, all others are dead cells.

Konnect

Once meristematic tissues have done their job, they transform into permanent tissues. These tissues don't divide any further but provide support and protection to the plant.

Phloem

Phloem tissues help in the transport of photosynthesis products to various parts of the plant body. It can transport food in a two way direction(i.e. both towards the shoot and root). Phloem tissue is made up of four different types of elements.

1. Sieve tubes
2. Companion cells
3. Parenchyma
4. Fibres

Among the phloem elements except phloem fibres, all are living cells. Sieve tube elements are long, tube-like and are placed end to end. Companion cells are seen associated with sieve tube elements. Phloem parenchyma mainly functions in storage. Phloem fibres provide mechanical strength.

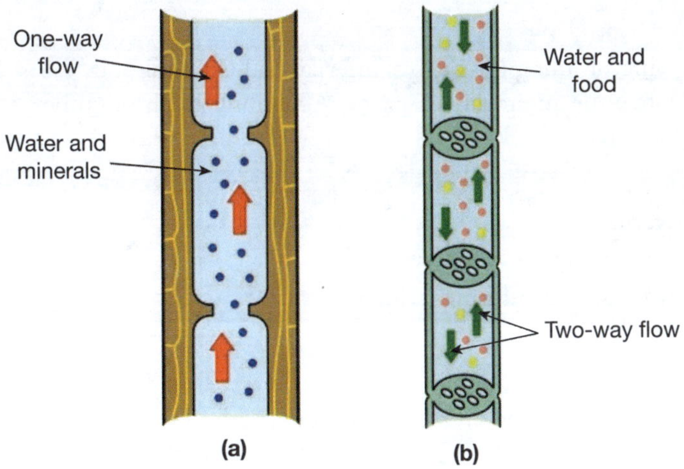

Figure 2.8 (a) Xylem (b) **Phloem**

Epidermal Tissue

It forms the outermost covering of the plant body. It consists of compactly arranged cells.

It is usually found as single continuous layer. Epidermal surface is coated with a thick waxy layer called cuticle, which prevents water loss. The specialized openings present on the epidermis are called stomata. Stomata are enclosed by a pair of kidney-shaped cells called guard cells. Guard cells regulate the opening and closing of stomata. Transpiration (loss of water in the form of water vapour) and gaseous exchange take place through stomata.

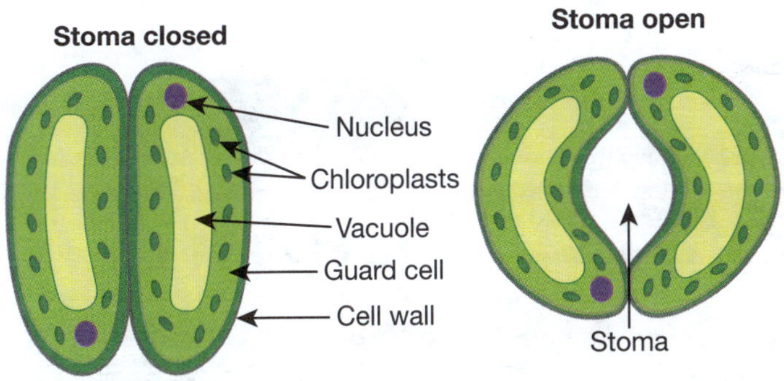

Figure 2.9 Illustration of opening and closing of stomata

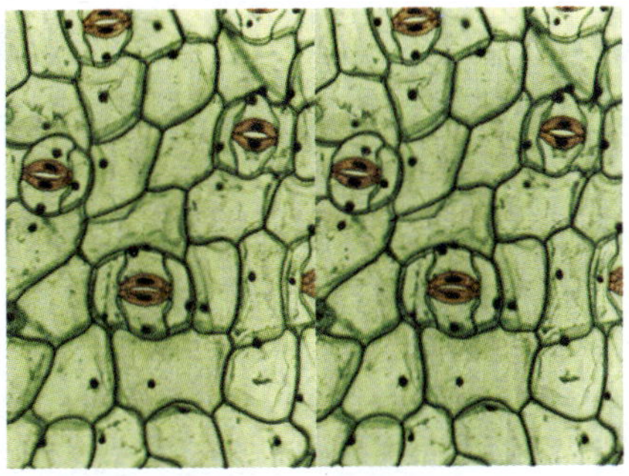

Figure 2.10 Microscopic view of guard cells and stomata in Spiderwort

Animal Tissue

Animals consist of four basic types of tissues which differ in location, structure and function as mentioned below.

1. Epithelial tissue
2. Connective tissue
3. Muscular tissue
4. Nervous tissue

These tissues are organized in a specific manner to form different types of organs.

Epithelial Tissue

Epithelial tissue provides a covering or lining for various internal and external body parts. It has protective function. The cells are compactly arranged with little intercellular spaces. According to the number of cell layers, epithelial tissue is divided into two types:

1. **Simple epithelium**
   - Composed of single layer of cells.
   - Forms lining of body cavities, ducts and tubes.
2. **Compound epithelium or stratified epithelium**
   - Consists of two or more cell layers.
   - Has protective function.

Info Bytes!

Epithelial tissues are the guardians of our body. They form the outer layer of our skin, protecting us from dust, bacteria, and much more.

According to the shape, epithelial tissue can be divided into four types:

1. **Squamous epithelium**
   - It consists of flat cells.
   - It is found in walls of blood vessels, skin, etc.
2. **Cuboid epithelium:** It consists of cube-shaped cells and is found in lining parts of the body, such as kidney tubules and the walls of respiratory bronchioles.
3. **Columnar epithelium**
   - It consists of tall pillar-like cells.
   - It is found in lining of stomach and intestine.
4. **Ciliated epithelium**
   - If the columnar or cuboidal cells bear cilia on their free surface, they are called ciliated epithelium.
   - Cilia (hair-like projections) move back and forth to move particles out of our body.
   - It is found in respiratory tract.

Info Bytes!

Columnar or cuboidal cells specialized for secretion are called glandular epithelium, for example, salivary glands.

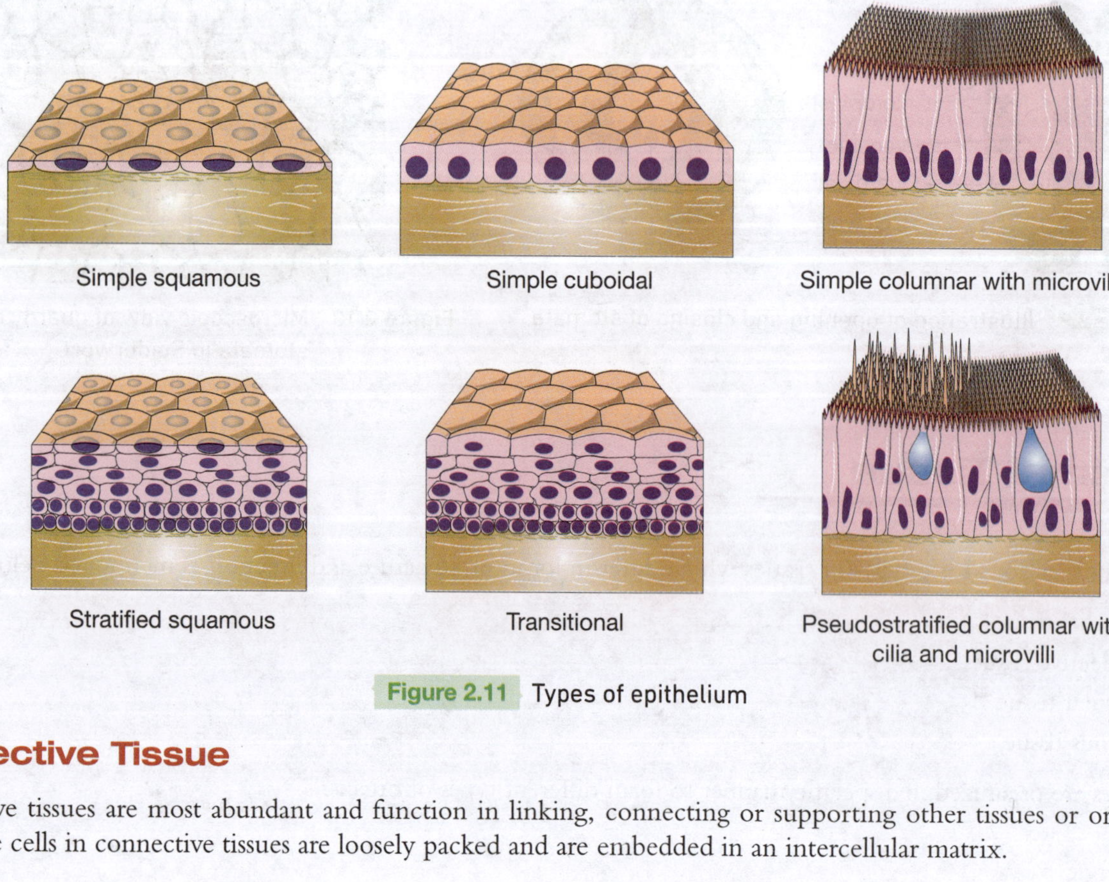

Figure 2.11 Types of epithelium

Connective Tissue

Connective tissues are most abundant and function in linking, connecting or supporting other tissues or organs in the body. The cells in connective tissues are loosely packed and are embedded in an intercellular matrix.

Different types of connective tissues are given below.

Areolar Tissue

- It is present beneath the skin, around blood vessels, nerves, etc.
- It acts as a packing or supporting tissue and fills space inside organs.

Adipose Tissue

- It is found beneath the skin and between internal organs.
- The excess nutrients in the body are converted into fats and are stored in this tissue.
- The cells of this tissue are called adipocytes.

Info Bytes!

Adipocytes can be divided into three categories: beige, brown, and white.

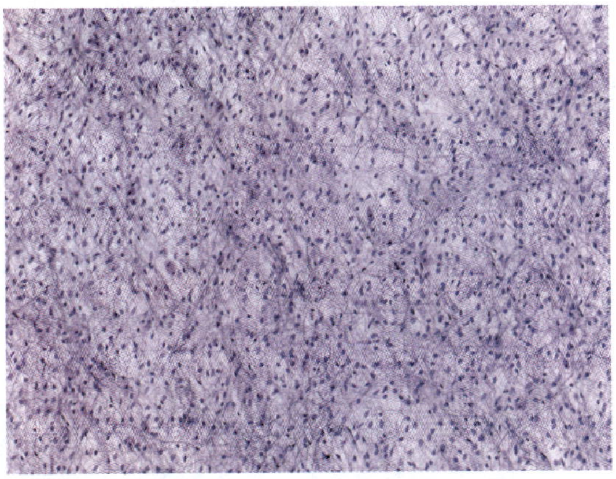

Figure 2.12 Microscopic view of areolar tissue

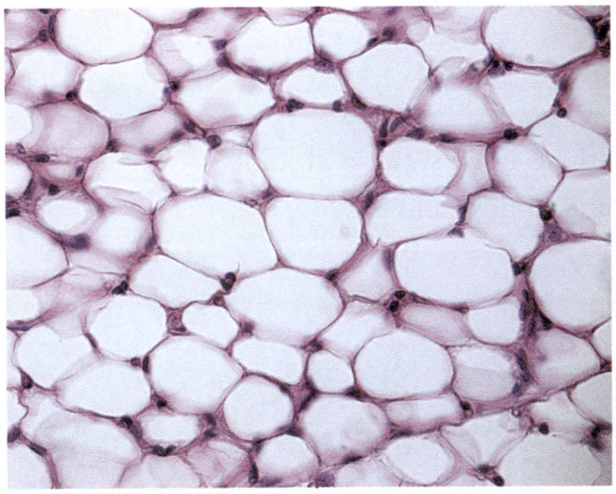

Figure 2.13 Microscopic view of adipose tissue

Blood

- It is a fluid connective tissue.
- It consists of cells, such as RBCs, WBCs and platelets.
- Blood circulates through the blood vessels—arteries, veins and capillaries.
- Its functions include transport of respiratory gases, nutrients, hormones and vitamins to various parts of body and excretory products from various parts to kidney and liver.

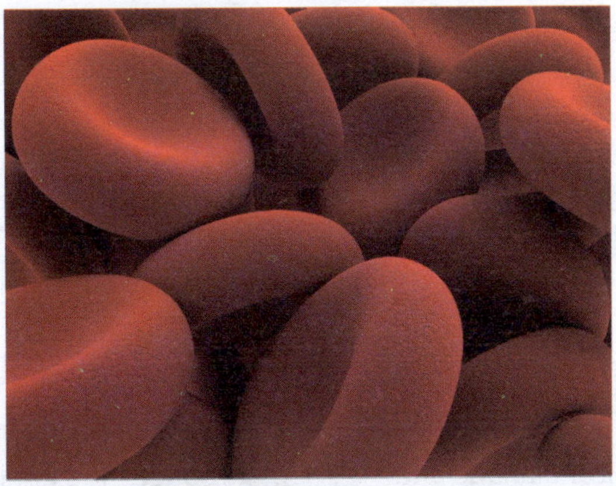

Figure 2.14 Red blood cells

Info Bytes!

Your ear and your nose might feel very different, but they both contain a type of connective tissue called cartilage.

Tendon

- The tissues that attach muscles to bones are called tendons.
- They have great tensile strength and less flexibility.

Ligament

- This tissue attaches bones to bones.
- It is elastic in nature.
- It has great strength.
- It strengthens the joint and allows normal movement.

Bones

- They provide structural framework to the body.
- They anchor the muscles and support the main organs of the body.

Cartilage

- It smoothens bone surfaces at joints.
- It is found in nose and ear.

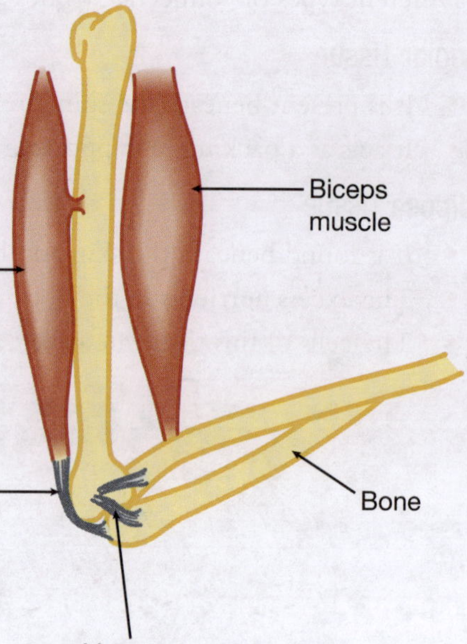

Figure 2.15 Illustration of tendon and ligament

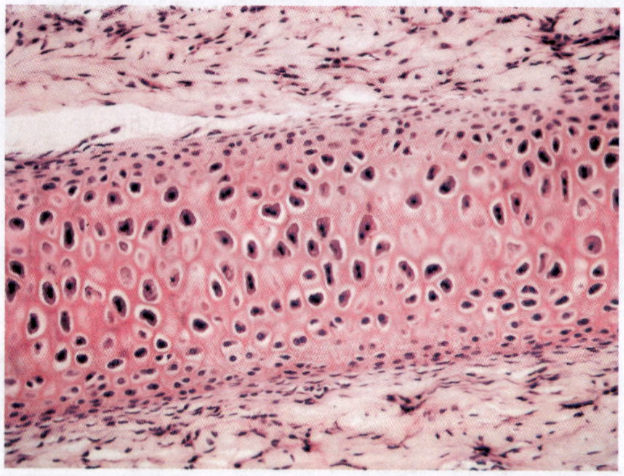

Figure 2.16 Microscopic view of bone tissue

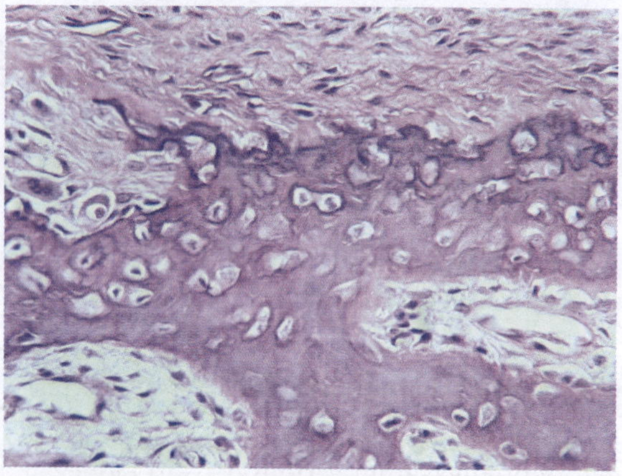

Figure 2.17 Microscopic view of cartilage

Table 2.1 Differences between bone and cartilage

Bone	Cartilage
1. Bones are hard, living and growing tissue.	1. Cartilage is a soft type of connective tissue.
2. It is non-elastic.	2. It is elastic in nature.
3. It is tough.	3. It is flexible.
4. It is formed of cells called osteocytes.	4. These are formed of cells called chondrocytes.
5. The matrix is made up of calcium and phosphate.	5. The matrix is made up of proteins and sugar.
6. It protects body against mechanical damage and assists in movement. It also provides shape and framework to the body.	6. It reduces friction in joints.

Muscular Tissue

Muscle tissue consists of many cylindrical, elongated cells called muscle fibres. Muscle fibres contract and relax in a coordinated fashion to cause movement. Muscles are of three types:

1. **Skeletal muscles**
   - They are attached to bones (muscles of limbs).
   - These are also known as voluntary muscles as we can contract these muscles according to our will.

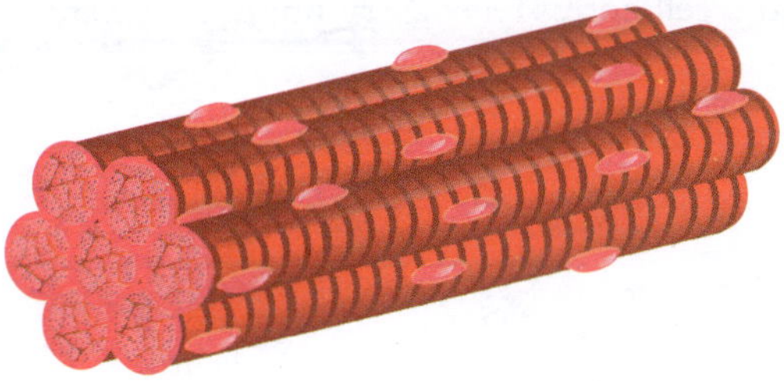
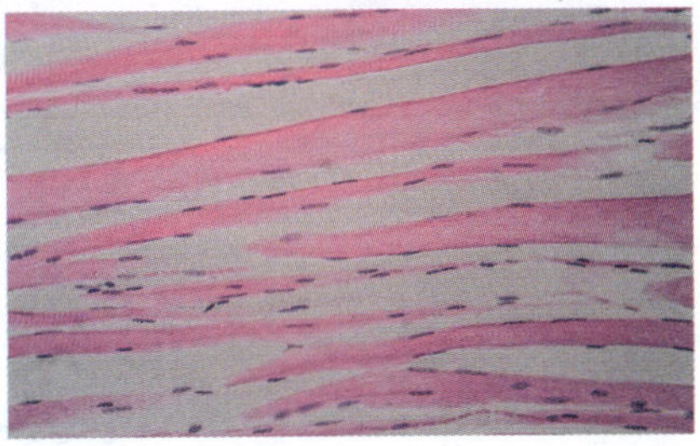

Figure 2.18 Skeletal muscle

2. **Smooth muscles**
   - They are found in the wall of alimentary canal, blood vessels, etc.
   - It is not possible to contract these muscles according to our will, so these are also known as involuntary muscles.

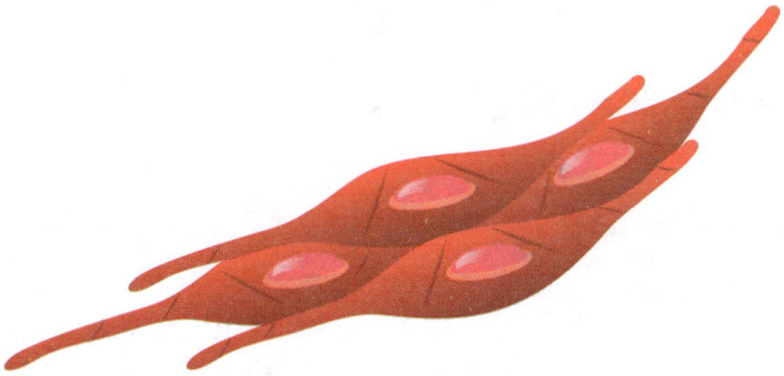
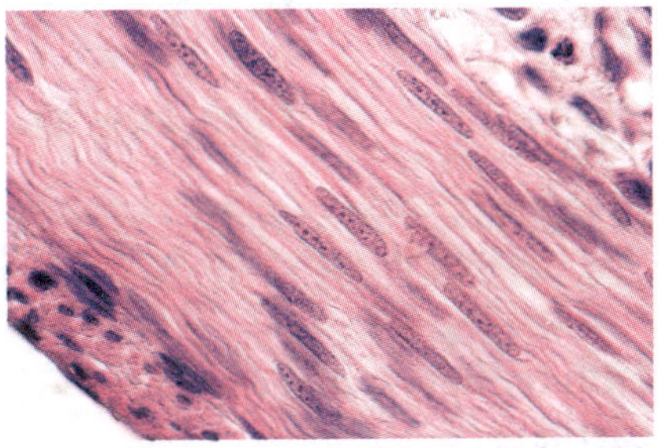

Figure 2.19 Smooth muscle

3. **Cardiac muscles**
   - They are found only on heart walls.
   - They are involuntary in nature.
   - These muscles show rhythmic contraction and relaxation throughout life.

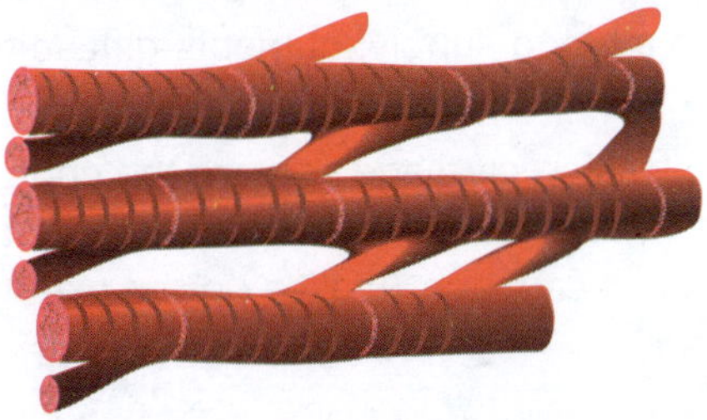
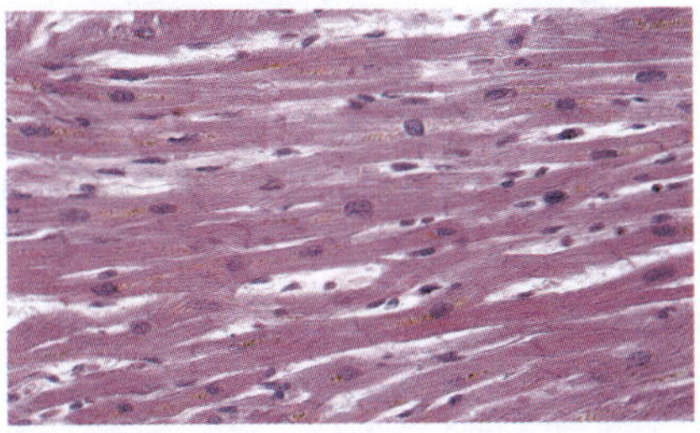

Figure 2.20 Cardiac muscle

Nervous Tissue

Cells of nervous tissue are called neurons. Neurons transmit information through electrical and chemical signals. Brain, spinal cord and nerves are made up of neurons. Neurons are protected by another type of cell called neuroglial cell. Neurons consist of three major parts:

1. **Cell body:** Contains nucleus and cytoplasm.
2. **Axon:** Longest part and carries impulses away from the cell body.
3. **Dendrites:** Short and branched parts arising from the cell body. They carry impulses towards cell body.

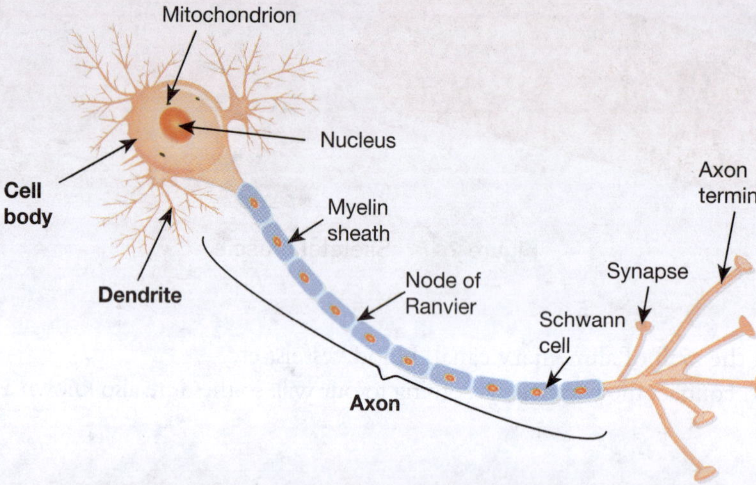

Figure 2.21 Structure of a typical neuron and its parts

Quick Recap

✔ **Differentiate between adipose tissue and cartilage.**

Adipose tissue and cartilage are specialized types of connective tissues serving different functions:

Adipose Tissue	Cartilage
Specialized for the storage of fat.	Provides flexible support and reduces friction between joints.
Contains adipocytes, cells that store fat droplets.	Matrix is semi-solid and contains chondrocytes, the cells responsible for producing the cartilaginous matrix.
Acts as an insulator, helping to maintain body temperature.	Does not have a blood supply; nutrients diffuse through the matrix.
Provides cushioning for organs and joints.	Types include hyaline cartilage (covers the ends of bones in joints), fibrocartilage (found in intervertebral discs), and elastic cartilage (makes up the external ear).

Body Movements

One of the important distinguishing features of living beings is movement. Movements can be observed in both animals and plants. Set of movements that result in change in position is called locomotion. Animals move usually for food, shelter, mating, etc., and the methods of locomotion depend upon their habitat and the demand of situation.

There are different kinds of structures that help in movement, such as cilia, flagella, pseudopodia and muscles.

Cilia

Cilia are minute hair-like organelles in eukaryotic cells. Cilia helps in movement of unicellular organisms. Ciliary movement can be observed in protozoans like *Paramoecium* and also in most of our internal organs that are lined by ciliated epithelium. For example, the coordinated movement of cilia in respiratory tract helps us in removing dust particles and foreign materials inhaled along with the atmospheric air.

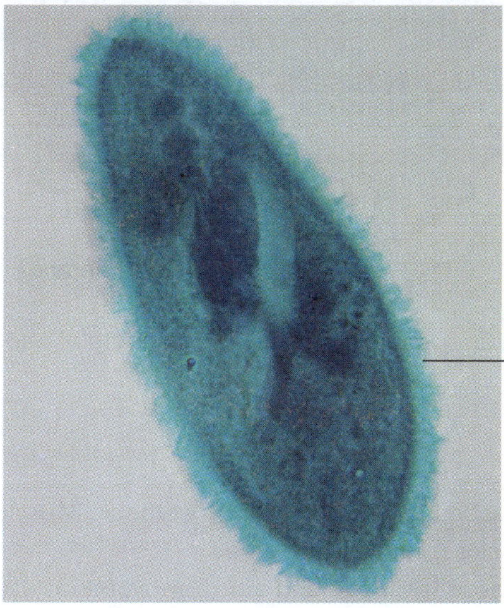

Figure 2.22 *Paramoecium* to display hair-like cilia

Flagella

Flagella are lash-like appendages that protrude from eukaryotic and prokaryotic cells. It is primarily used for locomotion but at times it also act as sensory organ. 'Flagellum' means 'a whip' which is used by the cell for its movement. Mammalian sperm cell is an example for eukaryotic cell bearing flagella. Sperm cell uses its flagellum to travel through the female reproductive tract.

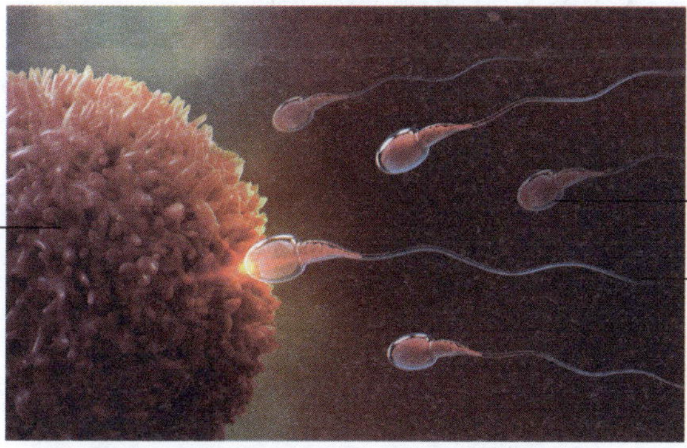

Figure 2.23 Sperm and egg cell

Pseudopodia (False Feet)

Pseudopodia are temporary projections of plasma membrane seen in eukaryotes. It can extend itself in any direction. Cells that show pseudopodia are usually referred to as amoeboids. Some blood cells in our body (leucocytes) exhibit amoeboid movement. The unicellular protozoan, *Amoeba* performs various activities by the formation of pseudopodia.

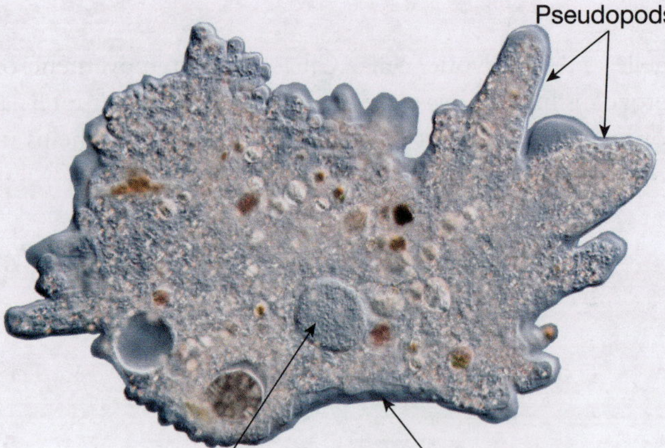

Figure 2.24 *Amoeba* moves with the help of pseudopodia

Muscles

Muscles are specialized tissues that contract and relax to cause movement. Muscles are of three types skeletal, smooth and cardiac muscles. There are over 600 muscles in our body.

Skeletal muscles attach to bones at various locations and aid in movement. The contraction and relaxation occur with the help of two proteins actin and myosin.

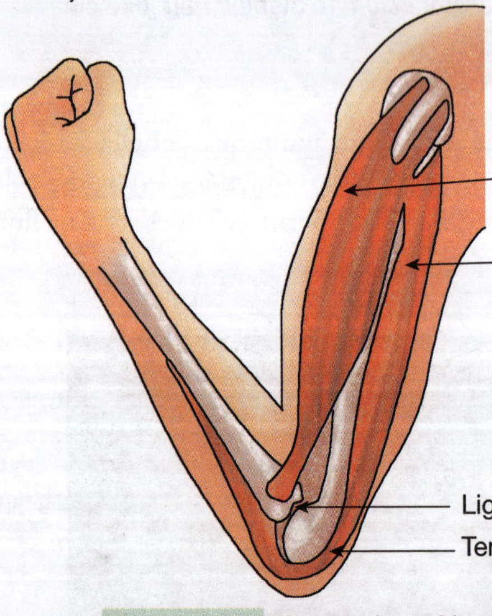

Figure 2.25 Illustration of human muscle

Info Bytes!

Your heart has cardiac muscles that work tirelessly, beating approximately 100,000 times a day.

Skeletal System

Skeletal system comprises a framework of bones and few cartilages. Human body (adult) comprises 206 bones and the skeletal system is divided in two:

1. Axial skeleton
2. Appendicular skeleton

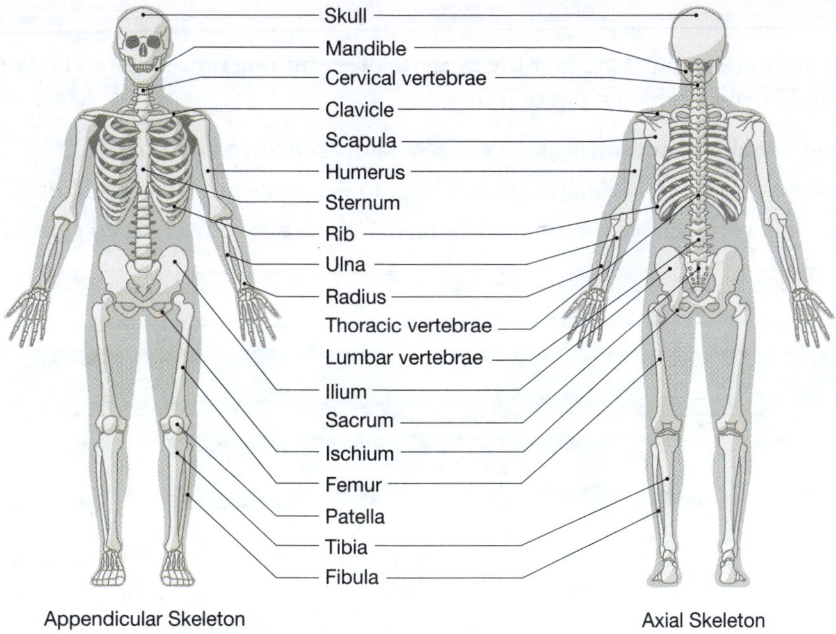

Figure 2.26 Human skeleton system

Axial Skeleton

It consists of 80 bones that are distributed along the main axis of the body. Axial skeleton includes:

- **Skull:** Hard, protective skeleton of head.
- **Vertebral column:** Extends from base of the skull and protects the spinal cord.
- **Sternum:** Flat bone found in the centre of chest.
- **Ribs:** Long, curved bones which form the ribcage.

Appendicular Skeleton

It supports the appendages, pectoral and pelvic girdles, for example, limbs. In human body, each limb is made up of 30 bones. The bones of hands are:

- Humerus
- Radius
- Ulna
- Carpals (wrist bones)
- Metacarpals (palm bones)
- Phalanges (digits)

The bones of lower limbs are:

- Femur (thigh bone)
- Patella
- Tibia
- Fibula
- Tarsals
- Metatarsals
- Phalanges

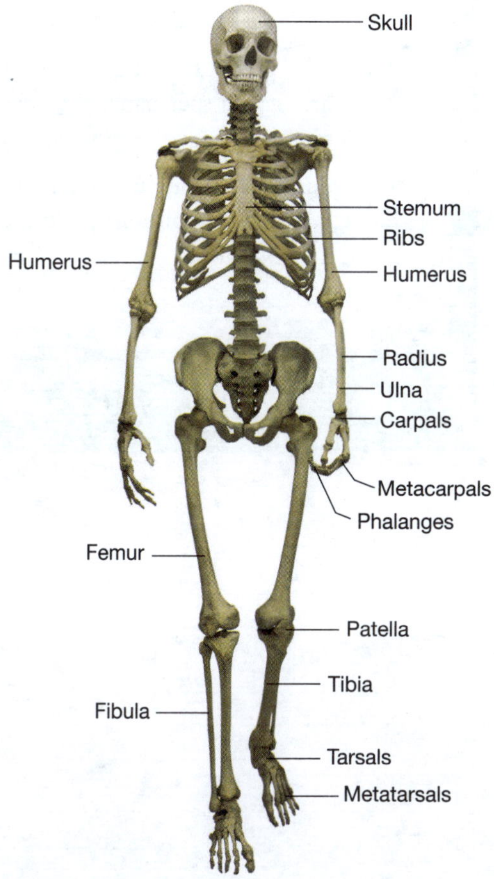

Figure 2.27 Human skeleton showing **major** bones in our body

Joints

A joint is the area where two bones are attached for the purpose of permitting movement of body parts. They are essential for all types of movements. There are three types of joints:

1. **Fibrous joints:** Do not allow movement, for example, joints between skull bones.
2. **Cartilaginous joints:** Permit limited movement, for example, joints in vertebral column.
3. **Synovial joints:** Allow considerable movement. Contain a fluid-filled cavity called **synovial cavity**, for example, knee joint.

POINTS TO REMEMBER

- ✔ Tissue is defined as a group of cells either similar or dissimilar that performs a specific function, for example epithelial tissue, muscular tissue, etc.
- ✔ Multicellular organisms exhibit division of labour.
- ✔ The plant tissue that can be divided throughout its life is called meristematic tissue.
- ✔ The plant tissues that do not undergo division are called permanent tissues. Examples are parenchyma, collenchyma, xylem, phloem, etc.
- ✔ Animals consist of four basic types of tissues which are Epithelial, Connective, Muscular and Nervous.
- ✔ Set of movements that result in change in position is called locomotion.
- ✔ Pseudopodia are temporary projections of plasma membrane seen in eukaryotes
- ✔ Muscles are specialized tissues that contract and relax to cause movement.
- ✔ Skeletal system comprises a framework of bones and few cartilages.
- ✔ A joint is the area where two bones are attached for the purpose of permitting movement of body parts.

DW

PRACTICE QUESTIONS CLASSROOM WING

Very Short Answer Type Questions

Directions for questions from 1 to 15:
Fill in the blanks in each question.

1. Phloem parenchyma mainly functions in ________.
2. Meristematic tissue converts to permanent tissue through a process called ________.
3. Set of movements that result in change in position is called ________.
4. In binary fission ________ division occurs first.
5. Mode of cell division in prokaryotes is ________.
6. Bone tissue constitutes cells called ________.
7. Muscles seen on heart wall are ________.
8. The part of neuron which contains nucleus is ________.
9. Plant tissues, according to their dividing abilities, can be divided into ____________ and ____________.
10. ____________ tissue provides a covering or lining for various internal and external body parts.
11. Blood is a ________ connective tissue.
12. The cells of nervous tissue are called ________.
13. ____________ cells in adipose tissue are responsible for storing fats.
14. One of the distinguishing features of living beings is ________.
15. The muscle types are skeletal, ________ and ________.

Directions for questions from 16 to 32:
For each of the following questions, four choices have been provided. Select the correct alternatives.

16. Which one of the following is a correct statement?
    (a) Sperm cells use cilia to travel through female reproductive tract.
    (b) Red blood corpuscles are capable of showing amoeboid movement.
    (c) Palm bones are also known as metacarpals.
    (d) Knee joint is an example for cartilaginous joint.
17. The hard protective covering of brain is called
    (a) Vertebral column (b) Cranium
    (c) Sternum (d) Ribs
18. Adult human body comprises
    (a) 206 bones (b) 300 bones
    (c) 204 bones (d) 200 bones
19. Meristem that occurs between mature tissues is
    (a) Lateral meristem (b) Cambium
    (c) Intercalary meristem (d) Apical meristem
20. Which one the following is a dead tissue?
    (a) Parenchyma (b) Collenchyma
    (c) Sieve-tube cells (d) Xylem tracheids
21. Match the following

A Coconut husk	i Xylem parenchyma
B Thin cell wall	ii Collenchyma
C Irregularly thickened cell wall	iii Sclerenchyma
D Lateral conduction of water	iv Parenchyma

	A	B	C	D
(a)	i	ii	iii	iv
(b)	ii	i	iv	iii
(c)	iii	iv	ii	i
(d)	iii	i	ii	iv

22. The type of tissue present in coconut husk is
    (a) Sclerenchyma (b) Collenchyma
    (c) Parenchyma (d) Meristem
23. Which of the following is NOT a type of meristematic tissue based on position?
    (a) Apical meristem (b) Intercalary Meristem
    (c) Lateral Meristem (d) Exterior Meristem
24. The primary function of sclerenchyma is
    (a) Photosynthesis
    (b) Gaseous exchange
    (c) To provide mechanical support
    (d) To store food

25. Which of the following elements in the phloem is dead?
(a) Sieve tubes (b) Companion cells
(c) Parenchyma (d) Fibres

26. Which type of epithelial tissue consists of tall pillar-like cells?
(a) Squamous epithelium (b) Cuboid epithelium
(c) Columnar epithelium (d) Ciliated epithelium

27. Which of the following tissues is responsible for storing excess nutrients as fats?
(a) Areolar Tissue (b) Adipose Tissue
(c) Blood (d) Tendon

28. What is the primary function of the muscle tissue?
(a) Protection (b) Movement
(c) Linking (d) Support

29. If a part of the body requires a protective lining due to constant friction, which type of epithelial tissue would you expect to find?
(a) Simple epithelium (b) Squamous epithelium
(c) Compound epithelium (d) Cuboid epithelium

30. Which of the following tissues has cells embedded in an intercellular matrix?
(a) Epithelial tissue (b) Connective tissue
(c) Muscular tissue (d) Nervous tissue

31. The tissue that connects bone to bone is
(a) Tendon (b) Areolar tissue
(c) Ligament (d) Adipose tissue

32. Match the following

A Adipose tissue	i Chondrocytes
B Bone	ii Blood
C Cartilage	iii Fat cell
D Platelets	iv Osteocyte

	A	B	C	D
(a)	iii	iv	i	ii
(b)	iv	i	ii	iii
(c)	iii	i	iv	ii
(d)	iv	ii	iii	i

Short Answer Type Questions

33. What is stomata and what is their significance in a plant?

34. Describe the main difference between simple and complex permanent tissues.

35. What role does the apical meristem play in the growth of plants?

36. How does the matrix composition differentiate between bone and cartilage?

37. Name the two proteins responsible for the contraction and relaxation of skeletal muscles.

38. Give a note on the structure of neuron.

39. Define pseudopodia.

40. Give a note on axial skeleton.

Essay Type Questions

41. Discuss the structure and functions of the three types of simple permanent tissues in plants.

42. (a) Differentiate between bone and cartilage.
(b) Make a comparison between tendon and ligament.

43. (a) How epithelial tissues have been classified according to their shape?
(b) What is ciliated epithelium, and why are they important in the respiratory tract?

PRACTICE QUESTIONS COMPETITION WING

Level 1: Apply your Concepts

Directions for questions from 1 to 5:
Fill in the blanks in each question.

1. ________ organisms exhibit division of labour.
2. Meristematic tissue that increases width of plant body is ________.
3. The dead simple permanent tissue is ________.
4. The element of xylem that provides structural support is ________.
5. The thick waxy coating present on the surface of epidermal cells is ________.

Level 2: Review your Concepts

6. You might have seen that even after grazing by herbivores, grasses regenerate from the remaining parts. Which tissue is responsible for this and where it is located?
7. Further growth of an onion root stops after the removal of tip portion. Why?
8. (a) Identify the parts.

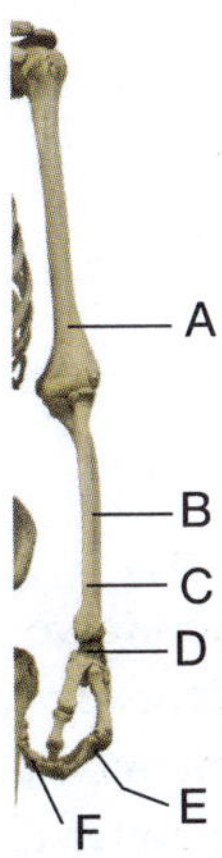

(b) It is possible to move the elbow freely. Which types of joints are present here that help in this movement?

9. Plants require less energy than animals. Do you think that this statement is correct? Explain your answer.

Level 3: Assess Your Concepts

10. Aakanksha was shown two slides of plant tissues; parenchyma and sclerenchyma. How did she identify sclerenchyma?
11. Generally shrubs and herbs are grown in open places and are exposed to strong winds. But they do not break. Why?
12. Arthritis is a common problem in aged people. Explain its connection with movement.
13. How is an earthworm able to move without having bones?

AT

PRACTICE QUESTIONS NEET SPECIAL WING

Multiple-Answer Type Questions

Questions number 1 to 5 are multiple-choice questions. Each question has FOUR options (a), (b), (c), and (d). ONE OR MORE THAN ONE of these four option(s) is/are the correct answer(s).

1. Organelles present in meristematic tissue include:
   (a) Golgi apparatus
   (b) Plastids
   (c) Vacuoles
   (d) Ribosomes

2. Which of the following tissue cannot be characterised as living mechanical tissue?
   (a) Collenchyma
   (b) Parenchyma
   (c) Sclerenchyma
   (d) Aerenchyma

3. Which of the following cells do not have nucleus as well as cytoplasm?
   (a) Stone cells
   (b) Sieve cells
   (c) Companion cells
   (d) Sclerenchyma

4. Skeletal muscles:
   (a) have striations
   (b) multinucleated
   (c) Spindle shaped
   (d) Voluntary

5. Functions of epithelial tissue include:
   (a) Forming lining of body cavities
   (b) Found in walls of blood vessels and skin
   (c) Found in respiratory tract
   (d) Has protective function

Comprehension-Based Questions

A. Read the paragraph given below and answer the questions number 6 to 11:

Connective tissue as the name suggests connects and supports various parts of the body and organs. Cells in the connective tissue are loosely arranged and are embedded within a jelly like matrix. Except for blood cells all the cells in the connective tissues secrete collagen or elastin fibres. These cells are also responsible for releasing different polysaccharides which forms the jelly like matrix which is present between the cells and fibres. Three major types of connective tissue include-Loose connective tissue present below the skin and as a packaging tissue around organs. E.g., Areolar tissue and Adipose tissue. Dense connective tissues like tendons and ligaments which connect muscles to bones and bone to bones respectively. Specialized connective tissues include- blood, bones and cartilage. Blood is the fluid connective tissue whereas bones provide the structural framework and cartilage smoothens bone surfaces at joints.

6. The connective tissue found in the tips of ears and nose is:
   (a) Areolar
   (b) Cartilage
   (c) Bone
   (d) Ligament

7. Collagen is a type of:
   (a) Globular protein
   (b) Fibrous protein
   (c) Lipid
   (d) Carbohydrate

8. Human erythrocytes are:
   (a) Nucleated and biconcave
   (b) Nucleated and biconvex
   (c) Enucleated and biconcave
   (d) Enucleated and biconvex

9. Find the incorrect statement out of the following:
   (a) Tendon is a dense connective tissue
   (b) Areolar is a loose connective tissue
   (c) Adipose acts as an insulating material
   (d) Cartilage increases friction in the joints

10. The difference between bone and cartilage is that:
    (a) Bones are soft and elastic whereas cartilage is hard
    (b) Bones have chondrocytes and cartilage have osteocytes
    (c) Bones reduce friction and cartilage provide protection against mechanical damage
    (d) Cartilage is made up of proteins and sugar whereas bones are made up of matrix of calcium and phosphate

11. Match the following:

Column – A	Column – B
(i) Blood	(a) Have tensile strength and less flexible
(ii) Tendon	(b) Elastic and stregthens joints for normal movement
(iii) Ligament	(c) Found between internal organs
(iv) Areolar	(d) Fluid tissue
(v) Adipose	(e) Fills spaces inside organs

B. Read the paragraph given below and answer the questions number 12 to 17:

The muscular system, skeleton system together help with the movement in our body. Skeletal system comprises a framework of bones and few cartilages. The adult human body contains 206 bones and the skeletal system is divided in two: Axial skeleton and Appendicular skeleton. Axial skeleton in total contains 80 bones and forms the main axis of the body. In contrast the appendicular skeleton supports the upper and lower limbs as well as the two girdles- pelvic and pectoral. Joints are the areas of attachment of the bones. They are essential for the smooth body movements. Based on the type of movements provided by the joints, there are three types of joints- fibrous joints, cartilaginous joints and synovial joints.

12. There are more bones in appendicular skeleton than axial skeleton.
(a) The statement is correct; appendicular skeleton consists of 80 bones and axial consists of 30 bones.
(b) The statement is incorrect; appendicular skeleton consists of 30 bones and axial consists of 80 bones.
(c) The statement is correct; appendicular skeleton consists of 126 bones and axial consists of 80 bones.
(d) The statement is incorrect; appendicular skeleton consists of 106 bones and axial consists of 80 bones.

13. Longest bone in human body is
(a) Patella
(b) Carpal
(c) Tibia
(d) Femur

14. Joint which is similar to knee joint
(a) Elbow joint
(b) Upper limb joined to the girdle
(c) Lower limb joined to the girdle
(d) Joints in vertebral column

15. Metatarsals are present in the
(a) Palms
(b) forelimb
(c) Soles of feet
(d) elbow

16. The main function of ribs is
(a) to form a cage
(b) to protect the vital organs inside
(c) to form an attachment
(d) forms the axis of the body

17. Match the following:

Column – A	Column – B
(i) Skull bones	(a) Cartilaginous joints
(ii) Knee joint	(b) Phalanges
(iii) Digits	(c) Synovial joint
(iv) Vertebral column	(d) Fibrous joints
(v) Wrist bones	(e) Carpals

ANSWER KEYS

Crossword

Across

2. Adipocytes 3. Flagella 7. Cuticle 8. Pseudopodia 9. Dendrites
12. Synovial Joint 13. Cartilage 14. Femur 15. Tendons

Down

1. Metacarpals 4. Epithelial tissues 5. Sclerenchyma 6. Epidermis 10. Osteocytes
11. Sternum

Classroom Wing

Very Short Answer Type Questions

1. Storage 2. Differentiation 3. locomotion 4. Nuclear 5. Binary fission
6. Osteocytes 7. Cardiac muscles 8. Cell body 9. Meristematic tissue, Permanent tissue
10. Epithelial 11. Fluid 12. Neurons 13. Adipocytes 14. Movement
15. Smooth, Cardiac 16. (c) 17. (b) 18. (a) 19. (c) 20. (d)
21. (c) 22. (a) 23. (d) 24. (c) 25. (d) 26. (c)
27. (b) 28. (b) 29. (c) 30. (b) 31. (c) 32. (a)

Competition Wing

Level 1: Apply your Concepts

1. Multicellular 2. Lateral meristem 3. Sclerenchyma 4. Xylem fibres 5. Cuticle

NEET Special Wing

Multiple-Answer Type Questions

1. (a, b, d) 2. (b, c, d) 3. (a, d) 4. (a, b, d) 5. (a, b, c, d)

Comprehension-Based Questions

6. (b) 7. (b) 8. (c) 9. (d) 10. (d)
11. (i) → (d); (ii) → (a); (iii) → (b); (iv) → (e); (v) → (c)
12. (c) 13. (d) 14. (a) 15. (c) 16. (b)
17. (i) → (d); (ii) → (c); (iii) → (b); (iv) → (a); (v) → (e)

Hints and Explanations

CLASSROOM WING

Short Answer Type Questions

33. Stomata are the specialized openings present on the epidermis of leaves and stems. They are enclosed by a pair of kidney-shaped cells called guard cells. Transpiration of water and gaseous exchange takes place through stomata.

34. Simple permanent tissues are made up of only one type of cell, whereas complex permanent tissues are composed of more than one type of cell.

35. The apical meristem is present at the growing tips of roots and shoots and helps in increasing the length of the root and stem.

36. Bones have a matrix made up of calcium and phosphate, making them hard and non-elastic. In contrast, cartilage has a matrix composed of proteins and sugar, giving it an elastic and flexible nature.

37. The two proteins responsible for the contraction and relaxation of skeletal muscles are actin and myosin.

38. Neurons are the basic unit of nervous tissue and are made up of three major parts: cell body, axons and dendrites. Cell body contains nucleus and cytoplasm and possesses many short, branched parts called dendrites. Dendrites carry impulses towards the cell body. The longest part of neurons that arises from cell body is called axon and it carries impulses away from the cell body.

39. Pseudopodia are temporary projections of plasma membrane seen in eukaryotes. Cells that show pseudopodia are usually referred to as amoeboids. *Amoeba* perform various activities, such as movement, food capturing, etc., with the help of pseudopodia. Amoeboid movement is also shown by some blood cells, such as leucocytes in human body.

40. Human axial skeleton is made up of 80 bones that are distributed along the main axis of the body. It includes skull, vertebral column, sternum and ribs. Skull functions as a hard protective covering of the brain, whereas vertebral column extends from base of the skull and protects the spinal cord. The flat bone found in the centre of the chest is called sternum and the long curved bones that form the ribcage are called ribs.

Essay Type Questions

41. Simple permanent tissues in plants provide essential services for the survival of the plant. The parenchyma is adaptable, taking part in a variety of vital processes. Collenchyma provides flexibility and mechanical strength, whereas sclerenchyma provides strong mechanical support, particularly in areas with dead tissues.

    Parenchyma: These are living tissues comprising cells that can be spherical, oval, polygonal, or elongated. They have a thin cell wall and a dense cytoplasm, and they participate in photosynthesis, gas exchange, and food storage. Chlorenchyma refers to parenchymal cells that contain chlorophyll and are involved in photosynthesis. Modified parenchyma, known as aerenchyma in some aquatic plants, has cells arranged with regular air spaces to aid in gas diffusion.

    Collenchyma: Collenchyma tissues are made up of living cells, and their cell walls are irregularly thickened at the corners. They may be oval, spherical, or polygonal in shape. Plants rely on them for mechanical support and flexibility, allowing them to bend without breaking.

    Sclerenchyma: Sclerenchyma tissues are dead and characterized by long cells with narrow lumen. Their walls are thickened due to lignin deposition. They play a pivotal role in providing mechanical support to various plant organs.

42. (a)

Bone	Cartilage
Hard tissue	Comparatively soft
Not elastic	Elastic
Tough	Flexible
Cells are called osteocytes	Cells are called chondrocytes
Matrix made of calcium and phosphate	Matrix made of proteins and sugar
Protects body against mechanical damage, assist movement	Smoothens bone surfaces at joints
Provides framework and shape for body	Reduces friction of joints

(b)

Tendon	Ligament
Connective tissue that attaches muscles to bones	Connective tissue that attaches bones to bones
Less flexibility and has great tensile strength	Elastic and has great strength

43. (a) Epithelial tissues have been classified into three types according to their shape, such as squamous, cuboidal and columnar epithelium. Squamous epithelial tissues are made up of flat cells and are usually found in the walls of blood vessels, skin, etc. Cuboidal cells are made up of cube-shaped cells that are found in ducts of glands. Columnar cells are made up of tall pillar-like cells and are usually found in the linings of stomach and intestine.

(b) The columnar or cuboidal epithelial cells that possess cilia on the free surface are called ciliated epithelial tissues. Cilia in the respiratory tract move back and forth and help in removing the dust particles that are inhaled during breathing.

COMPETITION WING

Level 2: Review your Concepts

6. The tissue responsible for the regeneration of parts eaten by grazing herbivores is intercalary meristem. It is a kind of meristematic tissue that has the ability to divide. Intercalary meristem is seen between mature tissues, on either side of the nodes and is also responsible for the increase in length of internodes.

7. The apical meristem, meristematic tissue responsible for the increase in length of a plant body (or here in this case root) is located at the root tip. Removal of root tip causes the removal of apical meristem and thus the growth of root stops.

8. (a) A – Humerus B – Radius
   C – Ulna D – Carpals
   E – Metacarpals F – Phalanges

   (b) The elbow contains synovial joint that allows considerable movement. It contains a fluid-filled cavity with synovial fluid. This fluid helps in lubrication.

9. Plants do not have to move in search of food as they prepare their own food through the process of photosynthesis. Whereas, animals are dependent on plants and other animals for food and have to travel to fulfill this requirement.

Level 3: Assess Your Concepts

10. She could identify sclerenchyma by the thickness of cell walls. The walls of sclerenchyma tissues are thickened due to lignin.

11. Aerial young parts of shrubs and herbs contain collenchyma tissues which provide flexibility and elasticity to plants to withstand winds.

12. Arthritis condition is marked by pain in joints. Hence, people find it difficult to move from one place to another as joints are primarily involved in movement of body parts.

13. During a movement, earthworm first extends front part of the body keeping the rear portion fixed to the ground. Then it fixes the front and releases the rear end of the body. Earthworm has muscles which repeatedly expand and contract to do so.

NEET SPECIAL WING

Multiple-Answer Type Questions

1. Meristematic tissue have very small or no vacuoles, all other organelles are present in very rudimentary forms. Its cell wall is very thin as the cells are constantly dividing.
2. Collenchyma with its thickenings provide plants mechanical strength with flexibility and hence called living mechanical tissue.
3. Sclerenchyma consists of stone cells which are dead and are devoid of cytoplasm as well as nucleus.
4. Striated muscles have striation and a single cell have many nuclei. These muscles are voluntary and are attached to skeleton, also called as skeletal muscles. It is the smooth muscles which have spindle shaped cells.
5. Epithelial tissue provides a covering or lining for various internal and external body parts. It has protective function. The cells are compactly arranged with little intercellular spaces. Different types of epithelial tissue is found lining the different parts of the body.

Comprehension-Based Questions

A.

6. Cartilage smoothens bone surfaces at joints and is found in nose and ear.
7. Collagen is a type of fibrous protein.
8. The RBC's of humans are enucleated and biconcave in shape due to the lack of nucleus.
9. Cartilage smoothens and reduces friction in the joints; hence option d is an incorrect statement.
10. Cartilage is made up of proteins and sugar whereas bones are made up of matrix of calcium and phosphate
11. Match the following:

    Blood is a type of fluid connective tissue.
    (i) (d)

    Tendons attach muscles to bones. They have great tensile strength and less flexibility.
    (ii) (a)

    Ligaments attaches bones to bones and is elastic in nature. It strengthens the joint and allows normal movement.
    (iii) (b)

    Areolar tissue is present beneath the skin, around blood vessels, nerves, etc. It acts as a packing or supporting tissue and fills space inside organs.
    (iv) (e)

    Adipose tissue is found beneath the skin and between internal organs. The excess nutrients in the body are converted into fats and are stored in this tissue.
    (v) (c)

B.

12. Appendicular skeleton has more bones (126 bones) than axial skeleton (80 bones). Thus, the given statement is correct.
13. The longest and also the strongest bone of the human body is femur.
14. Knee joint is similar to elbow joint; in that they are both synovial joints and give hinge like movements.
15. Metatarsals are found in the soles of the feet whereas metacarpals are found in the palm of the hands.
16. Ribs are extremely important as they protect the vital organs such as lungs and also aid in the right breathing movements.
17. Match the following:

    Fibrous joints do not allow movement, for example, joints between skull bones.
    (i) d

    Synovial joints allow considerable movement and contain a fluid-filed cavity called synovial cavity, for example, knee joint.
    (ii) c

    Digits contain small bones called phalanges.
    (iii) b

    Cartilaginous joints permit limited movement, for example, joints in vertebral column.
    (iv) a

    Wrist bones consists of bones called as carpals.
    (v) e

CHAPTER 3

Classification of Living Organisms

Remember

Before beginning this chapter, you should be able to:

- Understand the need for classifying organisms
- Remember the rules for writing scientific names
- Remember the basics of two- and three-kingdom systems of classification
- Recall the basic concept and the key indicators of Biological Classification

Key Ideas

After completing this chapter, you should be able to:

- Identify the hierarchy of classification
- Explain and apply the rules of binomial nomenclature
- Understand the five-kingdom classification
- Define the basic features of all the five kingdoms

A Tribute to Robert Harding Whittaker (1920-1980)

Robert Harding Whittaker (1920–1980) was a visionary biologist whose work in ecology and taxonomy revolutionised our understanding of how living organisms are classified. Whittaker's most notable contribution was the creation of the Five Kingdoms of Life classification system in 1969, which expanded on the traditional two-kingdom plant-animal system. Recognizing the enormous diversity of life on Earth, he introduced three new kingdoms: Protista, Fungi, and Monera.

Whittaker's system provided a comprehensive framework that accommodated microscopic organisms and bacteria, laying the groundwork for modern taxonomy. His ground-breaking research spanned plant ecology and biogeography, significantly improving our understanding of ecosystems and their dynamics.

Whittaker received numerous honours throughout his career, including the Ecological Society of America's prestigious Eminent Ecologist Award. His enduring legacy continues to shape how we classify and understand the diverse forms of life on our planet, emphasising the importance of his contributions to science.

FUN TIME

CROSSWORD

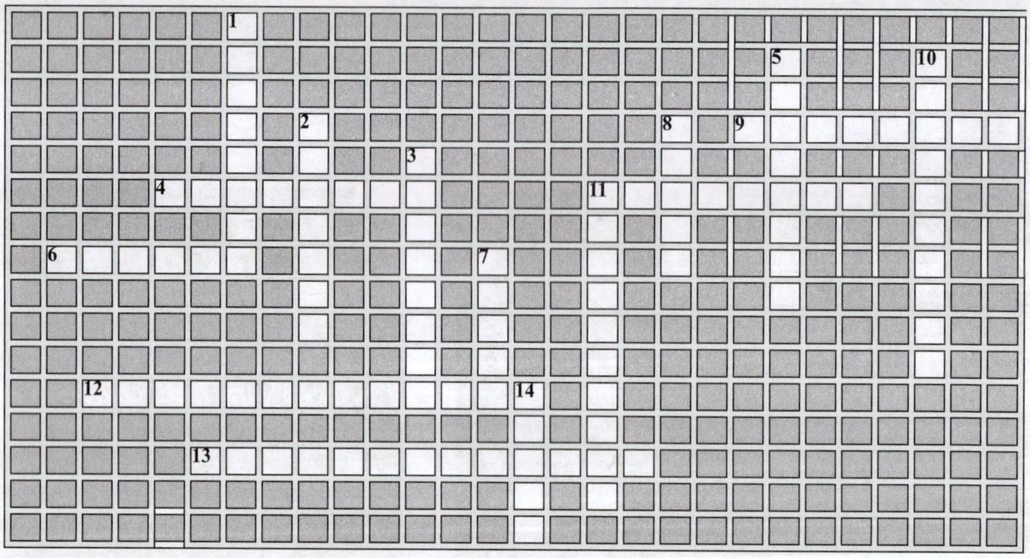

Across

4. Kingdom of eukaryotic, multicellular, heterotrophic organisms, like tigers
6. Kingdom including single-celled prokaryotic organisms like bacteria
9. Organisms with pores, commonly called sponges
11. A two-part formal system of naming living organisms
12. First true vascular plants with feather-like leaves, e.g., ferns
13. Common name for the roundworms, can be aquatic or terrestrial

Down

1. Worms with segmented bodies, such as the earthworm
2. The kingdom of chlorophyll-containing, eukaryotic organisms, i.e., plants.
3. The science of classifying living organisms into groups based on shared characteristics.
5. Kingdom of single-celled eukaryotes such as Amoeba
7. Simple, chlorophyll-bearing organisms, often aquatic, like Spirogyra
8. Kingdom of organisms including mushrooms and yeast, some are saprotrophytic.
10. Marine animals known as comb jellies, capable of bioluminescence
11. Primitive land plants, such as mosses and liverworts, needing water for reproduction
14. Bristle-like structures used for motility

INTRODUCTION

There are a large variety of living organisms in the world. It is nearly impossible to study all of them individually, but grouping them into convenient categories makes their studies possible. This process of categorizing the living organisms on the basis of their similarities and dissimilarities is called classification. Grouping or classification is done on the basis of some observable characteristics like their genetic constitution, characteristic features and also on the basis of their evolution. The scientific term used to represent these categories from Kingdom to species is called **taxon** (plu - Taxa). Classification of living organisms into different taxa on the basis of their characteristics is called **taxonomy**.

Hierarchy of Classification

Hierarchy is the taxonomical classification of living organisms into successive levels of complexity. There are seven levels of categories where 'kingdom' is the highest level and species is the lowest level. The various categories are as follows:

> **Info Bytes!**
> Carolus Linnaeus is known as the 'Father of Taxonomy'

Species: It is the basic or lowest level of classification. A group of organisms which can mate and produce offspring of their own kind with fundamental similarities is called species. For example, all mango plants are included in one species.

Genus: It consists of a group of related species that have some common characters. It is denoted with the first capital letter followed by lower case letters, for example, tiger and lion come under the same genus '*Panthera*'.

Family: It consists of a group of related genera, for example, lion, tiger and cat are included in the same family, that is, *Felidae*.

Order: A group of related families constitutes an order, for example, family *Canidae* (dogs) and *Felidae* (cats) come under the same order Carnivora.

Class: It consists of related orders, for example, class Mammalia includes orders Carnivora and Primata (apes, monkeys and humans).

Phylum: In animals, related classes are categorized into the phylum, whereas in plants they are categorized into divisions, for example, phylum Chordata constitutes of mammals along with birds, reptiles, amphibians and fish.

Kingdom: Phyla that have common characters are grouped into various kingdoms, such as plant kingdom (Plantae) or animal kingdom (Animalia).

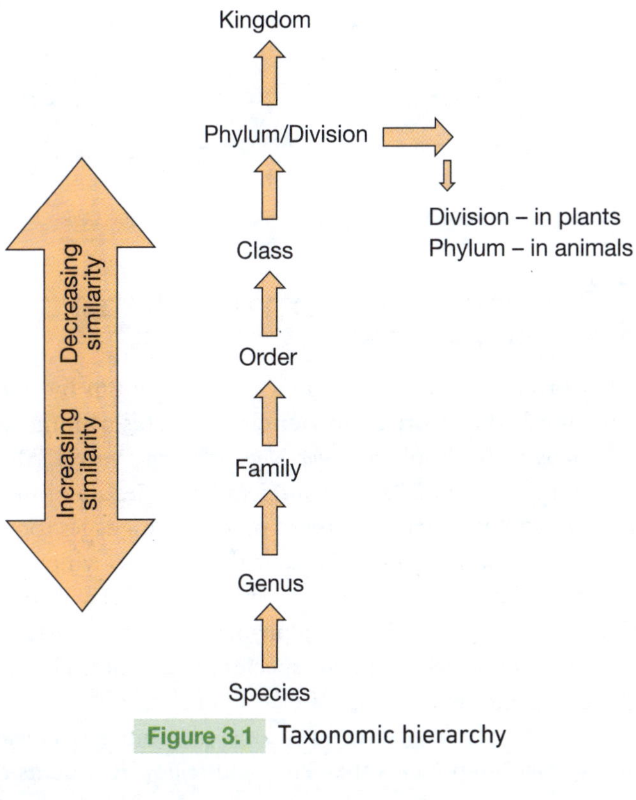

Figure 3.1 Taxonomic hierarchy

The levels of taxonomic hierarchy are explained with examples in the following figure:

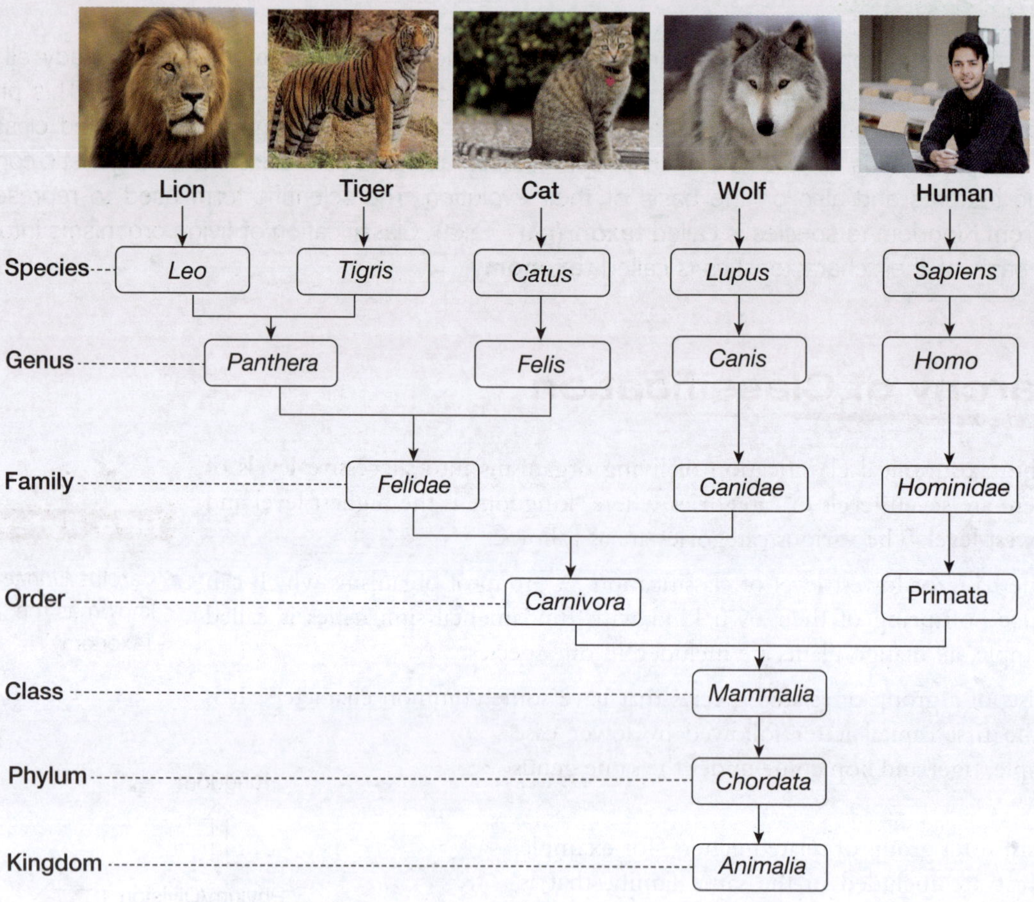

Figure 3.2 Taxonomic hierarchy of different animals

Binomial Nomenclature

The formal system of naming a living organism by giving it a name composed of two parts is called **binomial nomenclature**. This naming system was put forward by Carolus Linnaeus in his book *Systema Naturae* in the year 1758. He is regarded as the 'father of taxonomy'. Binomial names or scientific names are mostly derived from Latin but they can be based on other languages too. The first part of a scientific name represents the genus to which the species belong and the second part represents the species within the genus. When handwritten, the first alphabet of the first part, the genus, is always capitalized while the species name is not. However, both the genus and species name are always italicized.

For example, the scientific name of human is *Homo sapiens*, where *Homo* represents the genus and *sapiens* represents the name of species. Similarly, the scientific name of mango is *Mangifera indica*, where *Mangifera* represents genus and *indica* represents species.

The taxonomic hierarchy of human beings is explained as an example for better understanding.

Konnect

John Ray was a naturalist who coined the term 'species' for the first time in his book 'Historia Generalis'

Table 3.1 Taxonomic hierarchy of human beings

Taxonomic Rank	Example
Kingdom	Animalia
Phylum	Chordata
Class	Mammalia
Order	Primate
Family	Hominidae
Genus	***Homo***
Species	***sapiens***
Common name	Human

Need for Binomial Nomenclature

The living organisms, plants or animals, are usually known by their local names in a particular locality. The local names may vary from place to place, which can lead to confusion in identifying the organisms. Hence, in order to avoid this confusion, standardized naming is required. Providing a standard name that is universally accepted will help us in identifying the organism with the same name all over the world.

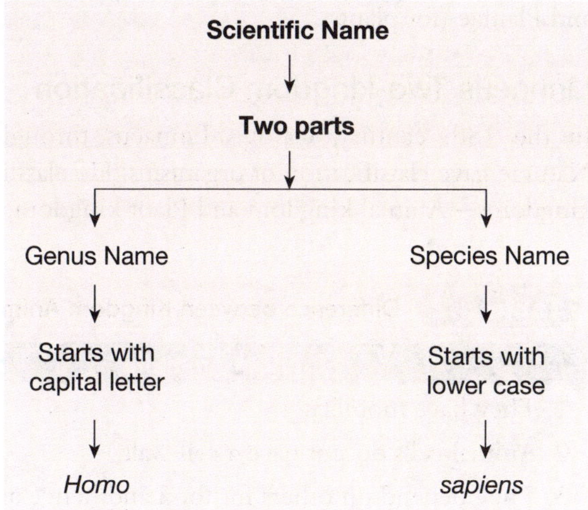

Figure 3.3 Division of a scientific name

Universal Rules of Nomenclature

The rules followed while giving scientific names to organisms are explained below:

- Biological names are generally Latin and are printed in italics and if handwritten, the genus and species names are separately underlined.
- The genus name starts with a capital letter, whereas the species name is written in lower case.
- Name of the author appears after the species name and is written in an abbreviated form, for example, *Mangifera indica* Linn. indicates that the species was first described by Linnaeus.

History of Classification

Aristotle, the Greek scientist, was one of the earliest scientists to classify living organisms on the basis of some simple morphological characters. He is known as the '**Father of Biology/Zoology**'. He classified organisms having red blood cells and those who doesn't have. He classified the living organisms into two groups, plants and animals. He further divided plants into trees, shrubs and herbs. Similarly, animals are divided into two groups: one with red blood and the other one without red blood. He also classified animals on the basis of their habitats, such as aquatic, terrestrial and aerial.

Aristotle's Classification

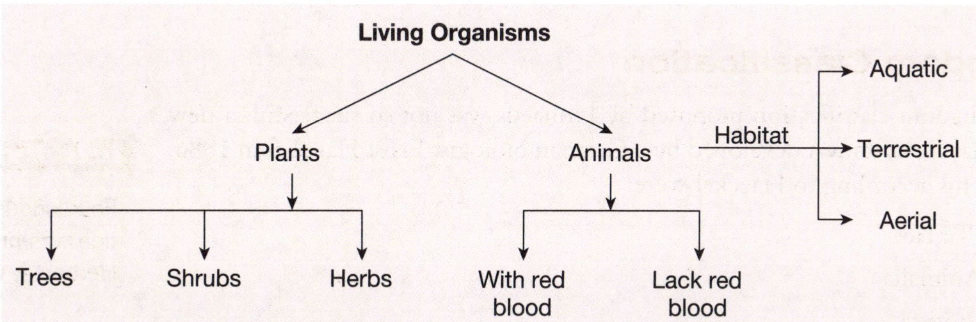

Figure 3.4 Aristotle's classification of living organisms

Theophrastus, Aristotle's student, is known as the 'Father of Botany' for his works on plants. Contributions of Theophrastus are also profound in the history of plant classification. He classified the plants into four major categories of trees, shrubs, subshrubs and herbs. Aristotle's classification had many demerits as many organisms do not fit to the groups. For example, frogs, when born, live in water and adult frogs live on land. Even with the limitations, Aristotle's system of classification was used until it was replaced by the classification system proposed by Carolus Linnaeus.

Two-kingdom Classification

Two-kingdom classification, which was used until recently, was introduced by Carolus Linnaeus. He classified all organisms into two kingdoms on the basis of nutrition and locomotion. The two kingdoms were Animalia (for animals) and Plantae (for plants).

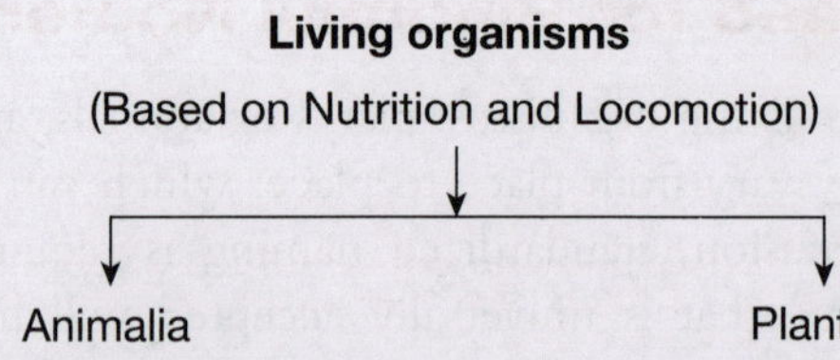

Figure 3.5 Division of organisms in two-kingdom classification

Linnaeus Two-kingdom Classification

In the 18th century, Carolus Linnaeus through his publication Systema Naturae gave classification of organisms. He classified the organisms into two kingdoms—Animal kingdom and Plant kingdom, on the basis of their modes of nutrition and locomotion.

Table 3.2 Difference between Kingdom Animalia and Plantae

Kingdom Animalia	Kingdom Plantae
1. They have mobility.	1. They cannot move.
2. Animal cells do not have a cell wall.	2. Plant cells have a cell wall.
3. They depend on others for food and hence are known as heterotrophs.	3. They can prepare their own food and hence are called autotrophs.
4. It has eukaryotic multicellular organisms.	4. It contains eukaryotic photosynthetic organisms.
5. They reproduce by sexual means of reproduction.	5. They reproduce both by asexual and sexual means of reproduction.
6. Example – All animals including human beings	6. Example – All plants

However there were certain demerits of the two-kingdom classification which are listed below:

- This system did not distinguish between
  - prokaryotes and eukaryotes
  - unicellular and multicellular organisms
  - photosynthetic and non-photosynthetic organisms
- A large number of organisms did not fall into any category, for example, *Euglena* (unicellular) had characters of both plants and animals.

Three-kingdom Classification

Since the two-kingdom classification proposed by Linnaeus was not so successful, a new three-kingdom classification was developed by a German biologist Ernst Haeckel in 1886. The three kingdoms according to Haeckel were:

1. Kingdom Plantae
2. Kingdom Animalia
3. Kingdom Protista

> **Info Bytes!**
> Four kingdom classification was proposed by Herbert F. Copeland.

While the first two kingdoms were same as in the earlier classification, a new kingdom of unicellular microorganisms was introduced. Kingdom Protista included protozoa, fungi, bacteria and other microorganisms. Protists are primarily aquatic in nature.

Five-kingdom Classification

Five-kingdom classification was proposed by an American ecologist, R. H. Whittaker (1969).

The main criteria for this classification were as follows:

- Cell type
- Cell wall
- Nuclear membrane
- Body organization
- Mode of nutrition

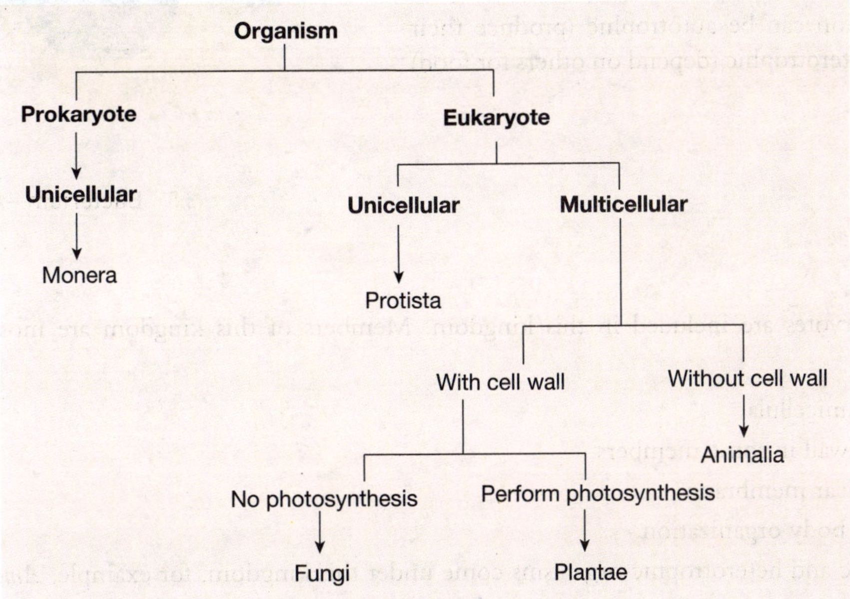

Figure 3.6 Flow chart showing five-kingdom classification

The five kingdoms are as follows:

1. Monera
2. Protista
3. Fungi
4. Plantae
5. Animalia

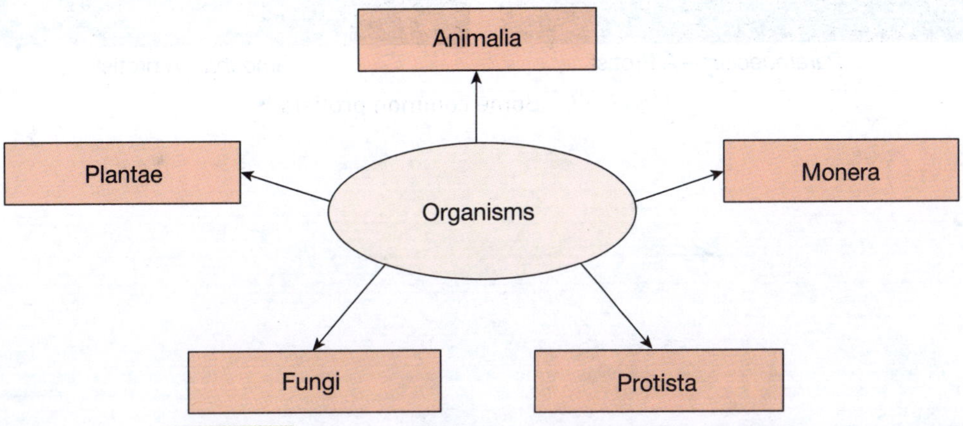

Figure 3.7 The five-kingdom classification of organisms

Monera

It includes prokaryotic organisms (bacteria), that is, both archaebacteria and eubacteria. Archaebacteria are found in most harsh habitats, such as extremely salty area. Eubacteria are the true bacteria, which are found everywhere including the human body.

It has the following features:

- Prokaryotic
- Unicellular
- Cell wall present
- Nuclear membrane absent
- Mode of nutrition can be autotrophic (produce their own food) or heterotrophic (depend on others for food)

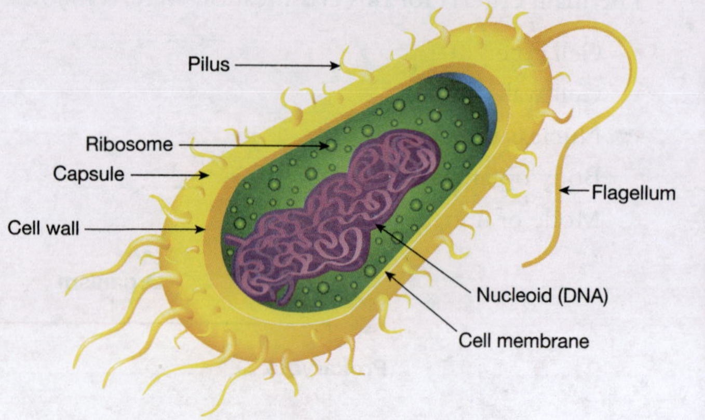

Figure 3.8 Bacterium—A Moneran

Protista

All single-celled eukaryotes are included in this kingdom. Members of this kingdom are mostly aquatic. It has the following features:

- Eukaryotic and unicellular
- Presence of cell wall in some members
- Presence of nuclear membrane
- Cellular level of body organization
- Both autotrophic and heterotrophic organisms come under this kingdom, for example, *Amoeba* and *Paramoecium*.

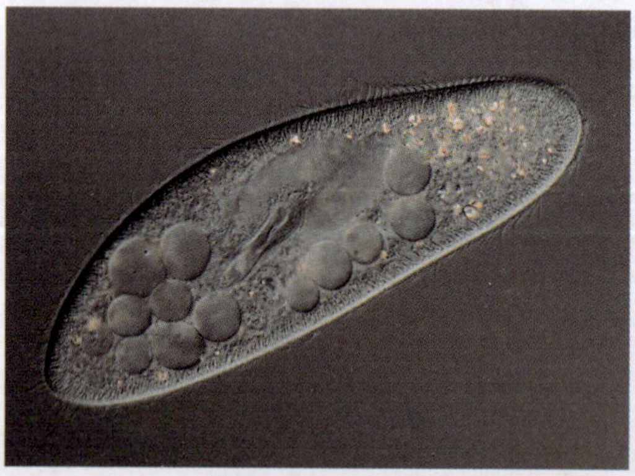

Paramoecium—A Protist

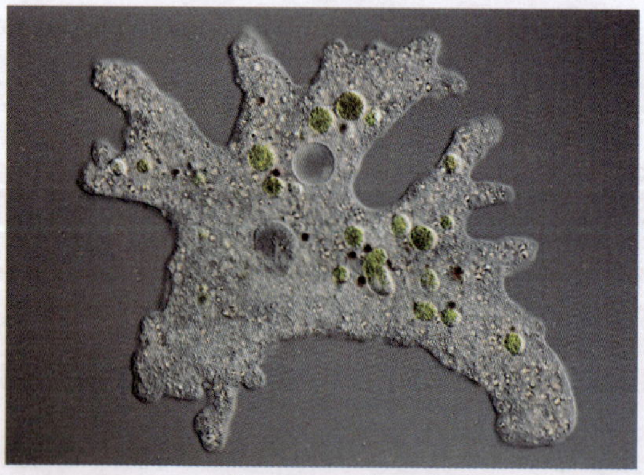

Amoeba—A protist

Figure 3.9 Some common protists

Fungi

Most of the fungi are multicellular organisms but unicellular fungi are also found such as yeast.

It has the following features:

- Eukaryotic in nature
- Presence of cell wall which is made up of chitin
- Nuclear membrane present
- Heterotrophic in nature, either saprophytic (feeds on dead and decaying matter) or parasitic (derives food from host organisms), for example, yeast and mushrooms.

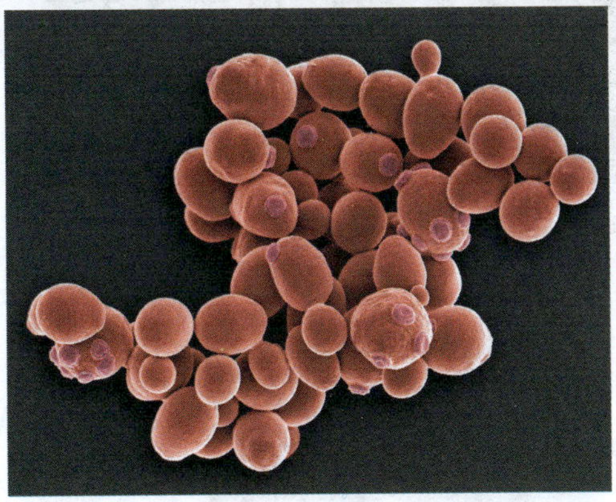

Yeast—A unicellular fungi

Mushroom—A multicellular fungi

Figure 3.10 Some common fungi

Plantae

All eukaryotic, chlorophyll-containing organisms are included in this kingdom, that is, all plants. They do not show locomotion and can store food in the form of starch. The reproduction is either through sexual or through vegetative means. They are multicellular and contain cells with cell wall which is made up of cellulose.

Kingdom Plantae includes the following:

1. Algae
2. Bryophytes
3. Pteridophytes
4. Gymnosperms
5. Angiosperms

Algae: They are simple, chlorophyll-bearing organisms that range from unicellular to multicellular. Plant body is in the form of a thallus, i.e., no clear distinction of true roots, stems and leaves. Most of the algae are autotrophs (synthesize their own food by the process of photosynthesis). They are mostly aquatic, for example, algae and *Spirogyra*. Some of them are also found on rocks or within plants and animals, for example, lichens.

Bryophytes: It is the collective term used for hornworts, liverworts and mosses. They are the simplest and most primitive land plants. As they are terrestrial but need water for completing their life cycle, they are called amphibians of plant kingdom. In these, plants possess stem-like and leaf-like structures but lack xylem and phloem (vascular tissues), for example, moss and liverworts. They prefer to grow in shady and damp places.

Pteridophytes: These were the first plant group to have true vascular system for the conduction of water, minerals and food. The word pteridophyte comes from the word 'Pteron' meaning feather and 'phyton' meaning plant. Thus, pteridophytes are those plants which possess feather-like leaves, for example, ferns.

Gymnosperms: These are vascular plants especially found in colder regions which produce naked seeds (not encased), that is, seeds are not enclosed in fruits. Gymnosperms produce male and female cones, which produce pollen grains and eggs, respectively. Male cones are generally smaller than female cones, for example, pines.

Angiosperms: These are flowering plants which reproduce through seeds which develop inside fruits. The reproductive structure, i.e., the flower houses both the male and female reproductive organs. The flower which has both male and female organs are called perfect flowers, for example, apples, cherries, orchids, etc. The flower which has only either male or female organ is called imperfect flower, for example, cucumber and corn.

Figure 3.11 Examples of different divisions under plant kingdom

Animalia

All eukaryotic, multicellular and heterotrophic animals come under this category. They lack cell wall. Most of them show mobility. Kingdom 'Animalia' is divided into different phyla as described below:

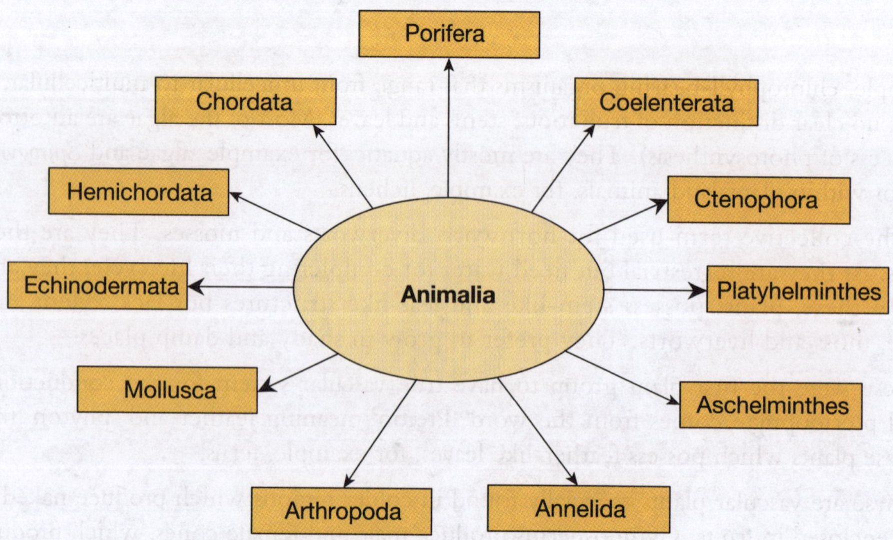

Figure 3.12 Different phyla under animal kingdom

Porifera: They are pore-bearing organisms (i.e., they have holes on their body). They are commonly known as sponges. Sponges are mostly asymmetrical but can also have radial symmetry and do not have a circulatory system. The food, oxygen, etc., reach the body by a water current through the holes.

Coelenterata (Cnidaria): They are aquatic animals that can be either non-motile or free swimming. They got the name due to the presence of specialized cells called cnidoblasts or cnidocytes on their body, for example, *Hydra* and jellyfish.

Ctenophora: They are commonly known as comb jellies and are exclusively marine. They have the ability to emit light (bioluminescence), for example, *Ctenoplana* and *Pleurobrachia*.

Sycon (Porifera) | Jellyfish (Cnidaria) | *Comb jelly* (Ctenophora)

Figure 3.13 Examples of phylum Porifera, Cnidaria and Ctenophora

Platyhelminthes: They are commonly known as flatworms as they have a flattened body. They are mostly found as endoparasites in animal's body, for example, tapeworm and liver fluke.

Aschelminthes: They are also called roundworms as their cross-sections are round in shape. They can be aquatic or terrestrial, free living or parasitic, for example, *Ascaris*.

Annelida: They may be aquatic or terrestrial. Their body is divided into many segments, and such a segmentation is called metamerism, for example, earthworm.

Liver fluke (Platyhelminthes) | *Ascaris* (Aschelminthes) | Earthworm (Annelida)

Figure 3.14 Examples of Phylum Platyhelminthes, Aschelminthes and Annelida

Arthropoda: They are the largest group of animals. They show segmentation in their body into head, thorax and abdomen. The significant feature of phylum 'Arthropoda' is the presence of 'jointed legs', for example, scorpion, prawns and butterflies.

Honey bee

Spider

Prawn

Millipede

Crab

Figure 3.15 Some examples of Phylum Arthropoda

Mollusca: They are the second largest phylum of animal kingdom. They can be terrestrial, marine or freshwater, for example, octopus and snails.

Echinodermata: They are spiny-skinned organisms and are exclusively marine animals, for example, starfish.

Hemichordata: This group includes worm-like marine animals, for example, *Balanoglossus* (commonly known as tongue worm).

Snail (Mollusca)

Starfish (Echinodermata)

Figure 3.16 Examples of phylum Mollusca, Echinodermata

Chordata: The organisms under this phylum are characterized by the presence of notochord (flexible rod-like structure), which later develops into a vertebral column. Notochord appears in the embryonic stage and in adults is converted to backbone.

Info Bytes!

Chordata is the third largest phylum in animal kingdom.

Phylum chordata includes the following classes:

1. Pisces (fish)
2. Amphibia (frogs)
3. Reptilia (crocodiles)
4. Aves (birds)
5. Mammalia (humans)

Fish (Pisces)

Frog (Amphibian)

Figure 3.17 Examples of classes pisces and amphibia

Crocodile (Reptilia)

Flock of birds (Aves)

Humans (Mammalia)

Figure 3.18 Examples of classes reptilia, aves and mammalia

Table 3.3 Characteristics of five kingdoms

Characters	Monera	Protista	Fungi	Plantae	Animalia
Cell type	Prokaryote	Eukaryote	Eukaryote	Eukaryote	Eukaryote
Cell wall	Present	Present in some	Present (chitin)	Present (cellulose)	Absent
Nuclear membrane	Absent	Present	Present	Present	Present
Body organization	Unicellular	Unicellular	Unicellular/ multicellular	Multicellular	Multicellular
Mode of nutrition	Autotrophic and heterotrophic	Autotrophic and heterotrophic	Heterotrophic	Autotrophic	Heterotrophic
Examples	Bacteria	*Amoeba*	Yeast	All green plants	Birds, humans, etc.

Quick Recap

✔ **Define the terms taxonomy and taxa.**

The wide variety of living organisms present on the earth can be grouped into different categories on the basis of some observable characters. The scientific terms used to represent these categories are called taxa. The classification of living organisms into different taxa on the basis of their characteristics is called taxonomy.

✔ **Define the terms phylum and species.**

The various divisions of living organisms, especially in the animal kingdom, based on major differences in body plan or organization, are termed as phyla. The most basic category in taxonomy where organisms share closely-related attributes and can interbreed to produce fertile offspring is called a species.

✔ **What is a family in the classification hierarchy, and can you provide an example?**

A family is a higher taxonomic rank than genus and species but lower than order. It is a group of related plants or animals that share common characteristics and evolutionary history. For example, the family *Felidae* includes a variety of cats, from domestic cats to lions and tigers.

✔ **Who is credited with developing the binomial nomenclature system, and why is it significant?**

The binomial nomenclature system was developed by Carolus Linnaeus. It is significant because it provides a standardized method to name and classify organisms, ensuring that each species has a unique and universally accepted name, making communication about species precise and clear. For instance, the rose plant's scientific name is *Rosa indica*, where *Rosa* represents the genus, and *indica* indicates the species.

✔ **Write a brief note on five-kingdom classification.**

Five-kingdom classification is the classification of living organisms into five kingdoms, such as Monera, Protista, Fungi, Plantae and Animalia. This method of classification was proposed by R. H. Whittaker. The main criteria for classification are as follows:

- Cell type
- Cell wall
- Nuclear membrane
- Body organization
- Mode of nutrition

✔ **What are different phyla under kingdom 'Animalia' and give examples for each?**

Porifera	-	Sponges
Coelenterata	-	*Hydra*
Ctenophora	-	*Ctenoplana*
Platyhelminthes	-	Tapeworms
Aschelminthes	-	*Ascaris*
Annelida	-	Earthworms
Arthropoda	-	Insects
Mollusca	-	Octopus
Echinodermata	-	Starfish
Hemichordata	-	*Balanoglossus*
Chordata	-	Humans

✔ **Write a note on the phylum 'Arthropoda'.**

They are the largest group of animals. They show segmentation in their body. The significant feature of phylum 'Arthropoda' is the presence of 'jointed legs', for example, prawns and butterflies.

✔ **What is the unique character of phylum 'Chordata'?**

The organisms under this phylum are characterized by the presence of notochord (flexible rod-like structure), which later develops into a vertebral column. Notochord appears in the embryonic stage and in adults it is converted to backbone.

✔ **What are roundworms and why are they called so?**

The organisms that come under phylum 'Aschelminthes' are also called roundworms as their cross-sections are round in shape. They can be aquatic or terrestrial, for example, *Ascaris*.

✔ **Define metamerism and give an example of organisms that show metamerism.**

Metamerism is the segmentation of body into a number of segments, for example, earthworms.

POINTS TO REMEMBER

- ✔ Classification of living organisms into different taxa on the basis of their characteristics is called taxonomy.
- ✔ Hierarchy is the taxonomical classification of living organisms into successive levels of complexity. There are seven levels of categories where 'kingdom' is the highest level and 'species' is the lowest level.
- ✔ The formal system of naming a living organism by giving it a name composed of two parts is called binomial nomenclature.
- ✔ Five-kingdom classification is the classification of living organisms into five kingdoms, such as Monera, Protista, Fungi, Plantae and Animalia.
- ✔ Kingdom Monera includes single-celled prokaryotic organisms (bacteria), that is, both archaebacteria and eubacteria.
- ✔ Kingdom Protista includes all single-celled eukaryotes, like Amoeba and Paramoecium.
- ✔ Kingdom Fungi includes saprotrophytic and multicellular organisms like mushrooms but unicellular fungi are also found such as yeast.
- ✔ All eukaryotic, chlorophyll-containing organisms are included in plant kingdom, that is all plants.
- ✔ All eukaryotic, multicellular and heterotrophic animals come under animal kingdom, example tiger, octopus, insects, etc.

DW

PRACTICE QUESTIONS CLASSROOM WING

Very Short Answer Type Questions

Directions for questions from 1 to 15:
Fill in the blanks in each question

1. ________ is known as the father of botany.
2. Organisms that can synthesize their own food are called ________.
3. The cell wall of fungi is made up of ________.
4. Chlorophyll-bearing eukaryotes come under the kingdom ________.
5. The ______ system of naming a living organism by giving it a name composed of two parts was put forward by Carolus Linnaeus.
6. Aristotle classified organisms having ______ blood cells and those who doesn't have.
7. A group of related species that have some common characters is termed as a ______.
8. The five-kingdom classification was proposed by ________ in the year ________.
9. ________ are the true bacteria found everywhere including the human body.
10. According to the mode of nutrition, organisms under kingdom 'Animalia' are ________.
11. Pore-bearing organisms come under the phylum '________'.
12. The ability to emit light is called ________.
13. Octopus comes under the phylum ________.
14. Jelly fish comes under the phylum ________.
15. The presence of jointed legs is the characteristic feature of phylum '________'.

Directions for questions from 16 to 30:
For each of the following questions, four choices have been provided. Select the correct alternative.

16. Which one of the following is not a name of family?
    (a) *Felidae* (b) *Canidae*
    (c) *Mammalia* (d) *Hominidae*
17. Select the mismatch
    A Lion - *Panthera*
    B Catus - *Felis*
    C Wolf - *Felis*
    D Tiger - *Canis*
    (a) A and B (b) C and D
    (c) A and C (d) B and C
18. Which is the highest level of taxonomical classification?
    (a) Genus (b) Species
    (c) Kingdom (d) Phylum
19. Who is regarded as the 'father of taxonomy'?
    (a) Aristotle (b) Theophrastus
    (c) Carolus Linnaeus (d) Ernst Haeckel
20. Which of the following organisms had characteristics of both plants and animals, and was difficult to classify in the two-kingdom system?
    (a) *Chlamydomonas* (b) *Paramecium*
    (c) *Euglena* (d) *Amoeba*
21. Which of the following organisms have a cell wall made up of chitin?
    (a) Plantae (b) Protista
    (c) Fungi (d) Animalia
22. The flower which has both male and female reproductive organs is known as:
    (a) Perfect flower (b) Imperfect flower
    (c) Bisexual flower (d) Unisexual flower
23. *Amoeba* and *Paramoecium* come under the kingdom
    (a) Plantae (b) Protista
    (c) Monera (d) Fungi
24. Plants that lack xylem and phloem are called
    (a) Bryophytes (b) Angiosperms
    (c) Gymnosperms (d) Pteridophytes
25. Match the following

A Aristotle	i Two-kingdom classification
B Theophrastus	ii Father of zoology
C Linnaeus	iii Five-kingdom classification
D Whittaker	iv Father of botany

	A	B	C	D
(a)	iv	iii	i	ii
(b)	ii	iv	i	iii
(c)	ii	i	iii	iv
(d)	iii	i	ii	iv

26. Which one of the following is exclusively marine?
(a) Mollusca (b) Echinodermata
(c) Aschelminthes (d) Coelenterata

27. Organisms under phylum 'Ctenophora' are also known as
(a) Roundworms (b) Comb jellies
(c) *Ctenoplana* (d) Flatworms

28. Match the following:

A *Octopus*	i Reptilia
B Starfish	ii Hemichordata
C *Balanoglossus*	iii Mollusca
D Chelone	iv Echinodermata

Option

	A	B	C	D
(a)	iii	iv	ii	i
(b)	iv	iii	i	ii
(c)	iii	ii	iv	i
(d)	ii	iv	i	iii

29. Bioluminescence was shown by the phylum
(a) Porifera (b) Ctenophora
(c) Coelentrata (d) Mollusca

30. Identify the word pair relationship.
________: Annelida
Jointed legs: ________

Short Answer Type Questions

31. What are the main features of the Protista kingdom?

32. Why are Bryophytes considered the amphibians of the plant kingdom?

33. How does the cellular organization of Monera differ from Protista?

34. Explain the significance of the presence of joint legs in Arthropoda.

35. What are bryophytes and pteridophytes?

36. Write a note on the phylum 'Cnidaria'.

37. What is notochord and write its significance.

38. What are the different classes under phylum 'Chordata'? Give examples for each.

Essay Type Questions

39. Describe the key distinguishing features of the five kingdoms: Monera, Protista, Fungi, Plantae, and Animalia, focusing on their cell type, presence of a cell wall, nuclear membrane, body organization, and mode of nutrition.

40. Explain classification of Kingdom Plantae.

41. What does it mean by hierarchy of classification?

PRACTICE QUESTIONS COMPETITION WING

Level 1: Apply your Concepts

Directions for questions from 1 to 5:
Fill in the blanks in each question

1. Bryophytes are terrestrial plants but need water for completing their life cycle, hence they are termed as ________ of the plant kingdom.
2. The type of bacteria that are found in harsh habitats, such as extremely salty areas, are known as ____________.
3. In the Plantae kingdom, ____________ are termed the amphibians of the plant kingdom due to their necessity for water to complete their life cycle.
4. ____________ are known for having the presence of 'jointed legs' and represent the largest group of animals.
5. The part of scientific name that starts with capital letter is ________.
6. Some of the organism's names are jumbled in the box given below. Arrange these terms correctly in the column that follows.

Ascaris	Snails	Roundworms	*Ctenoplana*
Jellyfish	*Pleurobrachia*	Starfish	Octopus
Balanoglossus	*Rana*	*Macropus*	*Chelone*

Phylum	Example
Cnidaria	________
Ctenophora	________
Aschelminthes	________
Mollusca	________
Echinodermata	________
Hemichordata	________
Chordata	________

Level 2: Review your Concepts

7. Ravi decides to make notes on a group of 20 different living organisms which he observes on a daily basis. How can the knowledge of taxonomy be helpful in this exercise?
8. Dogs and cats are different from each other. At the levels of hierarchy, are they grouped under any common taxon?
9. Tiger and lion have scientific names, *Panthera tigris* and *Panthera leo*, respectively. What similarities could be identified?
10. Bryopsida is called amphibian of the plants. What can be inferred about this plant?

Level 3: Assess Your Concepts

11. Plant body in higher plants is well-developed. Roots are the organs used for absorbing water and minerals. What is the equivalent of roots in the less developed lower plants?
12. Whittaker's five-kingdom classification was a more logical method of classification as compared to two-kingdom classification. Justify the statement.

AT

PRACTICE QUESTIONS NEET SPECIAL WING

Multiple-Answer Type Questions

Questions number 1 to 5 are multiple-choice questions. Each question has FOUR options (a), (b), (c), and (d). ONE OR MORE THAN ONE of these four option(s) is/are the correct answer(s).

1. Fungi are:
   (a) Eukaryotes
   (b) Prokaryotes
   (c) Have cell wall
   (d) Mostly multicellular

2. The characteristics of unicellular prokaryotes include:
   (a) Cell wall presence:
   (b) Nucleus absent
   (c) Cell wall and nucleus both absent
   (d) Both autotrophic and heterotrophic

3. Which of the following phyla have aquatic animals?
   (a) Porifera
   (b) Ctenophora
   (c) Cnidaria
   (d) Arthropoda

4. Which of the following developed for the first time in Annelids?
   (a) Metamerism
   (b) Jointed legs
   (c) Body segmentation
   (d) Spiny skin

5. Hemichordates are:
   (a) Flatworms
   (b) Worm like animals
   (c) Round worms
   (d) Tongue worms

Comprehension-Based Questions

A. Read the paragraph given below and answer the questions number 6 to 11:

An American ecologist Robert Whittaker in the year 1969 gave the five-kingdom classification of organisms. There were five major criteria based on which he classified the organisms which include-cell structure, body organisation, body organisation, mode of nutrition and phylogenetic relationships. The first kingdom is kingdom Monera which includes prokaryotic unicellular organisms like bacteria. Kingdom Protista includes unicellular eukaryotes like Amoeba and Paramoecium. The third one is Kingdom Fungi which includes eukaryotes containing cell walled saprophytes or parasites. Kingdom plantae consists of chlorophyll containing eukaryotes which are producers of the ecosystem. Lastly kingdom Animalia includes multicellular, eukaryotic heterotrophs which show mobility. Taxonomical classification follows a hierarchial system wherein the organisms are classified into successive levels of complexity.

6. In which of the following kingdom do organisms which cause tuberculosis belong to?
   (a) Monera
   (b) Protista
   (c) Fungi
   (d) Plantae

7. Which of the following organism does not show nuclear membrane?
   (a) Jelly fish
   (b) Amoeba
   (c) E.coli
   (d) Fern

8. Mushroom is an example of the Kingdom:
   (a) Monera
   (b) Protista
   (c) Fungi
   (d) Plantae

9. All different types of rose plants belong to the same:
   (a) Species
   (b) Genus
   (c) Family
   (d) Class

10. In the name *Mangifera indica*, the word Mangifera indicates:
    (a) Species
    (b) Genus
    (c) Family
    (d) Order

11. Match the following:

Column – A	Column – B
(i) Genus of lions and tigers	(a) Order
(ii) Group of related families	(b) Kingdom
(iii) Phyla with common characters	(c) Three kingdom classification
(iv) Ernst Haeckel	(d) Panthera
(v) Carolus Linnaeus	(e) Two kingdom classification

B. Read the paragraph given below and answer the questions number 12 to 17:

Taxonomy is the science which deals with the classification of organisms. All the organisms are classified into the five kingdoms. One of the five kingdoms is animal kingdom which consists of all eukaryotic, multicellular heterotrophs. The animals are further classified into different phyla, class, order, family, genus and species which is based on the characteristic features. Kingdom Animalia is divided into two major categories-Chordates and Non chordates based on the presence or absence of the notochord. Non-chordates consists of phyla such as Porifera, Coelenterata, Ctenophora, Platyhelminthes, Aschelminthes, Annelida, Arthropoda, Mollusca, Echinodermata and Hemichordata. Non-chordates are animals without the notochord which is a rod- like structure that supports the body. Chordates are animals which possess a notochord at some point of their life, with pharyngeal gill slits.

12. Which among the following animals are asymmetrical?
(a) Sponges
(b) Star fish
(c) Human
(d) Donkey

13. Body segmentation is a characteristic feature of:
(a) Ctenophora
(b) Echinodermata
(c) Hemichordata
(d) Annelida

14. Animals who have the ability of bioluminescence belong to:
(a) Cnidaria
(b) Ctenophora
(c) Aschelminthes
(d) Arthropoda

15. The specialized cells on the body of Coelenterates are called:
(a) Chondrocytes
(b) Osteocytes
(c) Fibroblasts
(d) Cnidocytes

16. Animals with jointed legs are found in Phylum:
(a) Arthropoda
(b) Annelia
(c) Echinodermata
(d) Aschelminthes

17. Match the following:

Column – A	Column – B
(i) Jellyfish	(a) Ctenophora
(ii) Comb jelly	(b) Arthropoda
(iii) Liver fluke	(c) Mollusca
(iv) Prawns	(d) Coelenterata
(v) Snails	(e) Platyhelminthes

ANSWER KEYS

Crossword

Across

4. Animalia **6.** Monera **9.** Porifera **11.** Binomial **12.** Pteridophytes **13.** Aschelminthes

Down

1. Annelida **2.** Plantae **3.** Taxonomy **5.** Protista **7.** Algae **8.** Fungi **10.** Ctenophora **11.** Bryophytes **14.** Setae

Classroom Wing

Very Short Answer Type Questions

1. Theophrastus **2.** Autotrophs **3.** Chitin **4.** Plantae **5.** Binomial Nomenclature **6.** Red **7.** Genus **8.** R. H. Whittaker, 1969 **9.** *Eubacteria* **10.** Heterotrophs **11.** Porifera **12.** Bioluminescence **13.** Mollusca **14.** Cnidaria **15.** Arthropoda **16.** (c) **17.** (b) **18.** (c) **19.** (c) **20.** (c) **21.** (c) **22.** (a) **23.** (b) **24.** (a) **25.** (b) **26.** (b) **27.** (b) **28.** (a) **29.** (b) **30.** Metamerism, Arthropoda

Competition Wing

Level 1: Apply your Concepts

1. Amphibians **2.** *Archaebacteria* **3.** Bryophytes **4.** Arthropoda **5.** Generic name

NEET Special Wing

Multiple-Answer Type Questions

1. (a, c, d) **2.** (a, b, d) **3.** (a, b, c) **4.** (a, c) **5.** (b, d)

Comprehension-Based Questions

6. (a) **7.** (c) **8.** (c) **9.** (a) **10.** (b)

11. (i) → (d); (ii) → (a); (iii) → (b); (iv) → (c); (v) → (e)

12. (a) **13.** (d) **14.** (b) **15.** (d) **16.** (a)

17. (i) → (d); (ii) → (a); (iii) → (e); (iv) → (b); (v) → (c)

Hints and Explanations

CLASSROOM WING

Short Answer Type Questions

31. Protista includes single-celled eukaryotes which are mostly aquatic. They can have a cell wall in some members, possess a nuclear membrane, have a cellular level of body organization, and can be either autotrophic or heterotrophic.

32. Bryophytes are considered the amphibians of the plant kingdom because they are terrestrial but require water to complete their life cycle.

33. Monera consists of prokaryotic cells with no nuclear membrane, whereas Protista consists of eukaryotic cells with a defined nuclear membrane.

34. Joint legs in Arthropoda provide these organisms with enhanced mobility and agility. This adaptation has played a significant role in their success, as evidenced by their vast diversity and widespread distribution.

35. Bryophytes and pteridophytes come under kingdom 'Plantae'. Bryophytes are usually known as 'amphibians of plant kingdom'. They possess stem and leaf-like structure but lack vascular tissues (xylem and phloem), for example, moss. Pteridophytes possess root, stem, leaves and also specialized tissues for conduction of water and other substances, for example, fern.

36. They are aquatic animals that can be either non-motile or free swimming. They got the name due to the presence of specialized cells called cnidoblasts or cnidocytes on their body, for example, *Hydra* and jellyfish.

37. Notochord is the flexible rod-like structure that later develops into a vertebral column. The organisms that possess notochord come under the phylum 'Chordata'. Notochord appears in the embryonic stage and is later converted into backbone (vertebral column).

38. The different classes under phylum 'Chordata' are as follows:

    Pisces – Fish
    Amphibia – Frogs
    Reptilia – Crocodiles
    Aves – Birds
    Mammalia – Humans

Essay Type Questions

39. The five-kingdom classification provides a comprehensive method for differentiating organisms based on a variety of characteristics. This kingdom, which begins with Monera, includes prokaryotic organisms, primarily bacteria, that lack a nuclear membrane. They have a cell wall and are primarily unicellular (Nutrition mode: autotrophic or heterotrophic).

    Protista are eukaryotic unicellular organisms that may or may not have a cell wall. They have a nuclear membrane, unlike Monera, and can be autotrophic or heterotrophic.

    Fungi are eukaryotic organisms that can be unicellular or multicellular. They have a distinct chitin cell wall and are purely heterotrophic, feeding on either saprophytic or parasitic means.

    Plantae is an umbrella term for all eukaryotic, chlorophyll-containing organisms with cellulose-based cell walls. These are multicellular, autotrophic organisms that rely on photosynthesis.

    Finally, Animalia contains eukaryotic, multicellular organisms without a cell wall. They have a nuclear membrane and feed on heterotrophic organisms. As a result, each kingdom has distinct characteristics that help distinguish it from the others, enhancing our understanding of the vast diversity of life on Earth.

40. Kingdom Plantae includes:
    - **Algae:** They are simple, chlorophyll bearing organisms that range from unicellular to multicellular organisms. They are mostly aquatic, e.g., *Spirogyra*.
    - **Bryophytes:** These are called 'amphibians of plant kingdom'. Plants possess stem and leaf-like structures but lack xylem and phloem (vascular tissues), e.g., moss.
    - **Pteridophytes:** Plant possess root, stem, leaves and specialized tissues for conduction of water and other substances, e.g., ferns.
    - **Gymnosperms:** They are non-flowering plants and produce naked seeds (not encased), e.g., pines.
    - **Angiosperms:** They are flowering plants and seed develop inside an organ which later forms fruit, e.g., orchids.

41. The taxonomical classification of living organisms into successive levels of complexity is called hierarchy of classification. There are seven levels of categories, such as species, genus, family, order, class, phylum and kingdom. Species is the lowest level whereas kingdom is the highest level.

COMPETITION WING

Level 1: Apply your Concepts

6.

Phylum	Example
Cnidaria	Jellyfish
Ctenophora	***Ctenoplana, Pleurobrachia***
Aschelminthes	***Ascaris***, Roundworms
Mollusca	***Octopus***, Snails
Echinodermata	Starfish
Hemichordata	***Balanglossus***
Chordata	***Rana***, ***Macropus***, ***Chelone***

Level 2: Review your Concepts

7. Ravi can broadly classify the organisms on the basis of the kingdom they belong to. After categorizing them into plants and animals, he can further group them according to their specific physical characters and features. For example, he can group trees and shrubs under kingdom Plantae and all the animals under kingdom Animalia. And so on, he can make further sub-groups with the help of knowledge of hierarchy of classification.

8. Cats and dogs are grouped under the same order Carnivora. Both the animals are meat-eating organisms. On the basis of this similarity, they are grouped under the same order.

9. Both lion and tiger belong to the same Genus, that is, *Panthera*. They are characterized by similar cranial (related to brain) features. They share some common anatomical features also.

10. Since Bryopsida is called amphibian of the plant kingdom, it must be a bryophyte. Bryophytes live in soil (land) but they require water as a medium to reproduce. Hence, they are called amphibians of plant kingdom.

Level 3: Assess Your Concepts

11. Lower plants have thallus-like structures, for example, algae. Thallus has root-like structures called rhizoids that serve the purpose of roots.

12. Two-kingdom classification was proposed by Carolus Linnaeus. He classified all organisms into two kingdoms on the basis of nutrition and locomotion. The two kingdoms were 'Animalia' (for animals) and 'Plantae' (for plants).

His system of classification had some demerits such as:

- This system did not distinguish between:
  - eukaryotes and prokaryotes,
  - unicellular and multicellular organisms,
  - photosynthetic and non-photosynthetic organisms.
- A large number of organisms did not fall into any category, for example, *Euglena* (unicellular) had characters of both plants and animals.

These demerits were rectified in five-kingdom classification, which was proposed by R. H Whittaker. The main criteria for classification were as follows:

- Cell type
- Cell wall
- Nuclear membrane
- Body organization
- Mode of nutrition

Organisms that are prokaryotes and unicellular in nature were placed under kingdom 'Monera'. Eukaryotic unicellular organisms were placed under kingdom 'Protista'. Eukaryotic heterotrophic organisms that included both unicellular and multicellular organisms were placed under kingdom 'Fungi'. Multicellular organisms that can perform photosynthesis were placed under kingdom 'Plantae'. Eukaryotic organisms that are multicellular and heterotrophic in nature were placed under kingdom 'Animalia'. They lack cell wall. Thus, more accurate method for classification was possible through five-kingdom classification.

NEET SPECIAL WING

Multiple-Answer Type Questions

1. Fungi are eukaryotic in nature and they possess cell wall which is made up of chitin. Most of the fungi are multicellular organisms but unicellular fungi are also found such as yeast.
2. Kingdom Monera includes prokaryotic organisms (bacteria), that is, both archaebacteria and eubacteria. They have cell wall, nucleus is absent. They can have both autotrophic and heterotrophic mode of nutrition.
3. Among the options given, aquatic organisms are found in Porifera, Ctenophora and Cnidaria. Arthropods are mostly terrestrial animals.
4. In Annelids, their body is divided into many segments, and this type of segmentation is called metamerism.
5. Hemichordata includes worm-like marine animals, for example, ***Balanoglossus*** commonly known as tongue worm.

Comprehension-Based Questions

A.

6. The causative agent for tuberculosis is bacteria and they belong to Kingdom Monera.
7. E.coli are bacteria which are prokaryotes which do not have a cell membrane, their nuclear material is present directly in the cytoplasm of the cell.
8. Mushrooms are parasitic fungi which derive food from host organisms.
9. A group of organisms which can reproduce and produce viable off spring of their own kind with fundamental similarities is called species. For example, all rose plants are included in one species.
10. In Binomial nomenclature , the first word indicates genus name and second word indicates species name. So, in ***Mangifera indica, Mangifera*** indicates genus name.
11. Match the following:

    Lions and tigers belong to the same genus Panthera, and they are a group of related species.
    (i) d

    A group of related families constitutes an order.
    (ii) a

    Phyla that have common characters are grouped into various kingdoms.
    (iii) b

    A new three kingdom classification was developed by a German biologist Ernst Haeckel in 1886. The three kingdoms according to Haeckel were: Kingdom Plantae, Kingdom Animalia and Kingdom Protista
    (iv) c

    Carolus Linnaeus classified all organisms into two kingdoms on the basis of nutrition and locomotion. The two kingdoms were Animalia (for animals) and Plantae (for plants).
    (v) e

B.

12. Sponges are animals that belong to phylum Porifera and are asymmetrical in nature.
13. Animals of phylum Annelida show a characteristic feature of segmented bodies.
14. Bioluminescence is a phenomenon where the animals can transmit their own light and this is a characteristic feature shown by the animals belonging to Phylum Ctenophora.
15. Coelenterates are aquatic animals that can be either non-motile or free swimming and are called so due to the presence of specialized cells called Cnidoblast or cnidocytes on their body
16. The significant feature of phylum 'Arthropoda' is the presence of 'jointed legs'
17. Match the following:

    Jelly fish belongs to Phylum Coelenterata having Cnidoblast.
    (i) d

Comb jelly is a common name given to animals belonging to phylum Ctenophora.
(ii) a

Liver fluke are flat worms and they belong to Phylum Platyhelminthes.
(iii) e

Prawns have jointed legs and belong to Phylum Arthropoda.
(iv) b

Snails have a hard calcareous shell to protect their soft bodies and belong to Phylum Mollusca.
(v) c

CHAPTER

4

Reproduction in Animals and Plants

Remember

Before beginning this chapter, you should be able to:

- Recall the basic features of flora and fauna
- Recall the basic concept of evolution
- Remember different modes of reproduction
- Understand the concept of cell division

Key Ideas

After completing this chapter, you should be able to:

- Describe the process of reproduction in animals
- Understand the concepts of adolescence and puberty
- Describe the process of reproduction in plants

A Tribute to Oscar Hertwig (1849-1922)

Oscar Hertwig (1849–1922) was a pioneer in reproductive biology, significantly expanding our understanding of life's perpetuation. The extensive contributions of this distinguished German biologist continue to reverberate profoundly within the field of biology, particularly in the study of reproduction in animals and plants.

Hertwig's monumental achievements are best summed up by his ground-breaking discovery of the sperm cell's pivotal role in fertilisation. This discovery fundamentally altered our perception of sexual reproduction. His careful observations and experiments established the foundation for modern embryology. His name will be forever linked to "Hertwig's rule," a seminal concept in embryology that has remained central to our understanding of this complex process.

Hertwig's dedication and innovative spirit earned him a slew of accolades and prestigious awards throughout his illustrious career, most notably the Copley Medal from the Royal Society, a testament to the extraordinary impact of his work.

FUN TIME

CROSSWORD

Across

5. Process of release of egg from the ovary in female
6. The part of the sperm which helps the sperm to penetrate through the egg during fertilisation.
8. The asexual reproduction in which the body of the organism is split into parts and each part develops into a new individual.
9. The passage which connects uterus to vagina
10. Plant in which leaves can give rise to new plants

Down

1. The type of pollination in which water is the pollinating agent
2. Uterine lining that gets thick before menstrual cycle
3. The part of the female reproductive tract in which zygote formation occurs
4. Release of semen into the vagina of the female during coitus
7. The transformation of young one into an adult with different morphological features

INTRODUCTION

The world we live in consists of living as well as non-living components and the striking difference between these two is the ability of living organisms to produce individuals of their own kind. This ability of living organisms is essential for their survival. Reproduction is a biological process by which an organism gives birth to its younger ones. It is important for the continuation of generations of living organisms on earth. It is a vital process without which species cannot survive for long. Reproduction is mainly of two types: Sexual reproduction and Asexual Reproduction

Reproduction in Animals

There are two modes of reproduction in animals. They can reproduce either by asexual reproduction in which only one individual is involved or sexual reproduction in which two individuals are involved. These are explained in detail in the following section:

Table 4.1 Difference between Asexual and Sexual Reproduction

Asexual Reproduction	Sexual Reproduction
1. Simple mode of reproduction.	1. Not as simple as asexual reproduction.
2. Only one parent is involved.	2. Usually two parents are involved.
3. Young ones produced are exactly identical to parents and are called clones.	3. Young ones produced are not identical to parents but resemble both parents.

Asexual Reproduction

As mentioned above also, asexual reproduction involves only one parent. Asexual reproduction can be observed in small animals, such as *Hydra*, *Amoeba*, etc. There are different modes of asexual reproduction. Some of them are given below:

Binary Fission

- This involves division of a parent organism into two younger ones, for example, *Amoeba* and *Paramoecium*.
  - Reproduction in *Amoeba* involves division of nucleus into two nuclei, followed by division of cytoplasm into two; so that each part receives a nucleus.
  - Other organism that can reproduce by binary fission is *Paramoecium*.

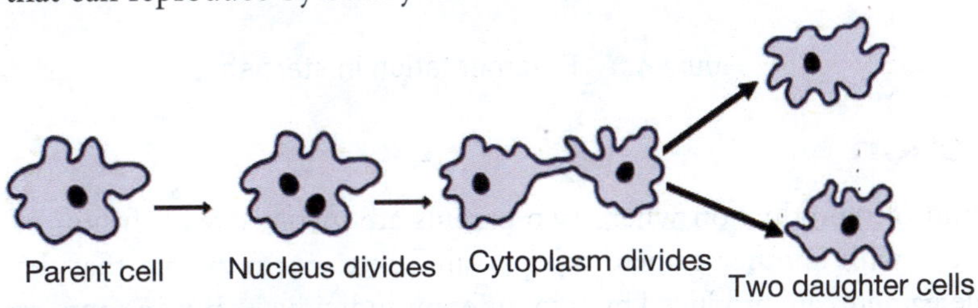

Figure 4.1 Binary fission in *Amoeba*

Budding

- It is also a kind of asexual reproduction which involves development of a new organism from the buds formed in parent's body, for example, *Hydra*, yeast, etc.
- In *Hydra*, a bud develops as an outgrowth that later on develops into new hydra. New offspring remains attached to parent body and detaches only after it is fully matured.

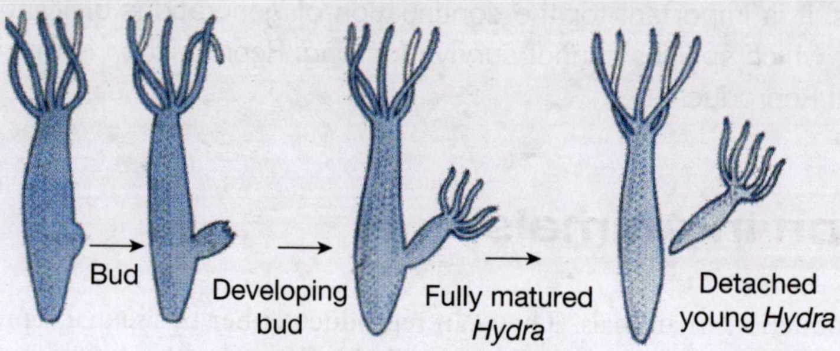

Figure 4.2 Budding in *Hydra*

Fragmentation

- Here, the parent body breaks into different fragments and each fragment develops into an organism, for example, Planaria.
- The offspring then produced are of similar type as the parent organism.

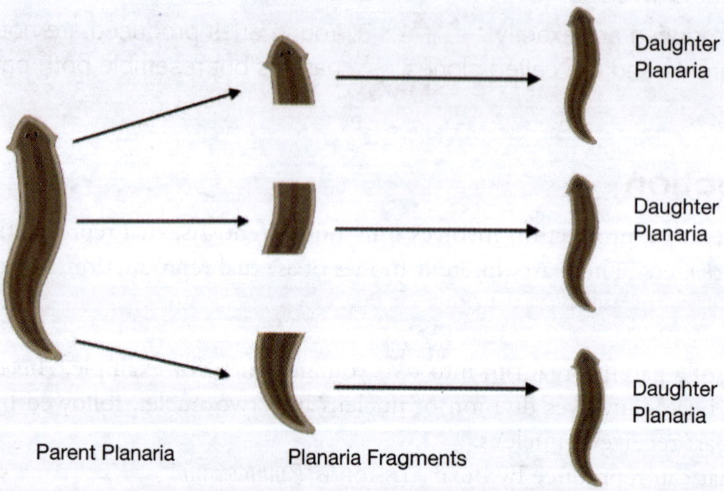

Figure 4.3 Fragmentation in starfish

Sexual Reproduction

Sexual reproduction is a kind of reproduction where two parents are involved with fusion of male and female gametes. Gamete is a cell that can fuse with another gamete of opposite sex to form zygote that develops into a younger one. Usually the male and female gametes are produced by two different individuals. But in some cases, both are produced by a single organism. Such organisms are called hermaphrodites (bisexual). A **hermaphrodite** possesses both male and female reproductive organs, for example, earthworm. Organisms that possess either male or female reproductive organs alone are called **unisexual organisms**, for example, humans. The male and female reproductive parts are dealt in detail below:

Male Reproductive Organs

In humans, the male reproductive organs include testes, scrotum, sperm ducts, accessory sex glands and penis.

Testes: A pair of testes are the male gonads that produce the male gametes called sperms. Millions of sperms are produced by the testes. They also produce testosterone, which is the primary male sex hormone.

Scrotum: It is a sac-like organ that houses the testes and helps to protects the testicles. It is present outside the body and maintains a low temperature required for sperm production.

Sperm ducts: These are tube like structures that helps to transport the sperms from testes to penis. They get mixed with fluids and is called semen. It is also known as vas deferens.

Accessory sex glands: They produce various substances that nourish the sperm, for example, prostate gland, seminal vesicles and bulbourethral gland.

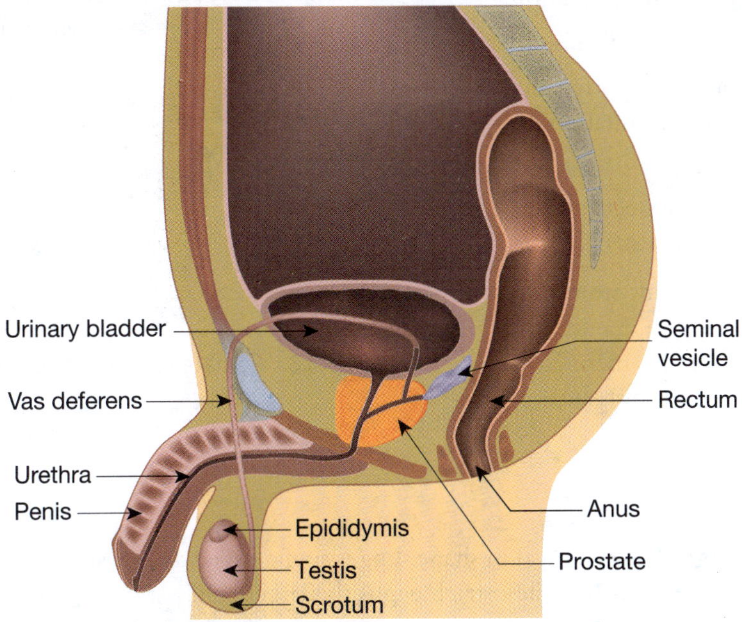

Figure 4.4 Male reproductive system

Info Bytes!
A woman's lifetime childbearing capacity is between 15 and 30.

Penis: Penis is the male external genitalia, which transfers and releases urine. It also transfers semen from the male reproductive tract into the reproductive tract of female during sexual intercourse.

Semen: Semen is the fluid that contains sperm. Apart from sperms, semen also contains other substances, like citric acid, free amino acids, fructose, enzymes, prostaglandins, etc., that nourish the sperm and also make their movement easy.

Sperm: Sperm is the male gamete. It is a single cell with three main parts:

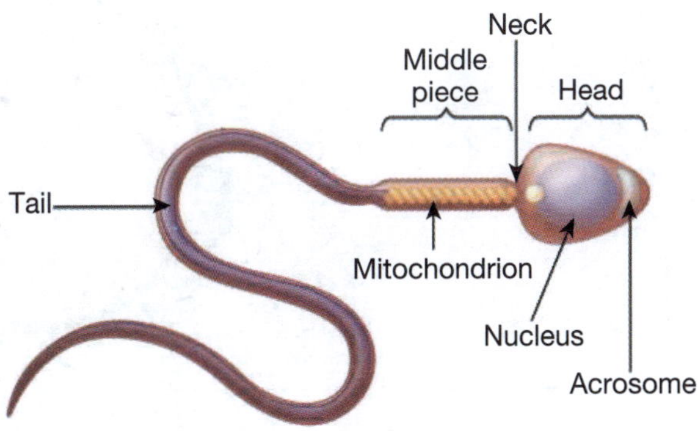

Figure 4.5 Structure of sperm

1. **Head:** Possesses nucleus and contains a structure called **acrosome** (which contains hydrolytic enzymes, like acrosin and hyaluronidase), that helps in penetrating female gamete.
2. **Middle piece:** Contains numerous mitochondria which produce energy for the movement of sperm tail and thereby facilitating sperm movement inside the female reproductive tract, which is essential for fertilization.
3. **Tail:** Helps in sperm movement inside the female reproductive tract.

Female Reproductive Organs

Female reproductive organs in human include a pair of ovaries, oviducts (fallopian tubes), uterus, cervix and vagina.

Ovaries: They produce female gamete that is known as female egg or **ovum**. There are two ovaries, right and left ovary. Every month a single matured egg is released from only one of the ovaries.

Oviduct or Fallopian tube: The tube structure present between the ovaries and uterus is called fallopian tube. Ovum released from ovary reaches uterus through fallopian tube.

Uterus: It is shaped as an inverted pear and is supported by ligaments attached to the pelvis. It is the site for implantation of the zygote and complete foetal development.

Cervix: Cervix is the lower part of uterus and connects uterus with vagina. The cavity of cervix is called cervical canal.

Vagina: Vagina is a tube-like structure that extends from the cervix to outside of the body. It is the site for sperm deposition at the time of coitus. It functions as a way for the menstrual flow and also as a passage for the baby to come out during vaginal delivery.

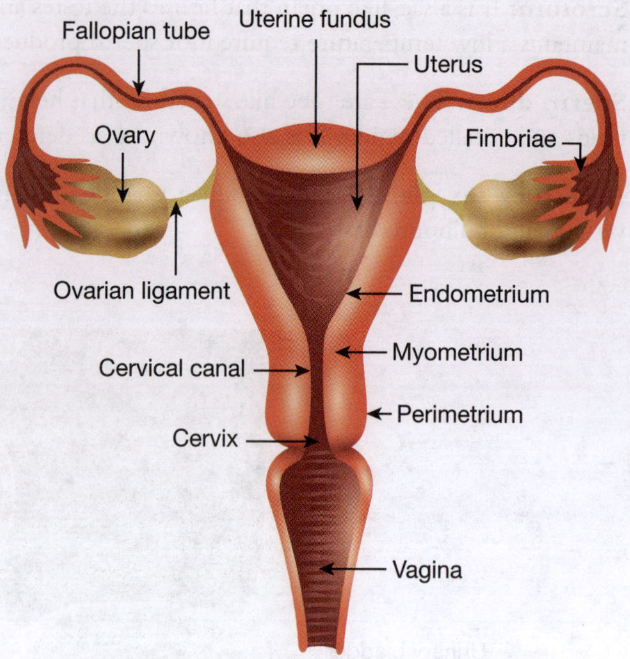

Figure 4.6 Female reproductive system

Ovum or Egg

The female gamete is known as an **ovum** or **egg**. It is spherical in shape. Egg is single celled and its size varies depending on the species. For example, the human egg is very small while ostrich egg is the largest cell.

The release of eggs from the ovaries is called ovulation.

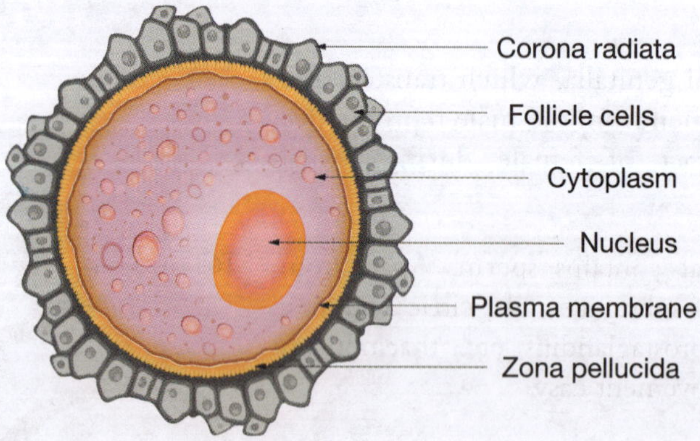

Figure 4.7 Structure of ovum

Fertilization

The fusion of male (sperm) and female gamete (ovum) is known as fertilization. During fertilization, nuclei of sperm and ovum fuse to form the zygote, which is the beginning of an individual. With the fusion of nucleus, the newly formed individual inherits characters of both parents, that is, mother and father. In humans, fertilization takes place at the fallopian tube. The sperms that are deposited inside the vagina by the penis during sexual intercourse move toward the fallopian tube and meet the egg that is released from

Info Bytes!

Sexual reproduction provides diversity in the genes of an offspring as it involves two different individuals.

the ovary after ovulation. The deposition of semen into the female vagina during copulation is called **insemination**. A single ejaculation of semen contains around 300 million sperms, out of which, only one sperm succeeds in fertilizing the egg.

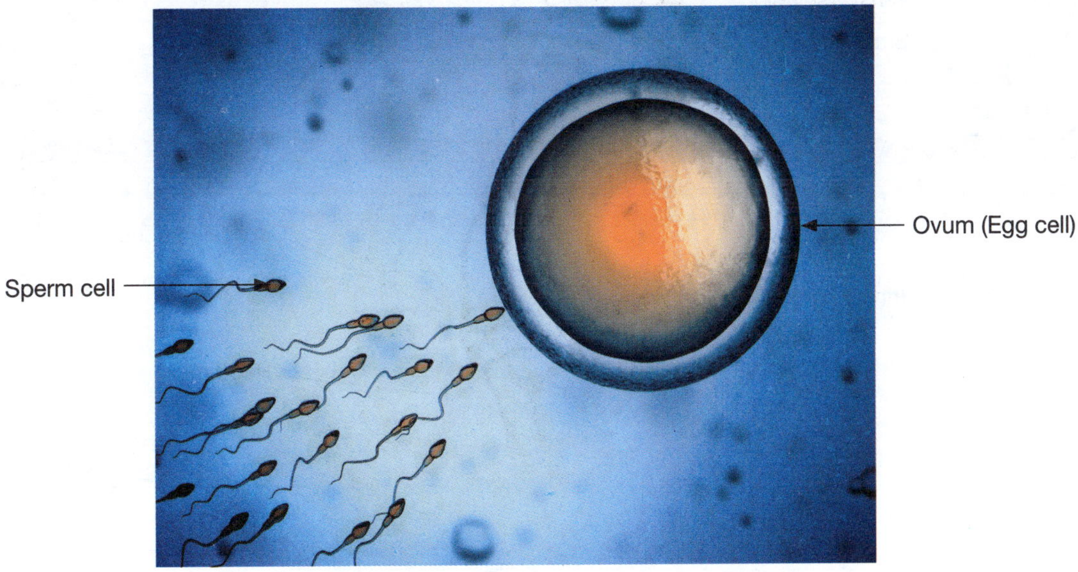

Figure 4.8 Fertilization of ovum by one sperm

Types of Fertilization

According to the place of fertilization, whether inside or outside the body. There are two types of fertilizations:

1. **Internal fertilization:**
    - Takes place inside the female body.
    - Male gametes are transferred to the body of female.
    - For example, humans, cows, dogs, hens, etc.
2. **External fertilization:**
    - Fertilization takes place outside the female body.
    - Usually takes place in the aquatic medium where gametes are released into the water.
    - For example, frog, fish, etc.

Development of Zygote to Embryo

Zygote formed after fertilization is a single cell, which then divides repeatedly to form embryo.

- Initial cell divisions of zygote take place at the **fallopian tube**, after which, the embryo moves to the uterus and gets embedded in the wall of the uterus and this process is called **implantation**.
- To enable implantation, the uterus goes through many changes, one of which is the increase in thickness of the inner lining of the uterus (**endometrium**).
- The embryo gradually develops inside the uterus and starts forming organs, such as hands, legs, head, eyes, etc. The nourishment required for the development of foetus is provided by the mother through the placenta.
- **Placenta** is an organ that connects the developing baby and mother. This structure provides oxygen and nutrients to the baby and also removes wastes from the baby's body.
- The stage of embryo in which all body parts can be identified is called **foetus**.
- Usually it takes around 38 weeks for complete development of the baby inside the uterus in humans.
- When the development is complete, mother gives birth to the baby.

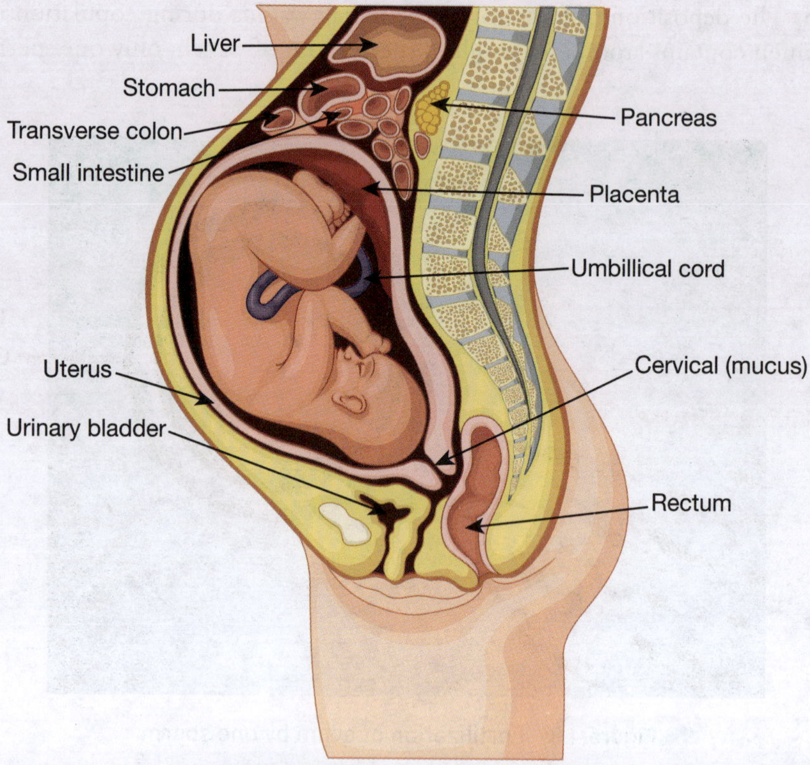

Figure 4.9 Human foetus in uterus

Stages of Human Reproduction

The sequence of events leading to fertilization are explained in the form of a flow chart.

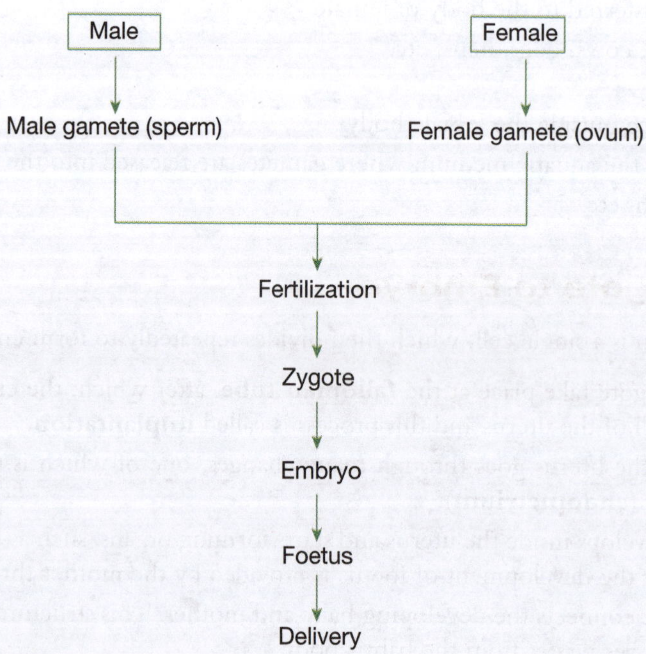

Figure 4.10 Sequence of events taking place in human fertilization

Growth and Development in Human Beings

Growth is defined as increase in the size and number of the cells. It is a gradual process that could be divided into following stages.

Infancy

This stage starts as soon as the child is born. It lasts till the age of two years. Growth occurs rapidly in this stage. The infants learn various activities like to sit, stand, walk, etc., in this stage.

Childhood

Generally, this stage ranges from the age of 2 to 12 years. Significant physical changes take place during childhood. This stage is marked by intellectual and social growth. The growth occurs at a steady rate.

Adolescence and Puberty

Adolescence meaning 'to grow up', is the period of life, where the body undergoes changes that lead to reproductive maturity. Adolescence begins around the age of 11 and lasts up to 18 or 19 years of age. It is a transitional stage from childhood to adulthood. **Puberty** is the time when an individual attains reproductive maturity. Many changes can be seen among children during puberty. Some of them are listed below:

- In boys, at puberty the voice box (larynx) can be seen as protruding parts of throat and is called **Adam's apple**.
- Increased activity of sweat and sebaceous gland is the reason why some people get acne and pimples at puberty.
- In girls, development of breasts and broadening of hips take place.

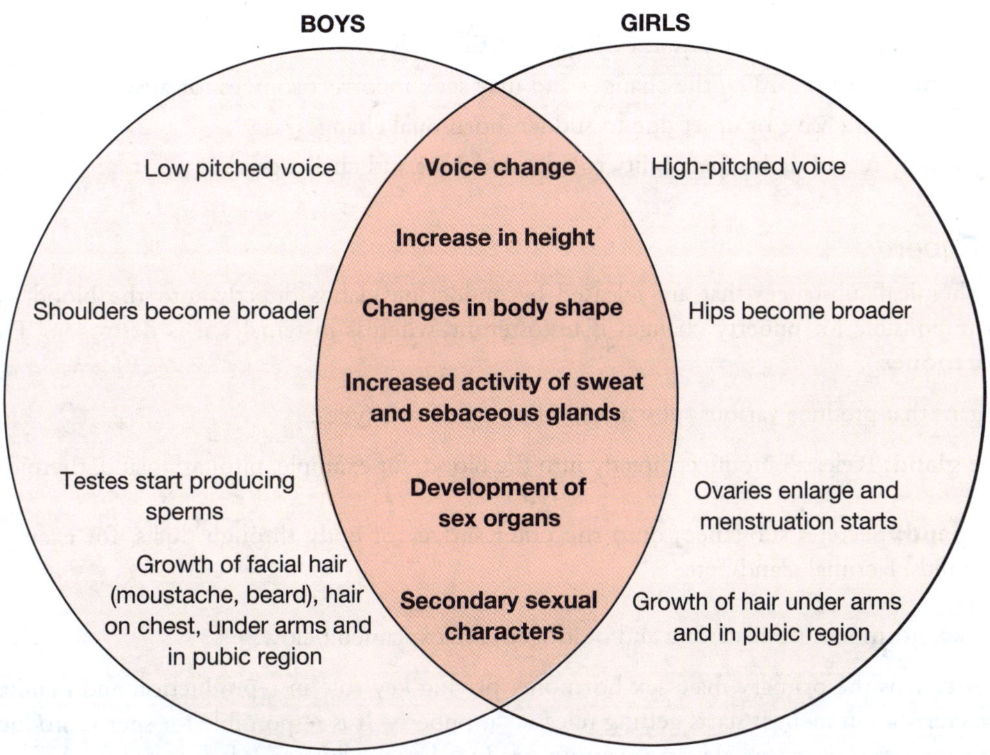

Figure 4.11 Changes seen in boys and girls at puberty

Role of Hormones

The various features that appear during puberty are called **secondary sex characters**. Unlike primary sex characters (development of sex organs), these features do not have direct involvement in reproduction but they help in distinguishing male from female. They are caused by hormones released at the time of puberty.

Following are the secondary sexual changes seen in boys:

- External genitalia (penis) increase in length.
- Shoulders get broader.
- Boys become more muscular.
- Hair grow on face (moustache, beard), chest, armpit, pubic regions.
- Voice becomes low pitched.

Following are the secondary sexual changes seen in girls:

- Breast development takes place.
- Hips get broader.
- Hair grow in armpits and pubic regions.
- Voice becomes high pitched.

From the above, it is clear that some of the changes at puberty are common to boys and girls while some others are unique. The unique changes are due to the changes in hormone released in boys and girls.

Problems related to adolescence:

Adolescence is marked by significant changes at physical, emotional, sexual and intellectual levels. Shift from childhood to adolescence is marked by adjustments that may lead to many problems discussed as follows:

- One may start to worry about the physical changes in the body.
- One may get inquisitive regarding the changes and may seek incorrect sources for answers.
- One may get easily offensive or upset due to sudden hormonal changes.
- One may get hasty regarding his/her ability to take decisions and challenges.

Hormones in Puberty

Hormones are chemical substances that are released by endocrine glands directly into the blood stream. The male hormone that is responsible for puberty changes is testosterone whereas in females it is oestrogen. These are together known as **sex hormones**.

Glands are organs that produce various substances. They are of two types:

1. **Endocrine gland:** Releases products directly into the blood, for example, pituitary gland, thyroid gland, testes and ovary, etc.
2. **Exocrine gland:** Secretes substances onto the outer surface of body through ducts, for example, sweat glands, mammary glands, lacrimal glands, etc.

The two primary sex hormones (testosterone and oestrogen) are explained below:

1. **Testosterone:** It is the primary male sex hormone, playing key role in reproduction and maintaining secondary sexual characteristics in men. It starts getting released at puberty. It is responsible for sperm production in men.
2. **Oestrogen:** It is the primary female sex hormone, produced by the ovaries. It is required for the normal functioning of female reproductive system and the release of ovum from ovaries.

Sex hormones are under the control of hormones released from the pituitary gland. It is explained in the following flow-diagram.

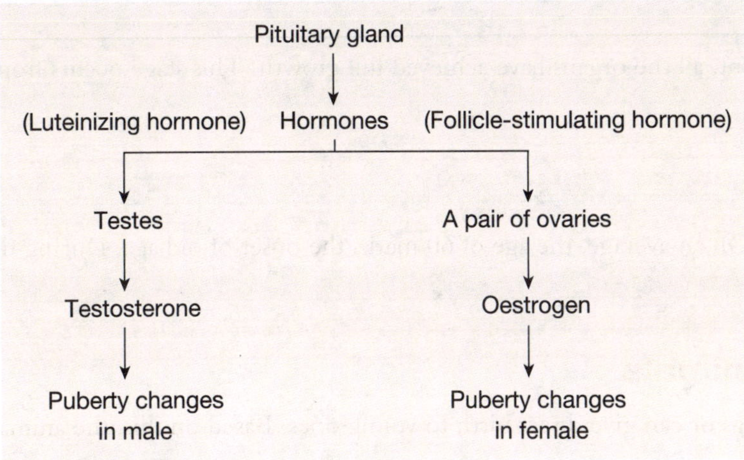

Figure 4.12 Hormonal regulation at the time of puberty

Konnect

In ovoviviparous animals, embryo develops inside the eggs and remains in the mother's body. Mother does not provide nutrition to the embryo. For example, shark.

Menstrual Cycle in Females

Menstruation is the periodic shedding of the endometrial lining of the uterus which comes out of the vagina in the form of bleeding and is repeated at an interval of every 28–30 days. The cycle of various events from one menstruation to the next one is called the menstrual cycle. Usually the release of ovum from ovary (ovulation) takes place at the middle of the menstrual cycle, that is, on the 14th day. During this period, uterus is also getting ready so as to receive the egg or released ovum, if it is fertilized. The lining of uterus becomes thick to provide a proper bed for the fertilized egg or zygote. If fertilization occurs, the fertilized egg develops into a baby (foetus) in the uterus; otherwise, the uterus sheds off its thick layer along with blood vessel and unfertilized ovum, which results in bleeding through the vagina. This is called **menstruation** which generally lasts for 3–5 days.

Info Bytes!

Certain women may be born with two vaginas or uteruses and be unaware of this until they experience irregular menstruation or heavy bleeding.

The first menstruation at puberty in a female is called **menarche**. Menstrual cycle stops at the age of 45–50 years and this is called **menopause**. The various events taking place in the menstrual cycle are represented below:

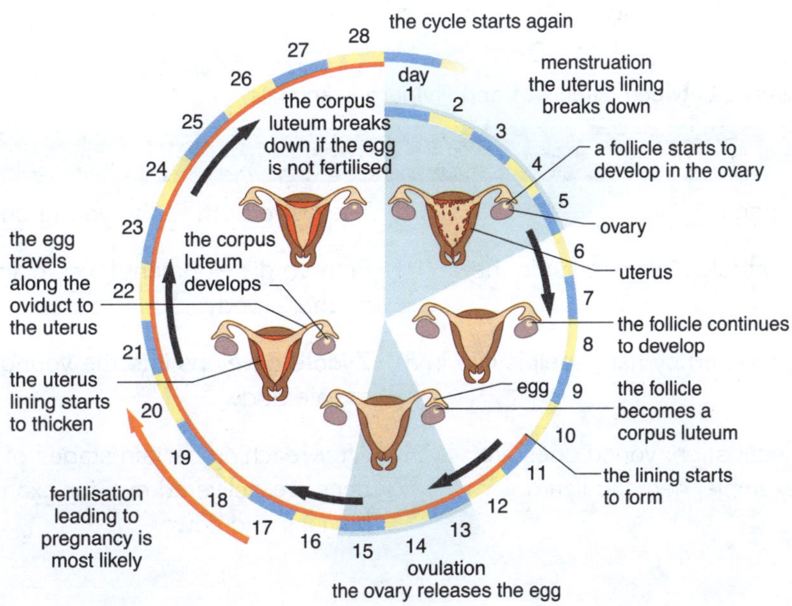

Figure 4.13 Cycle of events during a menstrual cycle

Adulthood

At this stage of human growth and development, all the organs have achieved full growth. This stage occurs from the age of 18.

Old Age

The beginning of this stage differs in people. On an average, the age of 60 marks the onset of old age. During this phase, bones become brittle and muscles get weak.

Viviparous and Oviparous Animals

After fertilization the mother can either lay eggs or can give direct birth to young ones. Based on this, the animals can be classified as oviparous and viviparous:

- **Oviparous:** They lay eggs. Development takes place outside mother's body. For example, hen, frogs, lizards, etc.
- **Viviparous:** They give birth to young ones directly. Development takes place inside mother's body, for example - humans, cow, dog, etc.

Figure 4.14 Oviparous animal—Hen

Figure 4.15 Viviparous animal—Cow

Table 4.2 Difference between oviparous and viviparous animals

Oviparous animals	Viviparous animals
These animals lay eggs.	They give birth to the young ones.
Embryo development takes place outside the mother's body.	Embryo development takes place within the mother's body.
The fertilized egg covered by hard shell is laid in a safe place.	Zygote develops into the young one within the female body.
After a period of incubation, young ones are hatched out, for example, hen and lizard.	After reaching certain stages of growth, young ones are delivered out, for example, humans and cows.

Metamorphosis

After the young ones are born or hatched out, there are two scenarios:

1. Young ones show similarities with adults and all body parts are present at the time of birth itself. These organisms gradually develop into adults.
2. Younger ones formed are distinct from the adults. They look different and even lack some of the features that are present in adults. For example, the young ones of frog look entirely different from the adults. Their development goes through a larval stage. The development of butterfly also shows metamorphosis.

Info Bytes!

In insects like silk moths, metamorphosis is controlled by insect hormones, whereas in frog it is controlled by thyroxine, produced by the thyroid gland.

Egg ⟶ Larva (Tadpole) ⟶ Adult

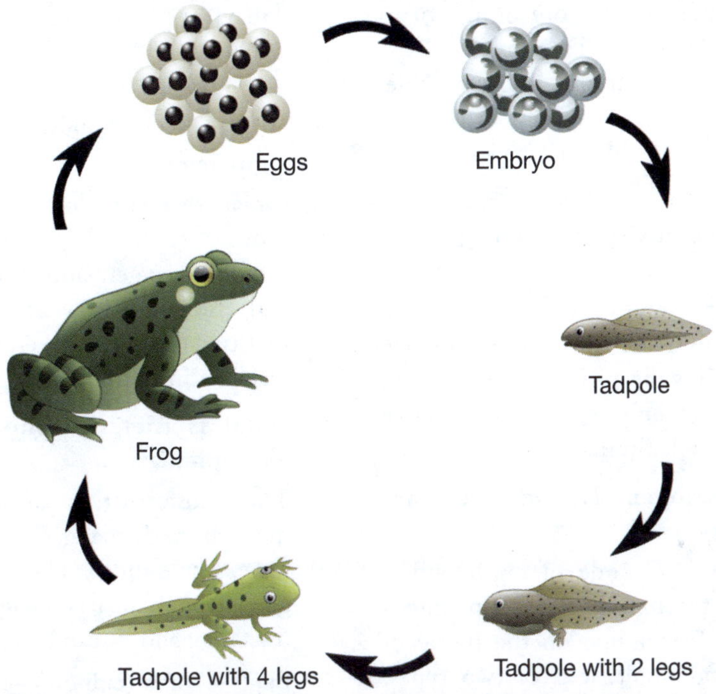

Figure 4.16 Metamorphosis in frog

Here, tadpole larva is different from the adult frog. The transformation of larva into adult through drastic changes is called metamorphosis.

Figure 4.17 Metamorphosis in butterfly

Quick Recap

✔ **Define budding. Give an example.**

Budding is a mode of asexual reproduction in which a new organism grows out as a small projection (or "bud") on the parent organism, eventually detaching and becoming independent. For example, yeast cells reproduce by budding where small buds grow from the parent yeast cell and then separate.

✔ **Define spore formation. Give an example.**

Spore formation is a mode of asexual reproduction where the organism forms spores, which are tiny cells protected by a thick wall. When conditions are favourable, these spores can develop into new organisms. For example, fungi like *Rhizopus* (bread mold) reproduce by forming spores.

✔ **What are dioecious species and give an example?**

Dioecious species are those species where individual organisms are either male or female but not both. This means one organism will have only male or only female reproductive organs. For example, humans are dioecious.

✔ **Define parthenogenesis and what are the different types?**

Parthenogenesis is a mode of reproduction in which an unfertilized egg develops into a new organism. Depending on the mode of development and result, it is of two types: obligate parthenogenesis, where sexual reproduction never occurs (e.g., in some lizards) and facultative parthenogenesis, where it happens occasionally (e.g., in honeybees).

✔ **Define oviduct.**

Oviduct, also known as fallopian tube is a tube-like structure present between the ovary and uterus. Ovum released from ovary reaches the uterus through the oviduct.

✔ **Define fertilization and what are the different types?**

Fertilization is the fusion of male and female gametes, that is, sperm and ovum, to form zygote. According to the place of fertilization, whether inside the body or outside, it is of two types: internal fertilization and external fertilization. Fertilization that takes place inside the body is called internal fertilization, for example, humans and fertilization that takes place outside the body is called external fertilization, for example, frogs.

✔ **Define implantation.**

The process by which the embryo gets embedded into the uterine wall is called implantation.

✔ **What is placenta and write its significance?**

Organ that connects developing foetus and mother is called placenta. This structure provides oxygen and nutrients to the baby and also removes wastes from the body of foetus. For example, embryo is attached to placenta in humans and elephants, etc.

✔ **What is metamorphosis and give one example?**

The transformation of larva into an adult through drastic changes is called metamorphosis, for example, frogs. The development in frogs goes through the larval stage. The development (metamorphosis) can be represented as:

Egg → Larva (tadpole) → Adult

✔ **What are secondary sexual characters?**

The various features that appear during puberty are called secondary sexual characters. Unlike primary sexual characters (development of sex organs), these features do not have direct involvement in reproduction but they help in distinguishing males from females. They are caused by hormones released at the time of puberty, for example, shoulders get broader and voice becomes deeper in boys whereas in girls, hips get broader and voice becomes high pitched.

Reproduction in Plants

Reproduction in plants is the process by which a new plant develops from a parent plant. In plants, reproduction is of two types:

1. Asexual reproduction
2. Sexual reproduction

Asexual Reproduction

Asexual reproduction is the development of a new plant from plant parts, such as leaf, root, stem, bud, etc., that is, from vegetative parts. The young ones produced are identical to the parent plants. The formation or fusion of gametes or fertilization is absent in this mode of reproduction. This method produces a large number of plants in a short period of time.

Plants reproduce asexually in two ways: spore formation and vegetative propagation.

Spore Formation

In this method, lower plant organisms produce globular structures called sporangia (singular: *sporangium*) which contain spores. When sporangia ripe, they burst open to release spores. These spores are very light and they have a hard protective coat. The spores develop in a same way as seedlings develop into plants. These method of asexual reproduction is seen in fungi, mosses, ferns, etc.

Vegetative Propagation

Vegetative propagation can be done in two ways:

1. Natural
2. Artificial

> **Info Bytes!**
> Mitosis is used in one type of asexual reproduction called vegetative propagation.

Natural Methods of Vegetative Propagation

Most plants reproduce vegetatively in nature by the help of various parts, like roots, stems and leaves. New plants can grow naturally from either of these parts, and are discussed in the following sections.

Roots

Plants like sweet potato and *Dahlia* can be propagated vegetatively from roots. These roots contain small buds, which are capable of generating a new plant whenever they are planted in the soil.

Figure 4.18 Tapioca plant is propagated through roots

Stem

New plants can be produced from the stem also. For example, plants like potato and onion could be propagated using their underground stem structures called tuber and bulb, respectively. Sugarcane is also an example for plants that could be propagated by planting segments of stems.

Figure 4.19 Plants propagated through stem

Leaves

In plants such as *Bryophyllum*, adventitious buds are present on the notched margins of the leaves. When these buds fall off and come in contact with moist soil, they give rise to new plants.

Figure 4.20 Leaf buds of *Bryophyllum*

Artificial Methods of Vegetative Propagation

Artificial means of vegetative propagation is used for those plants which produce very few seeds or non-viable seeds. These methods are done artificially for propagation of desired plants in a short period of time. Some of the examples are given below:

Cutting

Stem cutting is the most common method used in vegetative propagation. It involves cutting a portion of the stem bearing one or more nodes (capable of rooting) from the parent plant. This cutting is then placed in a rooting medium from where the plant either starts growing immediately or takes some time. Various chemical substances are used for promoting the growth. Examples of plants propagated by stem cutting include rose, *Hibiscus*, *Salvia*, etc.

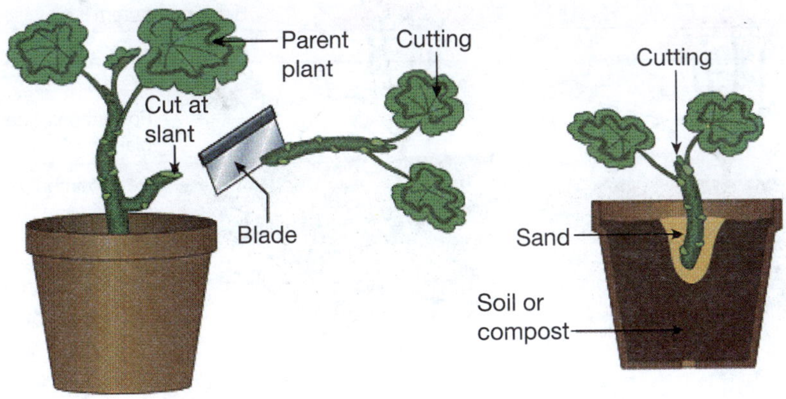

Figure 4.21 Stem cutting in a plant

Grafting

It is a technique in which parts of two different plants are connected or united artificially which later on develops as a single unique plant. For example, root and shoot of two different plants can be used for grafting. Here the shoot of the plant with superior quality is called **scion or graft** and root system of good quality taken for grafting is termed as **a stock**. Examples of plants propagated through grafting include apples, citrus, cherries, etc.

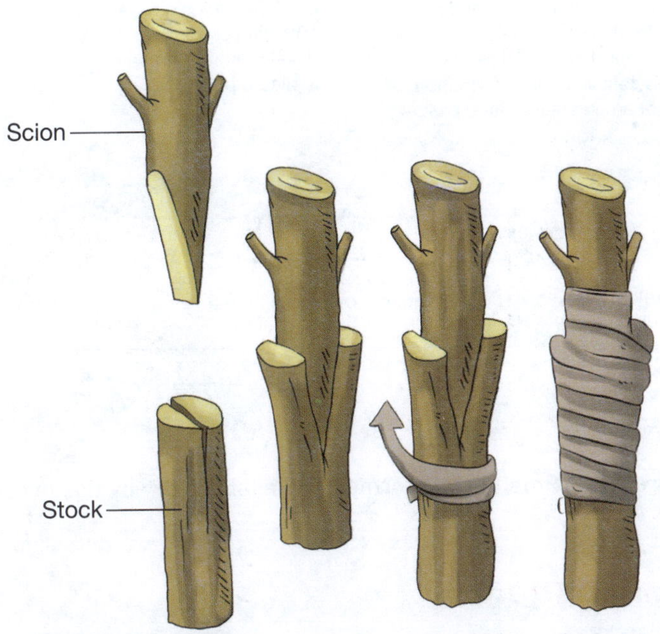

Figure 4.22 Grafting shown in a plant

Layering

Layering is a method used to develop roots on soft stems, while they are still attached to the plant. In a simple method, the stem is bent down and allowed to touch the soil, and from the point at which it touches the soil, new roots develop. Layering can also take place naturally. Examples of plants propagated by layering include *Rhododendron*, azalea, etc.

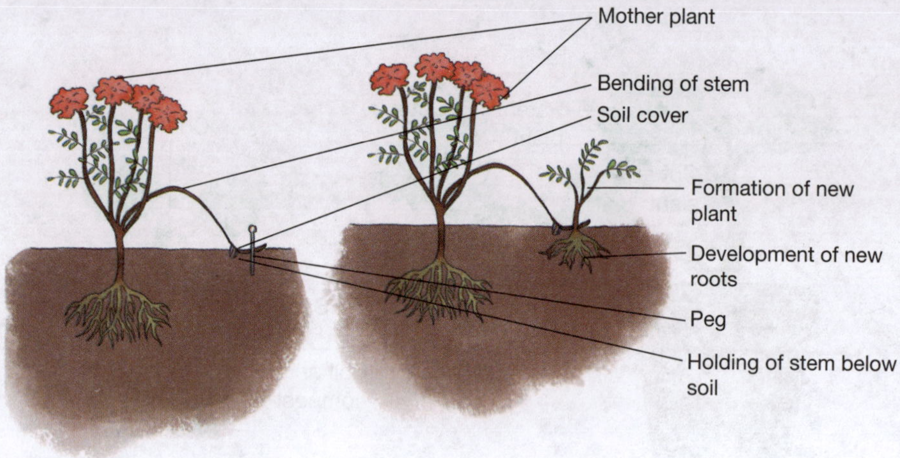

Figure 4.23 Layering shown in a plant

Plant Tissue Culture

Plant tissue culture involves cultivation or propagation of plants by growing or culturing plant cells, tissues or organs under controlled conditions in a laboratory. All the nutrients required for proper growth are provided artificially. After they have reached a particular stage of growth, the plantlets are transferred to separate pots or nursery to grow them into plants. Examples of plants propagated through this technique include tomato, apple, orchids, etc.

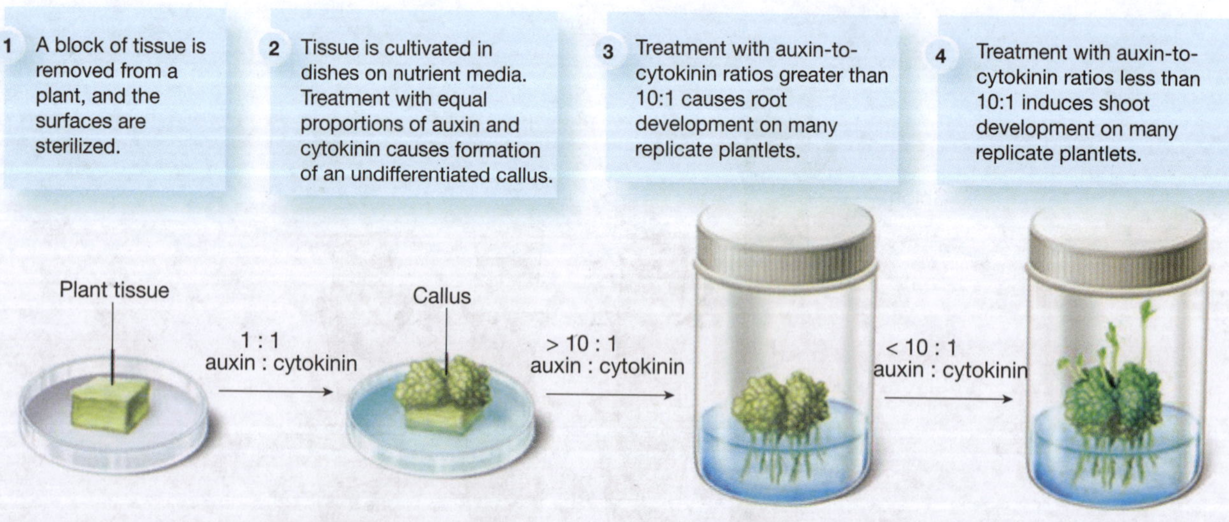

Figure 4.24 Small plants formed in the laboratory by tissue culture

Sexual Reproduction in Plants

Most of the higher plants reproduce sexually. Sexual reproduction in flowering plants involves the fusion of male and female gamete. Flower is the reproductive organ of plants which produces the gametes.

Structure of Flower

Flower is the attractive part of a plant that is found in various colours, shapes and fragrances. It is also the reproductive organ of a plant.

Following are the 4 main parts of a flower:

1. Calyx } Accessory floral organs that do not
2. Corolla } participate in reproduction
3. Stamen (Androecium) } Reproductive parts or
4. Carpel (Gynoecium) } essential floral organs

The individual unit of calyx are called **sepals** (which are small green coloured, leaf-like structures which protect the developing bud) and the individual unit of corolla are called **petals** (which are brightly coloured structures mainly for the attraction of pollinators).

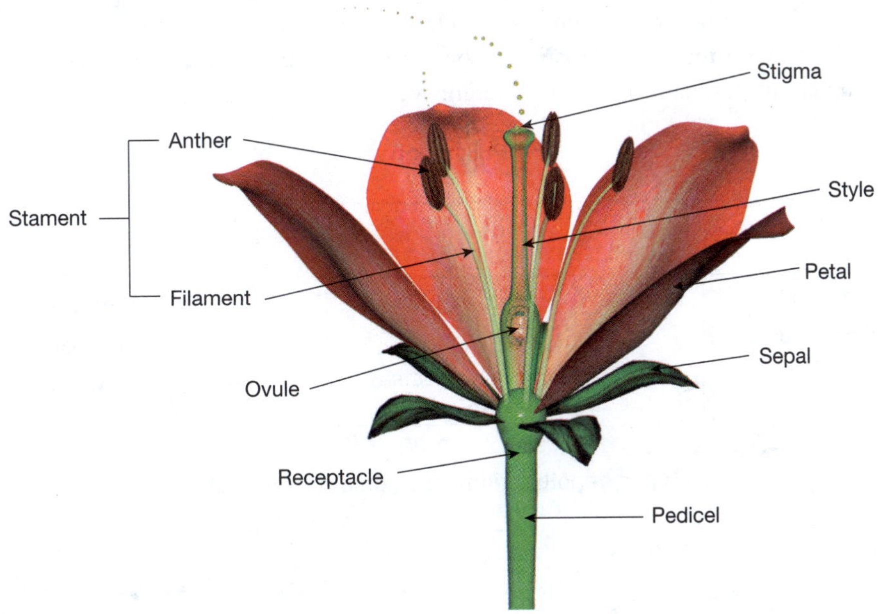

Figure 4.25 Longitudinal section of a flower **showing all parts**

Stamen or Androecium

Stamen is the male reproductive organ of a flower and male gamete is produced inside the stamen. Stamen has two parts: Anther and filament.

1. **Anther:** It is the structure bearing pollen grains located at the top of the filament of stamen.
2. **Filament:** It is a long, stalk-like structure that attaches the stamen with flower parts, such as petal.

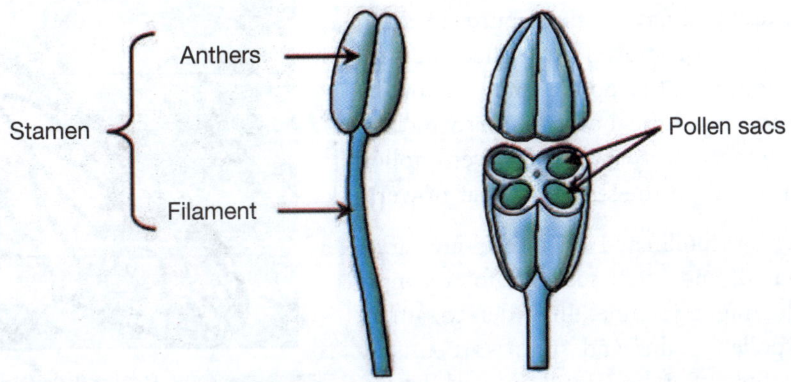

Figure 4.26 Parts of stamen

Carpel or Gynoecium

Gynoecium is the female reproductive organ of flower which encloses ovules and its individual unit is called **pistil**. It is the innermost part of a flower.

The pistil of a flower consists of the following three parts:

1. **Stigma:** It is at the tip of the pistil and forms the landing platform for pollen grains.
2. **Style:** It is the long, slender stalk which carries pollen grain from stigma to the ovary.
3. **Ovary:** This is the main reproductive organ of the flower, it encloses the unfertilized female gamete and the fertilized ovule.

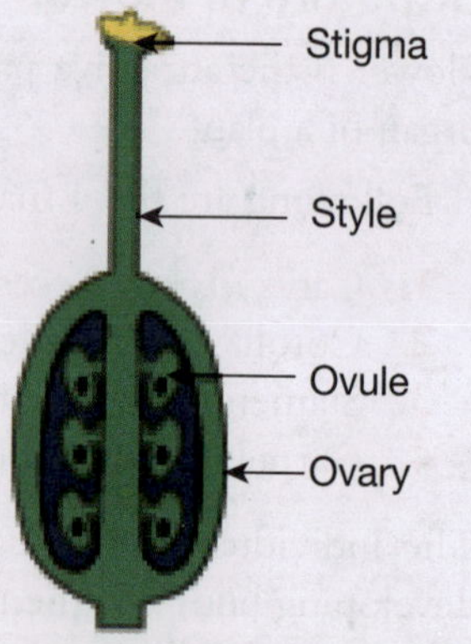

Figure 4.27 Parts of pistil

Pollination

The transfer of pollen grains from the male anther of a flower to the female stigma is termed as pollination. As pollen grains cannot move on their own, external agents, such as wind, water or animals are required for pollination. These are called **pollinating agents**. According to the type of pollinating agent bringing about pollination, it is of different types, as described below:

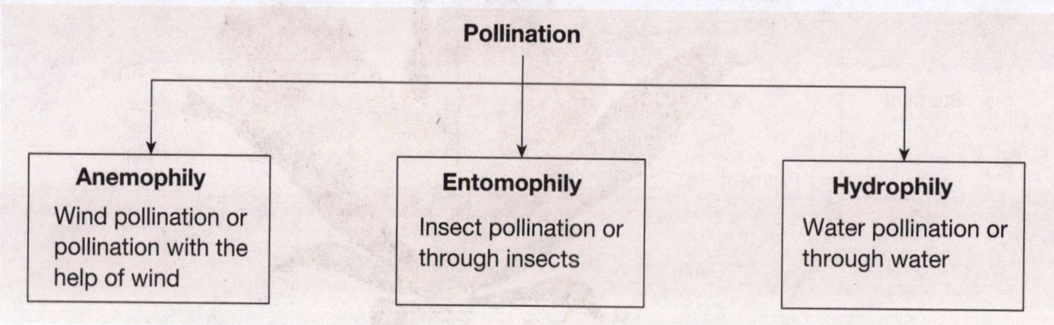

Figure 4.28 Types of pollination based on different pollinating agents

Natural Pollination

Natural pollination is of two types:

1. **Self-pollination:** In this process, pollen grains from anthers of a flower are transferred to the stigma of the same flower, or another flower of the same plant.
2. **Cross-pollination:** In this process, pollen grains from anther of a flower are transferred to the stigma of another flower on a different plant but of the same variety. Cross-pollination can be carried out by various agents which are known as pollinating agents, for example, insects, water, wind, etc.
    - **Pollination by insects:** This is the most common method of natural pollination. Bees, butterflies and other insects sit on the flowers to collect nectar/ juice. While doing so, the pollen grains from the anther get stuck onto the body of these insects. When these insects visit another flower, pollen grains get deposited on the stigma of that flower.

      Flowers which are pollinated by insects are large, brightly coloured, and often scented; for example rose, marigold, night jasmine. In order to attract insects their pollen grains and stigma are usually sticky. For example, strawberry and mustard flower.

FIG. 4.29 Butterfly sitting on a flower facilitating pollination

- **Pollination by water:** This type of pollination occurs in aquatic plants, like *Hydrilla* and *Vallisneria*. Flowers which are pollinated by water are in light weight so that they can easily float on water surface. These flowers do not produce nectar.
- **Pollination by wind:** In this type of pollination, pollen grains are carried by wind and get deposited on the stigma. So, pollen grains are produced in large quantities so that at least some have a chance to reach the stigma. Most wind-pollinated flowers are small, and have dry and light pollen grains which can be easily carried by wind; for example rice, maize and grass

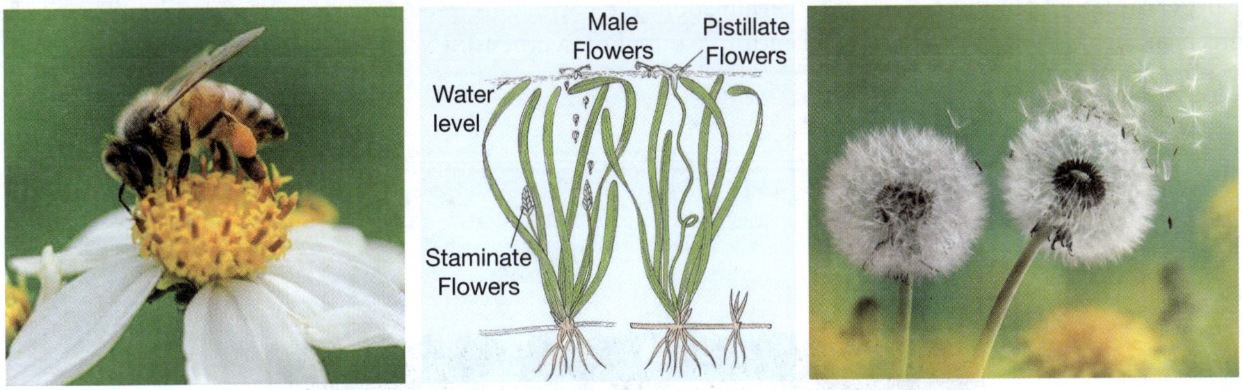

Figure 4.30 (a) Entomophily, (b) Hydrophily and (c) Anemophily

Artificial Pollination

In this process, two different varieties of plants are selected both with certain required characteristics, to produce a new variety of plants. This method leads to an increase in genetic diversity as different flowers will share and combine their genetic information to create unique offspring.

For example, a plant with *disease-resistance* property and another with *high-yielding* property could be selected. After selecting, they are made to cross-breed by artificial pollination to produce a new variety of plants which will have characteristics from both the parent plants.

Artificial cross pollination of rice is very common in the field of agriculture.

Info Bytes!

Scientists at the Indian Botanical Garden in West Bengal's Howrah district have carried out artificial pollination of the only double coconut tree in India, which bears the largest seed known to science.

Fertilization

The fusion of male and female gametes is called **fertilization**. During pollination, a large number of pollen grains are deposited on the stigma of a flower. Pollen grain starts to germinate and form a pollen tube downwards to the ovary. The male gamete within the pollen grain reaches the ovary through pollen tube and fuses with the female gamete to form the zygote. The zygote later on develops into an embryo which in turn develops into a young plant.

Seed Formation

Seed formation completes the process of reproduction in plants. **Seed** is an embryonic plant enclosed in a seed coat, with some food reserves (in the form of endosperm). Seed is formed inside the plant structure called fruit.

Seed Dispersal

It is the scattering of seeds over a large area so that they find a suitable place for germination. Dispersal is carried out by different agencies, like wind (Dandelion), water (coconut), animals (Cocklebur), etc. The dispersal of seeds is important as it helps the plants to germinate without competing with each other.

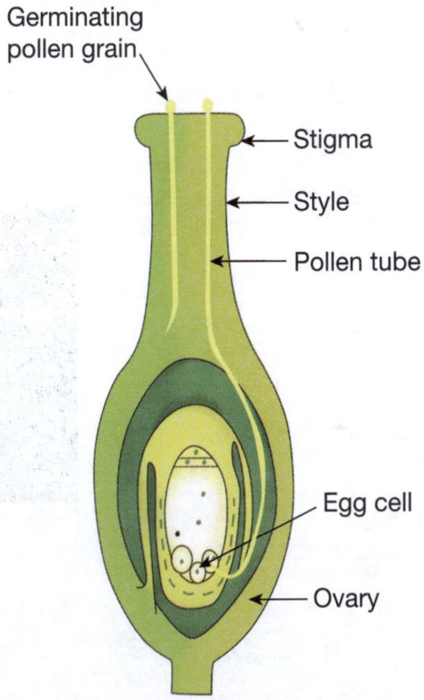

Figure 4.31 Growth of pollen grains leading to fertilization

Seed Germination

Seed germination is the process by which a new plant grows from the seed. After the seed has formed, it remains in a dormant state and waits for suitable conditions for germination. When it is provided with enough water and if temperature is also suitable, it starts germinating first giving rise to a seedling. The seedling initially attains nutrients from the seed itself, until it has grown enough to prepare its own food through photosynthesis.

There are two types of seed germination found in nature:

Epigeal germination: In this type of seed germination, the cotyledons (seed) emerge out of the soil. The cotyledons turn green and act as the first leaves of the plant (carry out photosynthesis). Examples are bean, castor, onion and papaya, etc.

Figure 4.32 Epigeal germination

Hypogeal germination: In this type of seed germination, the cotyledons (seed) remain inside the soil. They play no role in photosynthesis. Examples are pea, maize, etc.

Figure 4.33 Hypogeal germination

Quick Recap

✔ **Define vegetative propagation.**

Asexual reproduction in plants is called vegetative propagation. It is the development of new plants from plant parts, such as leaf, root, stem, bud, etc. The younger ones produced are identical to the parent plants. Large number of plants can be produced in a short period of time through vegetative propagation. It can be done in two ways: natural as well as artificial.

✔ **Write a note on female reproductive structures of a flower.**

Gynoecium or carpel is the female reproductive structure of a flower and its free unit is called pistil. Pistil comprises three parts known as stigma, style and ovary. Stigma functions as the landing platform for pollen grains. Ovary encloses the ovule where development of female gamete (egg) takes place. The elongated stalk that connects ovary with stigma is known as style.

✔ **Define fertilization.**

The fusion of male and female gametes is called fertilization. Large numbers of pollen grains are deposited on the stigma of a flower during pollination. Pollen grains start to germinate and form a pollen tube downwards to the ovary. The male gamete within the pollen grain reaches the ovary through the pollen tube and fuses with the female gamete to form the zygote. The zygote later on develops into an embryo which in turn develops into a young plant.

✔ **What is anemophily?**

Transfer of pollen grains from anther to stigma (pollination) with the help of wind is called wind pollination or anemophily.

✔ **What is hydrophily?**

Transfer of pollen grains from anther to stigma with the assistance of water is termed as water pollination or hydrophily. It is common in aquatic plants, and the pollen grains are either floated on water surfaces or are submerged.

POINTS TO REMEMBER

- ✔ Reproduction is an essential biological process by which an organism gives birth to its younger ones.
- ✔ Asexual Reproduction is that type of reproduction in which only one individual is involved, it is found in lower plants and animals, example, Binary fission in Amoeba.
- ✔ Sexual reproduction is a kind of reproduction where two parents are involved with fusion of male and female gametes. It is found in higher plants and animals, for example, Angiosperms and Humans.
- ✔ The fusion of male and female gametes is called fertilization.
- ✔ Adolescence is the period of life, where the body undergoes changes that lead to reproductive maturity.
- ✔ Vegetative propagation is the development of new plants from plant parts, such as leaf, root, stem, bud, etc.
- ✔ Plant tissue culture involves cultivation or propagation of plants by growing or culturing plant cells, tissues or organs under controlled conditions in a laboratory.
- ✔ The transfer of pollen grains from the male anther of a flower to the female stigma is termed as pollination.
- ✔ Seed germination is the process by which a new plant grows from the seed.

DW

PRACTICE QUESTIONS CLASSROOM WING

Very Short Answer Type Questions

Directions for questions from 1 to 25:
Fill in the blanks in each question.

1. Asexual reproduction involves only _______ parent.
2. The fusion of male (sperm) and female gamete (ovum) is known as _______.
3. The structure that connects the developing baby and mother, providing oxygen and nutrients to the baby, is called _______.
4. Ovum is produced by ________.
5. ________ is the largest cell.
6. In humans, fertilization takes place at ________.
7. Release of egg from ovaries is called ________.
8. In hens, fertilization takes place ________ the body.
9. The stage of embryo in which all body parts can be identified is called ________.
10. The organisms that lay eggs are ________.
11. Puberty is the time when an individual attains ________ maturity.
12. The first menstruation at puberty is called ________.
13. In frogs, metamorphosis is controlled by ________.
14. The gland that releases its contents directly into the blood are called ________.
15. Sweat gland is an example for ________.
16. Pollen grains are produced in ________.
17. The shoot part of the plant that is selected for grafting is called ________.
18. The method used to develop roots on soft stems is ________.
19. In potato, vegetative propagation can be done from ________.
20. The stalk that connects stigma and ovary is ________.
21. Ovule is located inside the ________.
22. The seedlings take in nutrients initially from ________.
23. Seed is enclosed in ________.
24. ________ act as the receiving part for pollen grains.
25. The long stalk that attaches stamen with the flower part is ________.

Directions for questions from 26 to 50:
For each of the following questions, four choices have been provided. Select the correct alternatives.

26. Male sex hormone is produced by
    (a) Male gonad (b) Prostate gland
    (c) Testes (d) Both (a) and (c)
27. Scrotum helps to maintain
    (a) Low pH (b) Low temperature
    (c) High temperature (d) High pH
28. Which one of the following is a wrong statement?
    (a) Testes are located outside the body.
    (b) Sperm production requires a temperature higher than normal internal temperature.
    (c) Semen constitutes sperm and also other substances that nourish the sperm.
    (d) Tail of sperm helps in the movement.
29. Match the following:

A Yeast	(i) *Hydra*
B *Amoeba*	(ii) Budding
C Budding	(iii) Starfish
D Fragmentation	(iv) Binary fission

	A	B	C	D
(a)	iv	ii	i	iii
(b)	ii	iv	iii	i
(c)	iv	ii	iii	i
(d)	ii	iv	i	iii

30. Which of the following statement/s is/are correct.
    I In *Amoeba*, nucleus and cytoplasm divide simultaneously during binary fission.
    II In budding, the new offspring detaches immediately from the parent.
    III In amoeba, cytoplasm divides first followed by the division of nucleus.
    IV In budding, the new offspring detaches after it is fully matured.
    (a) I and II (b) I and IV
    (c) III only (d) IV only

31. What is the primary male sex hormone?
(a) Ovum (b) Testosterone
(c) Prostaglandin (d) Acrosin

32. Where does fertilization take place in humans?
(a) Uterus (b) Vagina
(c) Fallopian tube (d) Ovary

33. The part of sperm that contains mitochondria
(a) Tail (b) Acrosome
(c) Middle piece (d) Head

34. The part of sperm that helps in the penetration of ovum is
(a) Acrosome (b) Nucleus
(c) Tail (d) Middle piece

35. Cervix is
(a) Upper part of the uterus
(b) Middle part of the fallopian tube
(c) Lower part of the uterus
(d) Lower part of the fallopian tube

36. Sexual reproduction involves formation of the male and female gametes by
(a) Same individual
(b) Different individuals of the opposite sex
(c) Different individuals of the same sex
(d) Both (a) and (b)

37. To enable implantation, usually the thickness of inner lining of the uterus
(a) Decreases
(b) Remains the same
(c) Increases
(d) First decreases and then remains the same.

38. In which of the following organisms, fertilization is not internal?
(a) Humans (b) Frogs
(c) Hens (d) Dogs

39. In a normal healthy person, a single ejaculation contains around ______ sperms
(a) 300 million (b) 150 billion
(c) 150 million (d) 300 billion

40. Sperm fuses with egg at
(a) Fallopian tube (b) Uterus
(c) Cervix (d) Vagina

41. Which one of the following is a wrong statement?
(a) Every month ovum will be released from both ovaries.
(b) Ovoviviparous animals do not provide nutrition to the developing embryo.
(c) In girls, voice becomes high pitched at puberty.
(d) Secondary sex characters do not have direct involvement in reproduction.

42. Identify the word pair relationship.
Frog: ________
Internal fertilization: ________

43. Match the following

A	Frog	i	Pituitary gland
B	Fish	ii	Metamorphosis
C	FSH	iii	External fertilization
D	LH	iv	Testes

	A	B	C	D
(a)	ii	iii	i	iv
(b)	iii	iv	i	ii
(c)	ii	iii	iv	i
(d)	iv	iii	ii	i

44. Usually ovulation takes place on
(a) 14th day
(b) Middle of menstrual cycle
(c) Towards the end of menstruation cycle
(d) Both (a) and (b)

45. Identify the word pair relationship
Endocrine gland : ________
________ : Sweat gland

46. Which one of the following is not a feature of viviparous animals?
(a) They give birth to young ones.
(b) Embryo development takes place inside the female body.
(c) Less embryonic care and protection.
(d) Provides nutrition to the foetus through placenta.

47. **Assertion (A):** Hen comes under oviparous animals
Reason (R): Oviparous animals give birth to young ones
(a) Both A and R are true and R is the correct explanation for A.
(b) Both A and R are true and R is the not the correct explanation for A.
(c) A is true and R is false
(d) A is false and R is true

48. **Assertion (A):** Pituitary gland is an exocrine gland
Reason (R): It releases it secretions directly into blood
(a) Both A and R are true and R is the correct explanation for A.
(b) Both A and R are true and R is the not the correct explanation for A.
(c) A is true and R is false
(d) A is false and R is true

49. The accessory floral parts are
(a) Sepal and tepal
(b) Sepal and petal
(c) Stamen and pistil
(d) Androecium and gynoecium

50. The unit of androecium is
(a) Stamen (b) Pistil
(c) Anther (d) Stigma

Short Answer Type Questions

51. What are hermaphrodites? Provide an example.

52. Describe the structure of the sperm.

53. How is sexual reproduction different from asexual reproduction in terms of offspring produced?

54. Write a note on reproduction of *Hydra*.

55. Differentiate between oviparous and viviparous animals.

56. List out the major secondary sex characters in girls.

57. Explain the role of pituitary gland in puberty changes?

58. Define a gland and what are its different types?

59. Name the male and female sex hormones in humans and the organs that produce them.

60. Define grafting and write its significance.

61. Which is the male reproductive structure in a flower? Mention about its parts.

62. Explain the method that is used to develop roots on soft stem.

63. What is pollination? Explain any three modes of pollination.

Essay Type Questions

64. Explain the development of the zygote into an embryo and its journey to becoming a foetus in the human reproductive system.

65. What are the main parts of a flower?

66. Explain seed germination.

67. Describe artificial methods of vegetative propagation.

PRACTICE QUESTIONS COMPETITION WING

Level 1: Apply your Concepts

Directions for questions from 1 to 5:
Fill in the blanks in each question.

1. The female gamete is called ________.
2. ________ is the male external genitalia.
3. Ovum released from ovary reaches uterus through ________.
4. Structure that connects uterus and vagina is ________.
5. ________ is an example for male accessory sex gland.

Directions for Questions 6 and 7:
Complete the table given below.

6. Complete the table with missing words

Characteristic	Male	Female
(a) Gamete	....	....
(b) Gonad	....	....
(c) External genitalia	....	....
(d) Motility of gamete	....	....
(e) Location of gonad	....	....

7. Complete the table given below.

Puberty changes	Male	Female
1. Voice change	....	....
2. Change in body shape	....	....
3. Sex organs development	....	....
4. Hair growth	....	....

Directions for question 8:

8. Arrange the following events in the correct order.

Foetus Ovulation Embryo
Zygote Delivery Fertilization

Directions for question 9:
Complete the chart with missing words.

9. (a)

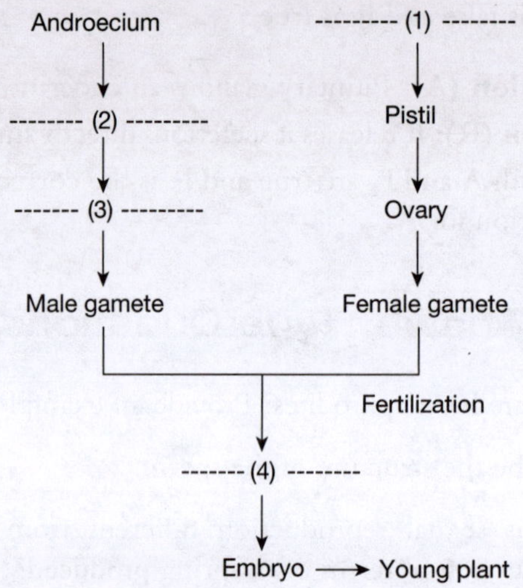

(b)

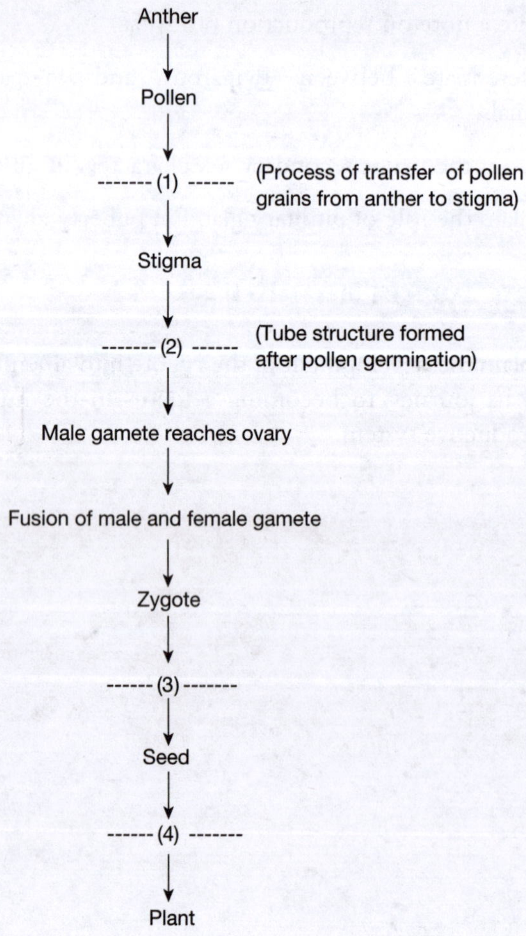

Level 2: Review your Concepts

10. The temperature inside the scrotum is two degrees less than the normal human body temperature. What could be the possible reason for this?

11. A single ejaculation of semen contains around 300 million sperms, whereas fertilization involves fusion of one male and one female gamete. How is fusion of more than one sperm avoided?

12. Genetic variation brings the diversity in traits of individuals of a population. Which one of the self-pollination and cross-pollination could bring more genetic diversity?

Level 3: Assess Your Concepts

13. A particular flower is brightly coloured and secrete nectar. The flower also secrete certain smell to attract insects. What can be inferred about its mode of pollination?

14. While growing, a seed derives nutrition from the endosperm. What happens to the mode of nutrition when the seed has matured to become a plant?

AT

PRACTICE QUESTIONS NEET SPECIAL WING

Multiple-Answer Type Questions

Questions number 1 to 5 are multiple-choice questions. Each question has FOUR options (a), (b), (c), and (d). ONE OR MORE THAN ONE of these four option(s) is/are the correct answer(s).

1. Which of the following is true about vegetative propagation in plants?
   (a) It takes place through spore formation
   (b) It is an asexual method
   (c) Roots, stem and leaves are involved
   (d) It can occur both naturally as well as artificially

2. Changes associated with adolescence in males includes:
   (a) Broader shoulders
   (b) Growth of facial hair
   (c) Broader hips
   (d) High pitched voice

3. In animals like humans and cows:
   (a) Embryo develops within the mother's body
   (b) Mothers give birth to young ones
   (c) After incubation young one hatch out
   (d) Fertilized egg is covered in a hard shell

4. In epigeal germination:
   (a) Cotyledons remain inside the soil
   (b) Cotyledons emerge out of the soil
   (c) Cotyledons act as first leaves
   (d) Cotyledons do not perform photosynthesis

5. Functions of primary sex hormones include:
   (a) Growth of thyroid gland
   (b) Maintaining secondary sexual characters
   (c) Released by exocrine glands
   (d) Required for sperm production and ovum release

Comprehension-Based Questions

A. Read the paragraph given below and answer the questions number 6 to 11:

Sexual reproduction in animals involves two parents with fusion of male and female gametes. Gamete is a sex cell that can fuse with another gamete of opposite sex to form zygote that develops into a progeny. Usually, the male and female gametes are produced by two different individuals. But in some cases, both are produced by a single organism. Such organisms are called hermaphrodites. A hermaphrodite possesses both male and female reproductive organs, for example, earthworm. Organisms that possess either male or female reproductive organs alone are called unisexual organisms. In humans sperms or male gametes are produced by the testes whereas in females eggs are produced by the ovary. In humans, the male reproductive organs include testes, scrotum, sperm ducts, accessory sex glands and penis. Female reproductive organs in human include a pair of ovaries, oviducts (fallopian tubes), uterus, cervix and vagina.

6. Fertilization in humans is:
   (a) Internal and takes place in uterus
   (b) External and takes place in vagina
   (c) Internal and takes place in fallopian tube
   (d) External and takes place in cervix

7. Prostate gland, seminal vesicles and bulbourethral gland are:
   (a) Part of the essential whorl
   (b) Part of non-essential whorl
   (c) Part of sexual reproductive tract
   (d) Accessory sex glands

8. Why is scrotal bag present outside the body?
   (a) to maintain equilibrium
   (b) to give proper balance and space to the organs in male body
   (c) to maintain a higher-than-normal temperature
   (d) to maintain a lower temperature than the body temperature

9. To enable a process A, uterus increases the thickening of its lining B. Label A and B.
   (a) A-Fertilization, B-Myometrium
   (b) A-Fertilization, B-Endometrium
   (c) A-Implantation, B-Myometrium
   (d) A-Implantation, B-Endometrium

10. There is a fluid that contains and nourishes the sperms. Name the fluid and the content which nourishes it.
(a) Semen; fructose
(b) Semen; prostaglandins
(c) Cerebrospinal fluid; fructose
(d) Cerebrospinal fluid; prostaglandins

11. Match the following:

Column – A	Column – B
(i) Penis	(a) Largest human cell
(ii) Vas deferens	(b) Connects uterus to vagina
(iii) Cervix	(c) Transports sperms from testes to penis
(iv) Ovum	(d) Contains hydrolytic enzymes
(v) Acrosome	(e) Male external copulatory organ

B. Read the paragraph given below and answer the questions number 12 to 17:

Reproduction is the process by which continuity of species takes place. There are two modes of reproduction- asexual and sexual reproduction. Asexual reproduction is a simple mode of reproduction wherein only one parent is involved. This process results in young ones which are identical to parents. Sexual reproduction on the other hand involves two parents and is much more complicated. Different types of asexual reproduction include binary fission, budding and fragmentation. For sexual reproduction male and female gametes are produced by two separate individuals, but in some cases a single organism contains both the gametes are produced by a single organism.

12. Asexual reproduction in spirogyra takes place by
(a) Binary fission
(b) Budding
(c) Fragmentation
(d) Both b and c

13. Which of the following organisms cannot divide by fragmentation?
(a) Unicellular organisms
(b) Star fish
(c) Spirogyra
(d) Sponges

14. The difference between sexual and asexual reproduction is
(a) Sexual reproduction produces clones
(b) Sexual reproduction takes a longer period of time
(c) Asexual reproduction produces similar progeny to parents
(d) Asexual mode is more complex

15. Budding is a mode of reproduction seen in
(a) Amoeba
(b) Hydra
(c) Humans
(d) Monkey

16. The haploid male gamete is called
(a) Ovum
(b) Zygote
(c) Endoderm
(d) Sperm

17. Match the following:

Column – A	Column – B
(i) Hydra	(a) Fragmentation
(ii) Binary fission	(b) Bisexual
(iii) Star fish	(c) Budding
(iv) Hermaphrodite	(d) Asexual reproduction
(v) Clones	(e) Paramoecium

ANSWER KEYS

Crossword

Across

5. Ovulation 6. Acrosome 8. Fragmentation 9. Cervix 10. Bryophyllum

Down

1. Hydrophily 2. Endometrium 3. Fallopian tube 4. Insemination 7. Metamorphosis

Classroom Wing

Very Short Answer Type Questions

1. One 2. Fertilization 3. Placenta 4. Ovary 5. Ostrich egg
6. Fallopian tube 7. Ovulation 8. Inside the body 9. Foetus 10. Oviparous
11. Reproductive 12. Menarche 13. Thyroxine 14. Endocrine gland
15. Exocrine gland 16. Anther 17. Scion 18. Layering 19. Underground stem
20. Style 21. Ovary 22. Seed 23. Seed coat 24. Stigma
25. Filament 26. (d) 27. (b) 28. (b) 29. (d) 30. (d)
31. (b) 32. (c) 33. (c) 34. (a) 35. (c) 36. (d)
37. (c) 38. (b) 39. (a) 40. (a) 41. (a)
42. External fertilization: Human 43. (a) 44. (d)
45. Pituitary gland: Exocrine gland 46. (c) 47. (c) 48. (d) 49. (b)
50. (a)

Competition Wing

Level 1: Apply your Concepts

1. Ovum or an egg 2. Penis 3. Fallopian tube 4. Cervix 5. Prostate gland

NEET Special Wing

Multiple-Answer Type Questions

1. (b, c, d) 2. (a, b) 3. (a, b) 4. (b, c) 5. (b, d)

Comprehension-Based Questions

6. (c) 7. (d) 8. (d) 9. (d) 10. (a)
11. (i) → (e); (ii) → (c); (iii) → (b); (iv) → (a); (v) → (d)
12. (c) 13. (a) 14. (b) 15. (b) 16. (a)
17. (i) → (c); (ii) → (e); (iii) → (a); (iv) → (b); (v) → (d)

Hints and Explanations

CLASSROOM WING

Short Answer Type Questions

51. Hermaphrodites are organisms that possess both male and female reproductive organs. An example is the earthworm.

    Unlike unisexual organisms, hermaphrodites have both types of reproductive organs, allowing them to produce both male and female gametes.

52. The sperm has three main parts: Head, Middle piece, and Tail. The Head contains the nucleus and acrosome. The Middle piece has many mitochondria. The Tail facilitates movement inside the female reproductive tract.

    Each part of the sperm has a specific function that aids in the process of fertilization, from penetration of the female gamete to movement towards it.

53. In asexual reproduction, offspring are clones and identical to the parent, while in sexual reproduction, offspring are not identical but resemble both parents.

    The involvement of two parents in sexual reproduction brings genetic diversity, leading to offspring that have traits from both parents, unlike asexual reproduction where only one parent's traits are passed down.

54. *Hydra* reproduces asexually through budding. Budding involves development of a new organism from the buds formed in the parent's body. In *Hydra*, a bud develops as an outgrowth that later on develops into new *Hydra*. New offspring remains attached to the parent body and detaches only after it is fully matured.

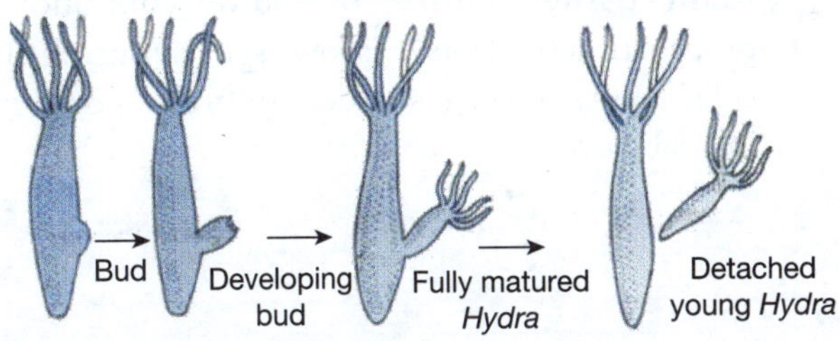

Budding in *Hydra*

55.

Oviparous animals	Viviparous animals
1. These animals lay eggs	They give birth to young ones
2. Embryonic development takes place outside the mother's body	Embryonic development takes place within the mother's body
3. The fertilized egg covered by hard shell laid in a safe place	Zygote develops into a young one within the female body
4. After a period of incubation, young ones are hatched out	After reaching certain stages of growth, young ones are delivered out
5. For example, hens	For example., humans

56.
- Breast development
- Hips get broader
- Hair growth in armpits and pubic regions
- Voice becomes high pitched

57. The puberty changes in males and females are controlled by male hormone 'testosterone' and female hormone 'oestrogen'. These sex hormones are under the control of hormones released from the pituitary gland which produces two hormones, namely, luteinizing hormone (LH) and follicle-stimulating hormone (FSH). LH acts on the testes and induces changes in males. Similarly, FSH acts on the ovaries and induces production of oestrogen that causes puberty changes in females.

58. Gland is an organ that produces various substances. They are of two types:

    - **Endocrine gland:** Releases products directly into the blood, for example, pituitary gland.
    - **Exocrine gland:** Secretes substances onto outer surface of body through ducts, for example, sweat gland.

59. The male hormone that is responsible for puberty changes is testosterone whereas in females it is oestrogen. These are together known as sex hormones. Testosterone is produced by testes whereas oestrogen is produced by ovaries.

60. Grafting is a method used for artificial vegetative propagation. It involves joining of parts of two different plants artificially which later develop into a single unique plant. For example, Root and shoot of two different plants can be used for grafting. Here the shoot of the plant with superior quality is called scion or graft and root system of good quality taken for grafting is termed as stock.

61. Stamen is the male reproductive organ of a flower and male gamete is produced inside the stamen. Stamen has two parts anther and filament. Pollen grains carrying male gamete are produced in the anther. Filament is the long stalk that attaches the stamen with floral parts, such as petal.

62. Layering is a method used to develop roots on soft stems, while it is still attached to the plants. In a simple method, the stem is bent down and allowed to touch the soil, and from the point at which it touches the soil, new roots develop. Layering can also take place naturally.

63. Transfer of pollen grains from anther to stigma is called pollination. As pollen grains cannot move by their own, external agents, such as wind, water or animal are required for pollination. According to this, pollination can be water pollination called hydrophily. Pollination through wind is called anemophily whereas pollination through bees or insects is called entomophily.

Essay Type Questions

64. When the nuclei of the sperm and ovum fuse after fertilisation, a zygote is formed. This single cell then divides into multiple cells to form an embryo. As the zygote moves through the Fallopian tube, the first cell divisions occur. The embryo then travels to the uterus, where it implants itself into the wall of the uterus. The uterus undergoes several changes to allow for successful implantation, including the thickening of its inner lining, known as the endometrium. As the embryo develops inside the uterus, it begins to form organs and body parts such as hands, legs, and eyes. The developing embryo is connected to the mother for nourishment via the placenta, which delivers essential nutrients and oxygen while also aiding in waste removal. The embryo is referred to as a foetus when all of its body parts are identifiable. After approximately 38 weeks of development in the human uterus, this entire process culminates in the birth of the baby.

65. The flower has four different parts, such as: calyx, corolla, androecium and gynoecium. Calyx and corolla together constitute the accessory floral parts as they do not participate in reproduction. Androecium and gynoecium are the essential parts that take part in reproduction. The units of androecium and gynoecium are stamen and pistil respectively.

66. Seed germination is the process by which a new plant grows from the seed. After the seed has formed, it remains in a dormant state and waits for suitable conditions for germination. When it is provided with enough water and if temperature is also suitable, it starts germinating first giving rise to a seedling. The seedling initially attains nutrients from the seed itself, until it has grown enough to prepare its own food through photosynthesis.

67. (i) **Cutting:** Pieces of plant parts such as root, stem, leaves are used for propagation.

(ii) **Grafting:** It is a technique in which parts of two different plants are connected or united artificially which later on develops as a single unique plant.

(iii) **Layering:** Layering is a method used to develop roots on soft stems while it is still attached to plant.

(iv) **Plant tissue culture:** It involves cultivation or propagation of plants by growing or culturing plant cells, tissues or organs under controlled conditions in a laboratory.

COMPETITION WING

Level 1: Apply your Concepts

6.

Characteristic	Male	Female
(a) Gametes	Sperm	Ovum
(b) Gonads	Testes	Ovaries
(c) External genitalia	Penis	Vagina
(d) Motility of gametes	Motile	Non-motile
(e) Location of gonads	Outside the body	Inside the body

7.

Puberty changes	Male	Female
Voice change	Deeper voice	High pitched voice
Change in body shape	Shoulders become broader	Hips get broader
Sex organs development	Testes start producing sperm	Ovaries enlarge and menstruation starts
Hair growth	Hair growth on face, chest, armpit and pubic regions	Hair growth in armpit and pubic region

8. Ovulation → Fertilization → Zygote → Embryo → Foetus → Delivery

9. (a) (1) Gynoecium (2) Stamen
(3) Anther (4) Zygote
(b) (1) Pollination (2) Pollen tube
(3) Embryo (4) Seedling

Level 2: Review your Concepts

10. A pair of testes are the male gonads which produce male gametes through the process of spermatogenesis. This process is affected by high temperatures (35°C). For spermatogenesis to occur under suitable conditions, temperature inside male gonads is two degrees less than normal human body temperature.

11. As soon as one male gamete (sperm) reaches the ovum and fertilizes it, the fertilized egg releases certain substances through a series of reaction that prevent further male gametes to fuse with it.

12. Self-pollination is the transfer of pollen from the anther to stigma of the same flower, or another flower on the same plant. Cross-pollination is the transfer of pollen from the anther of one flower to the stigma of another flower on a different individual of the same species. Hence, cross-pollination allows for more genetic diversity in plants.

Level 3: Assess Your Concepts

13. From the features described in the question, it can be inferred that the flower is insect-pollinated. Since, the insects get attracted to colours, smell and nectar, they assist in transfer of pollens.

14. When the seed has matured to become a plant, it derives nutrition through the process of photosynthesis which happens in the leaves and results in the formation of carbohydrates.

NEET SPECIAL WING

Multiple-Answer Type Questions

1. Asexual reproduction is the development of a new plant from plant parts, such as leaf, root, stem, bud, etc., that is, from vegetative parts. The young ones produced are identical to the parent plants. There are two types of asexual reproduction- natural as well as artificial. Artificial means of vegetative propagation is used for those plants which produce very few seeds or non-viable seeds. These methods are done artificially for propagation of desired plants in a short period of time.

2. Adolescence meaning 'to grow up', is the period of life, where the body undergoes changes that lead to reproductive maturity. Puberty is the time when an individual attains reproductive maturity. Many changes can be seen among children during puberty. In boys some of the changes include- low pitched voice, shoulders become broader, growth of facial hair, pubic hair as well as in the armpits, etc.

3. Viviparous animals give birth to young ones directly. Development takes place inside mother's body, for example - humans, cow, dog, etc.

4. In this type of seed germination, the cotyledons (seed) emerge out of the soil. The cotyledons turn green and act as the first leaves of the plant and carry out photosynthesis.

5. Hormones are chemical substances that are released by endocrine glands directly into the blood stream. The male hormone that is responsible for puberty changes is testosterone whereas in females it is oestrogen. These are together known as sex hormones.

Comprehension-Based Questions

A.

6. Fertilization in humans is internal and takes place inside the female reproductive tract. The process of fertilization takes place in the fallopian tubes.

7. Accessory sex glands produce various substances that nourish the sperm, for example, prostate gland, seminal vesicles and bulbourethral gland.

8. The scrotal bags which contain testes are present outside the abdominal cavity. This ensures that a lower temperature in maintained there than the body temperature which helps in sperm production.

9. Initial cell divisions of zygote take place at the fallopian tube, after which, the embryo moves to the uterus and gets embedded in the wall of the uterus and this process is called implantation. To enable implantation, the uterus goes through many changes, one of which is the increase in thickness of the inner lining of the uterus that is endometrium.

10. Semen is the fluid that contains sperm. Apart from sperms, semen also contains other substances, like citric acid, free amino acids, etc., that nourish the sperm.

11. Match the following:

Penis is the male external genitalia, which transfers and releases urine. It also transfers semen from the male reproductive tract into the reproductive tract of female during sexual intercourse.
(i) (e)

Sperm ducts are tube like structures that helps to transport the sperms from testes to penis. They get mixed with fluids and is called semen. It is also known as vas deferens.
(ii) (c)

Cervix is the lower part of uterus and connects uterus with vagina.
(iii) (b)

The female gamete is known as an ovum or egg. It is spherical in shape. Egg is single celled and its size varies depending on the species.
(iv) (a)

The head of the sperm possesses nucleus and contains a structure called acrosome (which contains hydrolytic enzymes, like acrosin and hyaluronidase), that helps in penetrating female gamete.
(v) (d)

B.

12. Mature spirogyra breaks down into small fragments, each new fragment develops into new individual.

13. Multicellular organisms show fragmentation, unicellular organisms cannot show fragmentation as it involves

breaking off of fragments of the parent organism to form progeny.

14. Sexual reproduction is more complex , involves two parents of the opposite sex and takes a longer period of time.

15. Hydra shows budding and amoeba undergoes binary fission whereas both humans and monkeys show sexual reproduction.

16. The haploid male gamete formed in case of humans in the testes is called sperm. It is motile and has tail for movement.

17. Match the following:

Budding is the asexual mode of reproduction seen in Hydra.
(i) (c)

Paramoecium shows binary fission, where first the nucleus is divided and then the cytoplasm.
(ii) (e)

In star fish after a period of maturation each fragment formed of the body is capable of growing into an individual and this method of reproduction is called fragmentation.
(iii) (a)

Bisexual organisms which produce bo0th male and female gametes are called hermaphrodites.
(iv) (b)

In asexual reproduction, the progeny formed is exactly identical to the parents and are called as clones.
(v) (d)

[illegible] shows binary fission, while the [illegible] nucleus is divided and then the cytoplasm [illegible]

[illegible]

[illegible] after a period of [illegible] the [illegible] part of the [illegible] and the [illegible] of [illegible] called [illegible]

[illegible]

[illegible] which [illegible] called hermaphrodites.

[illegible]

[illegible] sexual reproduction, the [illegible] formed [illegible] the parent and are called [illegible]

[illegible]

budding off of daughter [illegible] organism [illegible]

14. Sexual reproduction [illegible]

15. Hydra shows budding and [illegible] but [illegible] reproduction.

16. The [illegible] is called [illegible]

17. Match the following:

[illegible] is the asexual mode of reproduction seen in [illegible]

CHAPTER

5

Microorganisms and Human Health

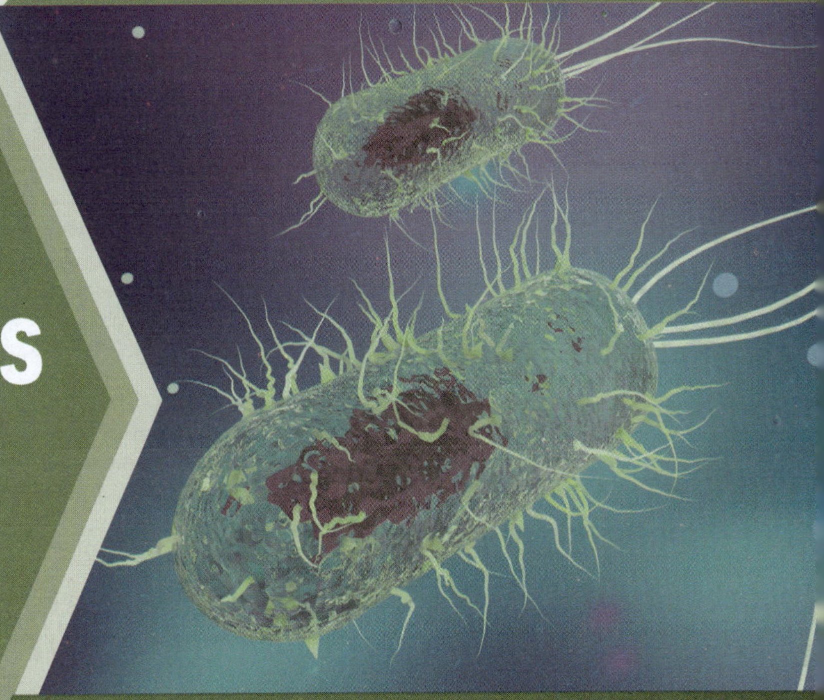

Remember

Before beginning this chapter, you should be able to:

- Recall the major categories of microorganisms
- Remember the structure, shape and nutrition in common microorganisms
- Understand the basic reproduction concepts in microorganisms

Key Ideas

After completing this chapter, you should be able to:

- Understand the basic concepts related to microorganisms
- Identify useful and harmful microorganisms
- Describe immune system and its components
- Discuss common human diseases

A Tribute to Louis Pasteur (1822-1895)

Louis Pasteur (1822–1895) was a pioneering French microbiologist whose work changed the course of medicine and microbiology forever. His work not only changed our understanding of microorganisms, but it also changed medical practises.

Pasteurization, Pasteur's most famous contribution, was a game changer. By inventing this method for heat-treating beverages and food, he made them safer to consume by killing harmful microorganisms. This breakthrough significantly reduced disease spread and vastly improved public health.

Pasteur's germ theory of disease reshaped medical science beyond pasteurisation. His experiments demonstrated that microorganisms were to blame for a wide range of illnesses, challenging previously held beliefs. This discovery ushered in a new era of medical knowledge and the development of effective disease prevention and treatment strategies.

One of his most notable accomplishments was the development of the first rabies vaccine in 1885. This life-saving vaccine saved countless lives and solidified his legacy as an immunisation pioneer.

Louis Pasteur's contributions to science and public health earned him numerous honours, including the prestigious Copley Medal and the French Legion of Honour. His work continues to inspire scientists, and his name will always be associated with the Pasteur Institute, a prestigious research institute dedicated to the study of infectious diseases.

FUN TIME

CROSSWORD

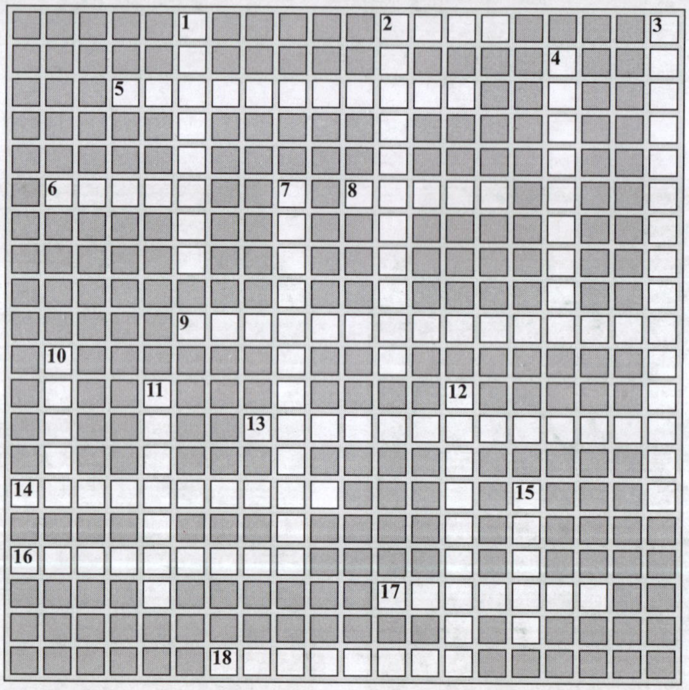

Across

2. The jelly-like substance prepared from red algae used as medium growth of many microbes in laboratory
5. The white blood cells which are produced in bone marrow
6. The class of microbes which mostly cause skin infections
8. The microorganism which has no life outside the living cell
9. The diseases caused due to the abnormality in DNA
13. Bacteria responsible for the curdling of milk
14. The vaccine discovered by Alexander Fleming
16. A substance which can initiate immune response
17. The condition of overweight caused due to lifestyle
18. The toxic substances produced by the pathogenic microbes

Down

1. The ability of a person to resist the attack of a disease or infection
2. The medicines which are likely to kill the bacteria invading the living cells
3. The diseases which develop over a period of time and persist for long time in the system
4. The edible member of algae
7. The principle behind the usage of yeast for wine making
10. Microorganisms which are autotrophic
11. The live or attenuated microbes which are injected into the body to produce antibodies for a pathogen
12. The microbes which cause infectious diseases
15. Solidifying agent prepared from red algae

INTRODUCTION

The organisms that cannot be seen with the naked eyes and can be viewed only under the microscope are called **microorganisms** or **microbes**. **Microbes** are diverse and include bacteria, fungi, protozoa and some algae. Viruses are also microscopic but they are generally considered as non-living. They reproduce only inside a host cell, which can be bacteria, plants or animals. There are some microorganisms that are unicellular, that is, they are made up of only one cell, for example, bacteria, whereas there are some microorganisms that are made up of more than once cells and are called **multicellular microorganisms**, for example, moulds.

Microorganisms

Microorganisms are broadly divided into four groups: algae, bacteria, fungi and protozoa.

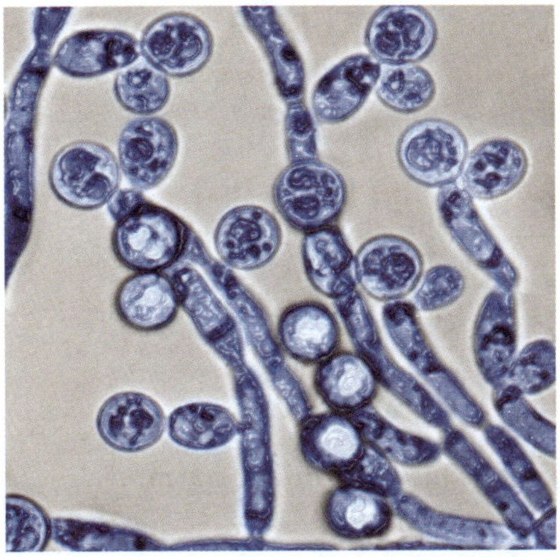

Fungi

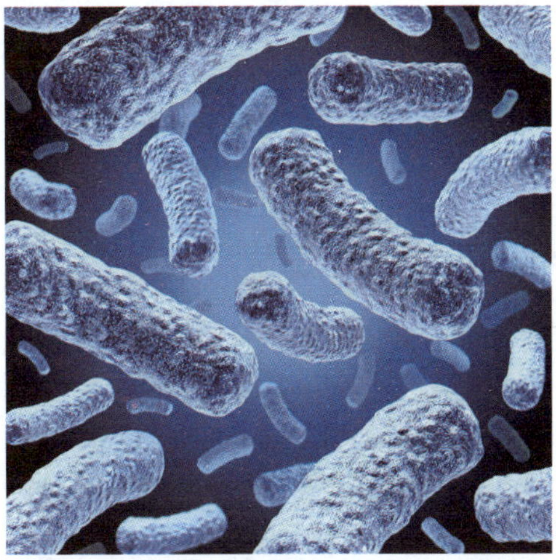

Bacteria

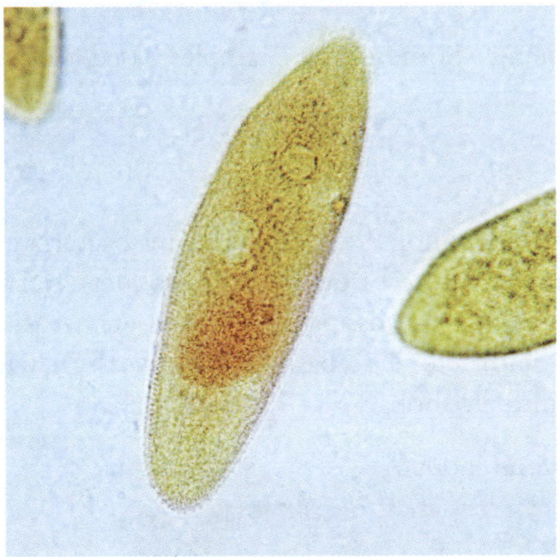

Protozoan

Algae

Figure 5.1 Common microorganisms (bacteria, fungi, protozoan, algae)

Microorganisms could be found anywhere in the biosphere, that is, in soil, oceans, air, hot springs, deserts, etc. They are even present inside the body of animals. The study of microorganisms is termed as **microbiology**. Depending upon their effects on human health, there are two types of microbes, namely useful or harmful.

Info Bytes!

Antonie van Leeuwenhoek is called 'Father of Microbiology'.

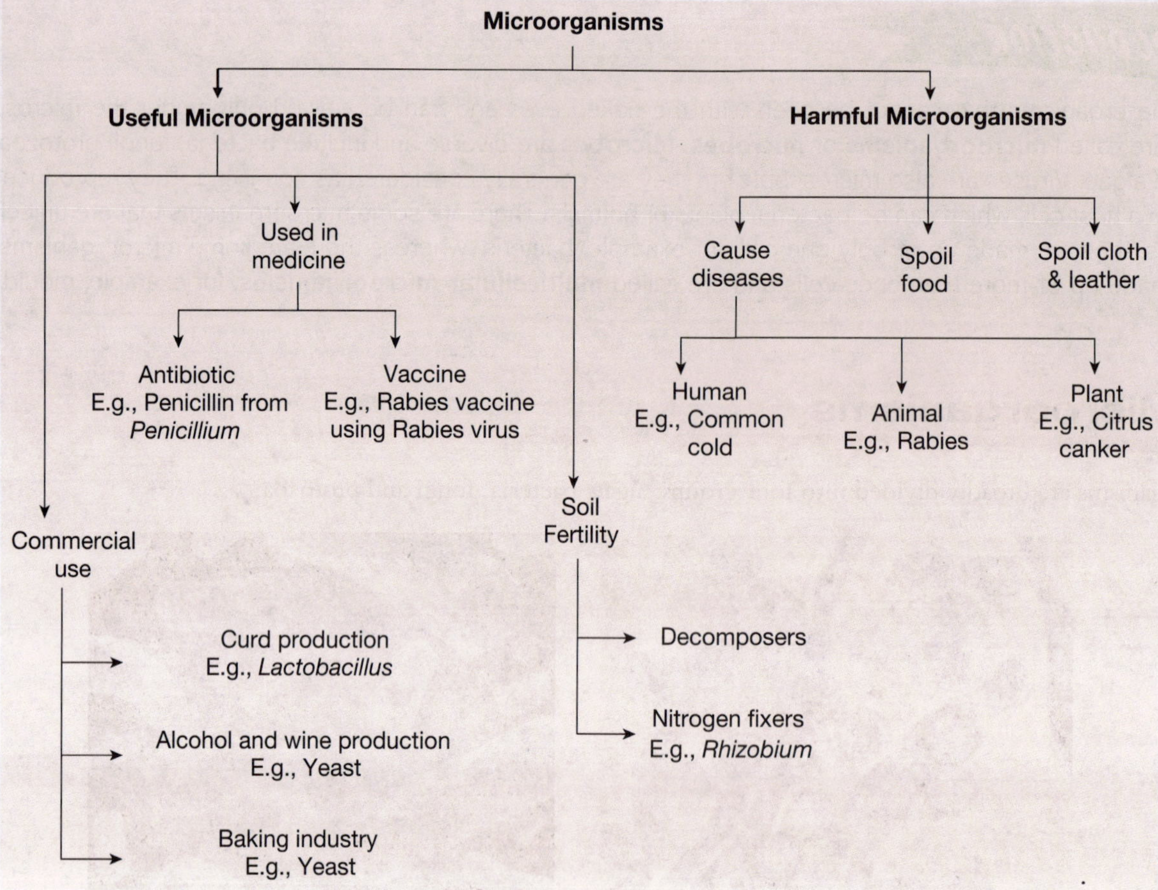

Figure 5.2 Classification of microorganisms into useful and harmful

Useful Microorganisms

There are many microorganisms that are beneficial to human beings. Some of the examples based on their uses are given below:

Microorganisms in Food Industry

Microorganisms are widely used for the production of curd, bread, alcohol, etc. Curd contains bacteria called *Lactobacillus* that convert milk into curd. Bacteria can also be used in the manufacture of other dairy products such as yogurt,cheese and vinegar, etc. Yeast can be used in the baking industry for making breads, pastries, cakes, etc. Yeast can also be used in the large-scale production of alcohol, wine, vinegar (acetic acid), etc. The basis of using yeast in wine production is fermentation. Fermentation is the process of converting sugar into alcohol.

Table 5.1 Useful microorganisms in food industry

Microorganism	Use
Lactobacillus	Curd production
Saccharomyces cerevisiae (Yeast)	Bread production
Acetobacter malorum (bacteria)	Vinegar production
Gluconacetobacter azotocaptans (bacteria)	Acetic acid production
Penicillium notatum mold	Antibiotic production

Figure 5.3 Vinegar, produced by the action of bacteria, is used for pickling

Info Bytes!

Chlorella (a green alga) is taken as a food supplement.

Microorganisms in Medicinal Industry

Microorganisms are used to make antibiotics. These antibiotics are used to kill or stop the growth of other disease-causing microorganisms. A simple example is penicillin. Penicillin can be obtained from the fungus *Penicillium*. These antibiotics can be used to cure many diseases that are caused by microorganisms, (except viral diseases). Microorganisms can also be used in the production of vaccine. A **vaccine** is a biological preparation that consists of either dead or weakened microbes. When a vaccine is introduced into the body, the body produces antibodies against the vaccine, which remains in the body and protects the body from attack by the same microbe in the future. The common examples are rabies and tuberculosis vaccines.

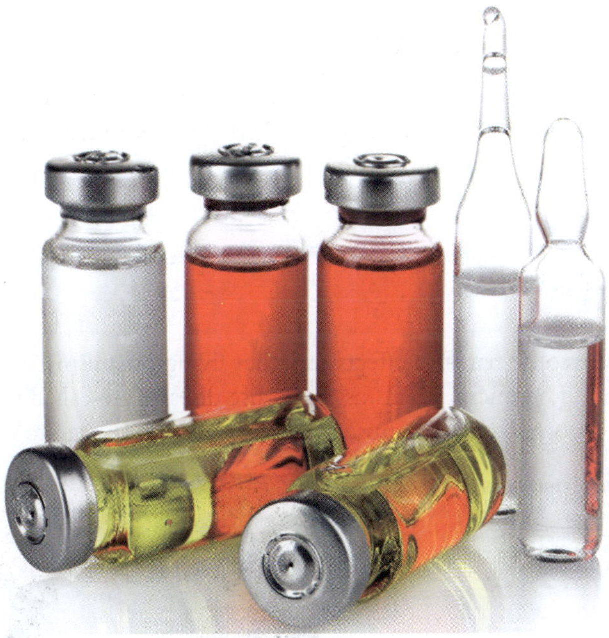

Figure 5.4 Medical vials containing vaccines

Info Bytes!

Regular hand washing can reduce the chances of getting diseases by up to 50%.

Sir Alexander Fleming was the person who introduced to the world, the greatest discovery of that time, the antibiotic 'Penicillin'. It saved the lives of thousands of soldiers during the second world war. He was awarded the Nobel Prize in Physiology or Medicine along with Florey and Chain in the year 1945. Florey and Chain developed processes to produce penicillin in sufficient quantites to become widely available.

Konnect

Antibodies are the substances produced by the body to fight against foreign particles called antigens.

Microorganisms in Agricultural Practices

Microorganisms act as decomposers in the soil that decompose the dead plant and animal wastes. Decomposition releases organic nutrients to the soil that can be again used up by plants. Microbes increase soil fertility by fixing atmospheric nitrogen, for example, *Rhizobium*. This microbe lives in root nodules of leguminous plants and increases the nitrogen content in the soil. Leguminous plants are of great interest in agriculture as they are disease resistant, can fix free nitrogen from the environment and hence it helps the plant to grow, for example - beans,peas, soybeans, and lentils etc.

Figure 5.5 Root nodules of leguminous plants

Microorganisms in Commercial Industries

There are many microbes that are used in the manufacturing or processing of various products used commercially. For example, there are certain bacteria that are used to manufacture linen. Red algae produces 'Algin' that is used for thickening cosmetics and food products like jelly. Red algae also produces 'Agar' that is used as a solidifying agent in microbial research at a large scale.

Harmful Microorganisms

Besides their several uses, microorganisms also cause some harmful effects on other living organisms. Microorganisms cause a number of diseases in humans, animals and plants. The microorganisms that cause diseases are called pathogens. The most common are viruses that cause common cold. Microorganisms also cause food spoilage and damage to clothes, leather, etc.

Table 5.2 Common diseases caused by microorganisms

Microorganism	Disease
Rhinovirus	Common cold
Bordetella pertussis	Whooping cough
Rubeola virus	Measles
Varicella zoster virus	Chicken pox
Treponema pallidum	Syphillis
Vibrio Cholerae	Cholera

Figure 5.6 Fruit spoilage

As microorganisms are everywhere in the biosphere, and some can also cause diseases, it is important to maintain good health.

Human Health and Immunity

Health may be referred to as the well being of an individual in all aspects, that is, physically, mentally and socially. While immunity is the ability of a person to resist infections and remain disease free. It can be achieved and enhanced by providing the antibodies to a person against that particular disease.

Immunity are of two types:

1. **Innate immunity:** Inborn immunity or immunity that is inherited from parents, for example, skin (prevents entry of foreign invaders).
2. **Acquired immunity:** Immunity acquired after birth is called acquired immunity or adaptive immunity, for example, Immunity to chickenpox.

Health of an individual depends on many factors. Some of them are given below:

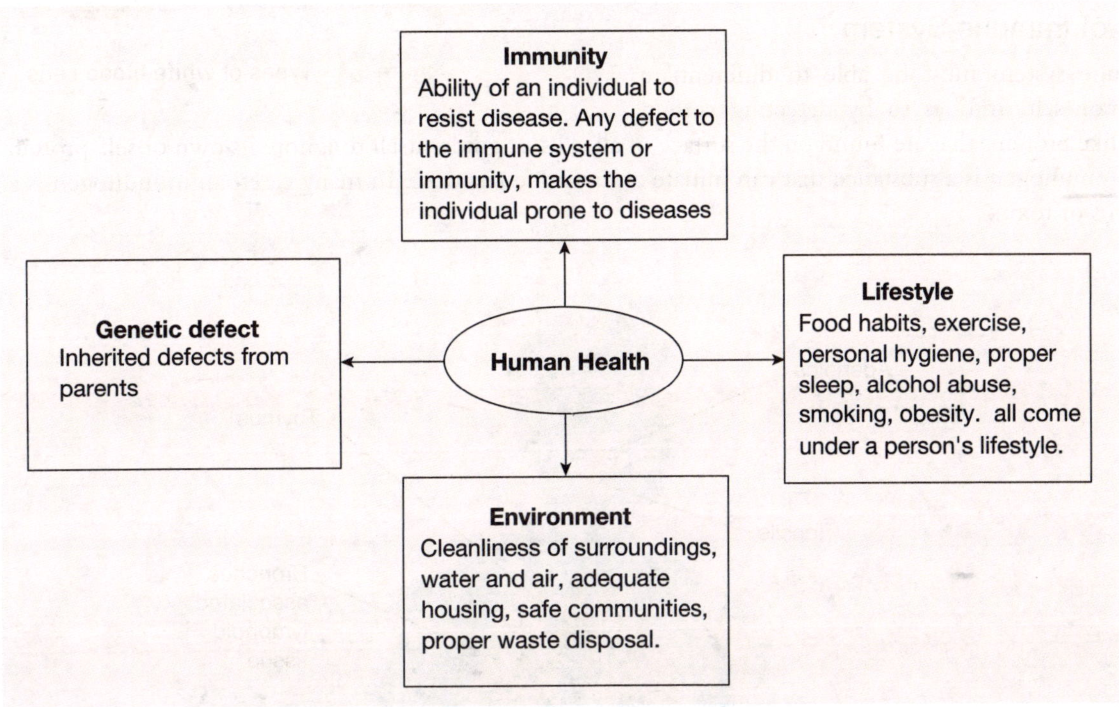

Figure 5.7 Factors contributing towards human health

Immune System

Human immune system is composed of a network of cells, tissues, organs that function together to defend us against infectious microbes (bacteria, virus, etc.). The coordinated response of the immune system towards any foreign particles is known as immune response. The white blood cells and the various lymphatic organs constitute the components of immune system. It protects the individual's body from the microorganisms such as bacteria and viruses.

Components of Immune System

The immune system forms the first line of defense against foreign particles which seek entry inside our body. Skin is the first barrier of the immune system which prevents entry of disease causing microorganisms (pathogens). Upon gaining entry inside a living body, the pathogens are encountered with various blood cells which specialize in neutralizing and killing pathogens. These are discussed below in detail:

White Blood Cells

Lymphocytes, monocytes, macrophages, neutrophils, eosinophils and basophils all come under white blood cells and provide immunity to the body against infectious diseases and foreign invaders.

Organs

Thymus and bone marrow are the primary lymphoid organs where development of lymphocytes take place whereas spleen, tonsils, lymph vessels and lymph nodes are the secondary lymphoid organs where immune responses are initiated.

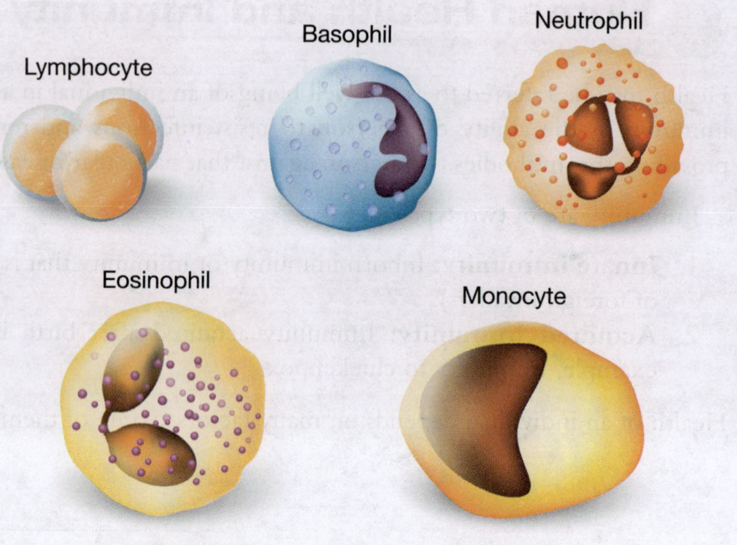

Figure 5.8 Types of white blood cells

Working of Immune System

Our immune system must be able to differentiate self from non-self. It does so by detecting certain molecules like proteins that are found on the surface of all cells. It guides itself to ignore its own or self-proteins at an early stage. An immunogen is a substance that can initiate an immune response. In many cases, an immunogen is a bacterium, fungus, virus or toxin.

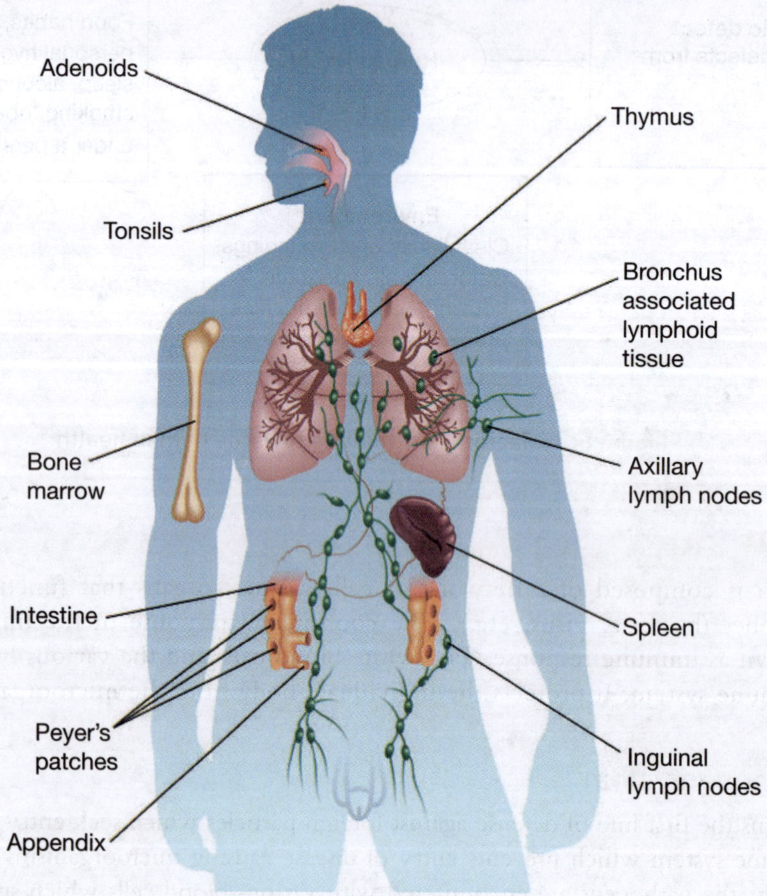

Figure 5.9 Lymphatic system-showing all lymphoid organs present in the body

Human Diseases

Whenever the system in human body gets disturbed due to attack of microorganism or malfunctioning of any organ, we are prone to get a disease. **Disease** can be referred to as the state of disturbed ease, or being uncomfortable. Disease affects the proper functioning or structure of body organs or systems. The changes in the body due to diseases give rise to certain signs and symptoms.

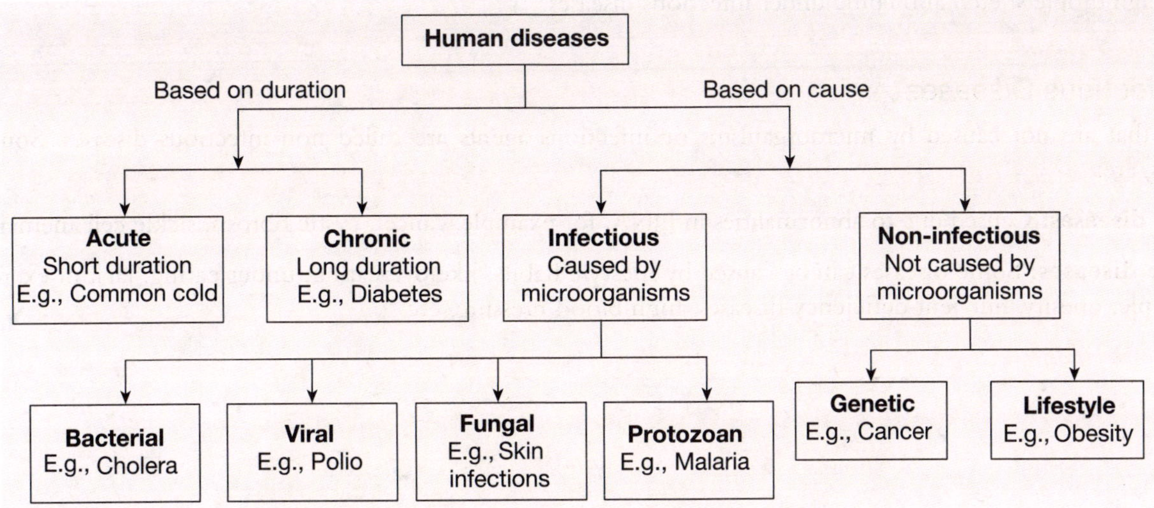

Figure 5.10 Types of diseases based on duration and cause

Type of Diseases

According to the duration of diseases, they can be divided into two types, that is, **acute** and **chronic**. An acute disease is the one in which the symptoms appear suddenly, worsen rapidly and then disappear as it heals, example, flu or common cold. Whereas a chronic disease is the one which develops gradually and worsens over a long period of time, example, chronic back pain.

Table 5.3 Points of difference between acute and chronic diseases

Acute diseases	Chronic diseases
Lasts for a short period often only a few days	Lasts for a long period of time, sometimes can be life-long
Sudden onset of symptoms and worsen rapidly	Develops gradually and worsens over time
Will not have time to cause major effects on human health if treated in time	Affects our normal health, for example, weight loss, tiredness, etc.
Can be cured	Require extended care or sometimes even hospitalization
For example, common cold	For example, diabetes

According to whether or not caused by microorganisms, diseases are of two types:

1. Infectious
2. Non-infectious

Infectious Diseases

Following are the characteristics of infectious diseases:

- Infectious diseases are caused by pathogens, such as bacteria, viruses, fungi and protozoa, like chicken-pox, TB, etc.
- Multicellular organisms like worms can also cause infectious diseases like filariasis.
- Diseases that can spread from one person to another are called communicable diseases.
- Diseases that spread through air, water, food, physical contact with patient, sexual contact, aerosols (sneeze or cough droplets, etc.) also come under infectious diseases.

Non-infectious Diseases

Diseases that are not caused by microorganisms or infectious agents are called non-infectious diseases. Some of the examples, are:

Genetic diseases: Caused due to abnormalities in DNA, for example, cancer, cystic fibrosis, sickle cell anemia etc

Lifestyle diseases: Some diseases can be caused by lifestyle habits, like overeating, under eating, lack of exercise, etc., for example, obesity, nutrient deficiency diseases, high blood pressure, etc.

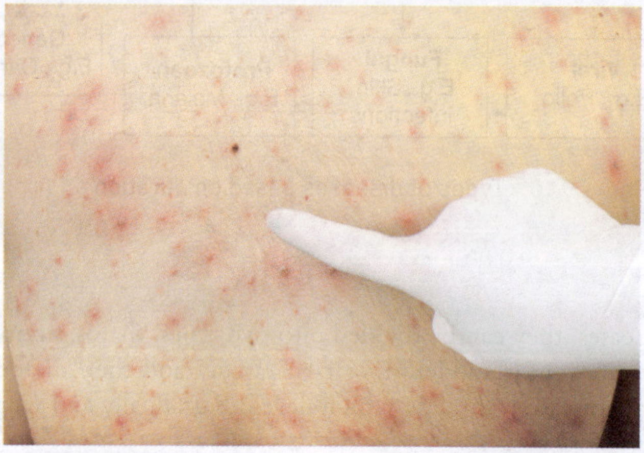

Figure 5.11 Chicken pox— an infectious disease

Drug and Alcohol Abuse

Abuse of drug and alcohol can have serious consequences on human health. Nowadays, drug abuse is very common among teenagers who later on get addicted to it.

Smoking: Tobacco is mainly used for smoking and inhaling, tobacco smoke can cause diseases of heart; lungs, etc.

Alcohol abuse: Excessive alcohol consumption is called alcohol abuse. It can have many ill effects on human health, such as nutrient deficiency, liver diseases, fertility problems, etc.

Ways to Maintain Proper Health

'Health is wealth', hence maintaining proper health is very essential. Some of the measures that can be taken to maintain proper health are:

- **Healthy food habits:**
  - Eat nutrient-rich food or balanced diet
  - Avoid junk foods
  - Include more vegetables, fruits into the diet
  - Have food that is properly cooked

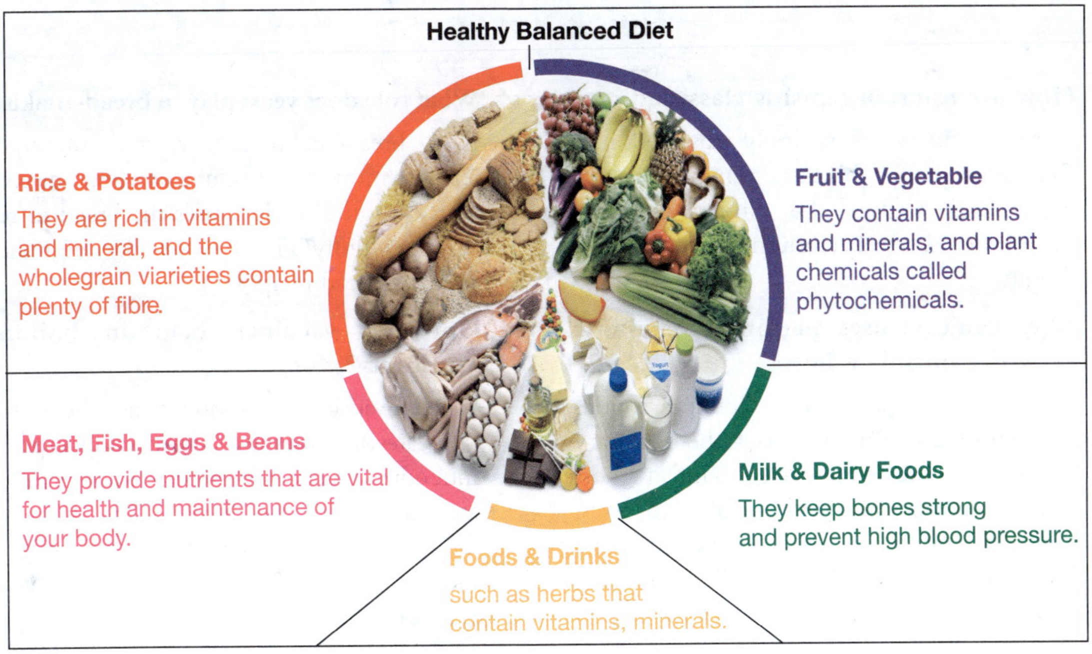

Figure 5.12 Balanced diet components

- **Proper exercise:** Exercising regularly in any form lowers the risk of various diseases. It also helps to maintain an active metabolism.
- **Avoid drug and alcohol abuse:** Intake of drugs and excessive consumption of alcohol may lead to adverse health effects, such as liver damage, kidney diseases, neural diseases, etc.
- **Maintain personal and public hygiene**
  - Always keep personal hygiene
  - Drink boiled water
  - Do not leave food uncovered
  - Keep the surroundings clean
  - Proper waste disposal
- **Control of disease spreading**
  - Diseases spread by mosquitoes can be controlled by avoiding water stagnation, using mosquito nets, repellents, etc.
  - Diseases spread by droplets from sneezing or cough can be prevented by using towels to mask nose while sneezing.
  - Avoid breeding of flies.

Quick Recap

✔ **How are microorganisms classified?**

Microorganisms are typically classified into five major groups: bacteria, fungi, protozoa, algae, and viruses. For instance, while *Escherichia coli* is a bacterium, *Penicillium* is a fungus.

✔ **Why can't viruses perform metabolic activities outside a host?**

Viruses cannot perform metabolic activities on their own because they lack the necessary cellular machinery. They need to infect a host cell to replicate and perform life processes, which is why they're often considered at the boundary between living and non-living entities.

✔ **What role does yeast play in bread-making?**

In bread-making, yeast undergoes fermentation to produce carbon dioxide. This carbon dioxide causes the bread to rise, making it fluffy. Thus, yeast is a key ingredient in many bread recipes.

✔ **How do vaccines help in building immunity?**

When a vaccine is introduced into the body, it stimulates the immune system to produce specific antibodies against a particular microorganism without causing the disease. This "memory" allows the immune system to quickly recognize and combat the microorganism if encountered again in the future.

POINTS TO REMEMBER

- ✔ The organisms which are too small to be seen by naked eye and are visible only through microscopes are called microorganisms.
- ✔ The study of microorganisms is termed as microbiology.
- ✔ Microorganisms are widely used for the production of curd, bread, alcohol, antibiotics, etc.
- ✔ Microorganisms can also be harmful and cause a number of diseases in humans, animals and plants.
- ✔ Health is referred to as the well being of an individual in all aspects, that is, physically, mentally and socially.
- ✔ Immunity is the ability of an individual to resist diseases.
- ✔ The coordinated response of the immune system towards any foreign particles is known as an immune response.
- ✔ Diseases that can spread from one person to another are called communicable diseases, example common cold.
- ✔ Diseases that do not spread from one person to another are called non-communicable diseases, for example, diabetes.
- ✔ Health can be maintained by following some good habits, such as eating nutrient-rich food or balanced diet, avoiding junk foods, including more vegetables and fruits into the diet and exercise.

PRACTICE QUESTIONS CLASSROOM WING

Very Short Answer Type Questions

Directions for questions from 1 to 5:
Fill in the blanks in each question.

1. Curd contains bacteria called __________ that convert milk into curd.
2. A __________ is a biological preparation that consists of either dead or weakened microbes.
3. Leguminous plants are of interest in agriculture as they can fix free nitrogen due to the microbe __________.
4. ___ is a substance that can initiate an immune response, often a bacterium, fungus, or toxin.
5. Genetic diseases arise due to abnormalities in ________.

Directions for questions from 6 to 12:
For each of the following questions, four choices have been provided. Select the correct alternatives.

6. Who introduced the antibiotic 'Penicillin' to the world?
   (a) Florey
   (b) Chain
   (c) Sir Alexander Fleming
   (d) None of the above
7. Which of the following is NOT a characteristic of infectious diseases?
   (a) Caused by pathogens
   (b) Easy person-to-person spread
   (c) Caused due to abnormalities in DNA
   (d) Spread through air, water, food
8. What prevents the entry of foreign invaders as part of the innate immunity?
   (a) Blood (b) White blood cells
   (c) Skin (d) Vaccines
9. What makes leguminous plants significant in agriculture?
   (a) They are predominantly found everywhere.
   (b) They contain Rhizobium in their root nodules which increases the soil's nitrogen content.
   (c) They undergo fermentation.
   (d) They produce antibiotics.
10. What plays a critical role in distinguishing 'self' from 'non-self' in the human immune system?
    (a) Lymph nodes
    (b) Bone marrow
    (c) Molecules like proteins on the surface of cells
    (d) Red blood cells
11. **Assertion (A):** Yeast can be used commercially to produce alcohol
    Reason (R): Yeast can perform fermentation
    (a) Both A and R are true and R is the correct explanation for A.
    (b) Both A and R are true and R is the not the correct explanation for A.
    (c) A is true and R is false
    (d) A is false and R is true
12. **Assertion (A):** Immunity to chickenpox is considered as acquired immunity.
    Reason (R): Immunity that is inherited from parents is considered as acquired immunity
    (a) Both A and R are true and R is the correct explanation for A.
    (b) Both A and R are true and R is not the correct explanation for A.
    (c) A is true and R is false
    (d) A is false and R is true

Short Answer Type Questions

13. Explain the role of microorganisms in improving soil fertility.

14. Explain the importance of Sir Alexander Fleming's discovery in relation to microorganisms.

15. Write down the differences between acute and chronic diseases.

16. What's the significance of nitrogen-fixing bacteria for plants?

17. Why are foreign particles called antigens?

Essay Type Questions

18. (a) Microorganisms can be harmful to humans. Justify the statement.

    (b) Explain the use of microorganisms in medicine.

19. (a) Define immunity and what are the different types?

    (b) What are various elements in an immune system?

PRACTICE QUESTIONS COMPETITION WING

Level 1: Apply your Concepts

Directions for questions from 1 to 5:
Fill in the blanks in each question.

1. The process by which yeast converts sugar into alcohol is known as ________.
2. A form of asexual reproduction in yeast, where a small bud forms and then detaches as a separate cell, is called ________.
3. Certain microbes that convert milk into yogurt produce an acid known as ________.
4. The process by which dead organic matter is broken down into simpler inorganic substances is termed ___.
5. Immunity to chickenpox is an example for ________ immunity.

Level 2: Review your Concepts

6. Nivin was observing his mother making wine using grapes. He saw that she is adding some amount of yeast into it. What do you think, what will be the reason for using yeast?
7. How environment affects someone's health?
8. A vaccine comprises the microbes that are able to cause diseases. How does a vaccine, then, not cause any harm when it is injected in our body?
9. Why is immunity to chicken pox an acquired immunity?

Level 3: Assess Your Concepts

10. A virus is living inside its host cell and is able to survive and reproduce. What happens when the same virus is removed out of the host cell?
11. Microorganisms like bacteria are reason behind a number of diseases some of which are even fatal. Should all microorganisms be considered harmful for humans?

AT

PRACTICE QUESTIONS NEET SPECIAL WING

Multiple-Answer Type Questions

Questions number 1 to 5 are multiple-choice questions. Each question has FOUR options (a), (b), (c), and (d). ONE OR MORE THAN ONE of these four option(s) is/are the correct answer(s).

1. Identify harmful microbes from the following:
   (a) Rhinovirus
   (b) *Treponema pallidum*
   (c) *Varicella zoster*
   (e) *Penicillium*
2. Which of the following are examples of innate immunity?
   (a) Digestive enzymes in mouth
   (b) Antibody production
   (c) Mucus and chemical secretions
   (d) Acid present in the stomach
3. Which of the following are components of the lymphatic system?
   (a) Thymus
   (b) Liver
   (c) Bone marrow
   (d) Tonsils
4. Identify non infectious diseases from the following:
   (a) Sickle cell anaemia
   (b) Tuberculosis
   (c) Cystic fibrosis
   (d) Tetanus
5. What steps should be taken for disease control?
   (a) Wear masks
   (b) Keeping food always covered
   (c) Prevent water stagnation
   (d) Using mosquito repellent

Comprehension-Based Questions

A. Read the paragraph given below and answer the questions number 6 to 11:

Disease is defined as any malfunctioning occurring in the body. Anything that disturbs good health is called as disease. Diseases are caused due to a variety of reasons and hence diseases are broadly classified into many types such as physical disorders, mental health disorders, infectious and non-infectious diseases, nutritional deficiency diseases, genetic disorders, degenerative diseases, social diseases etc. Depending on the duration and the onset of the diseases, diseases are also classified as acute and chronic diseases. In acute diseases the changes occur very fast and lasts for a short period of time. On the other hand, the onset of chronic disease is very slow but the disease can be either progressive of last for a longer period of time. The most common classification of diseases is to divide them into communicable or non-communicable diseases. Communicable or infectious diseases can be transmitted from a diseased person to s healthy person whereas non infectious diseases do not spread from person to person.

6. Haemophilia and colour blindness are examples of:
   (a) Genetic diseases
   (b) Deficiency diseases
   (c) Vector borne diseases
   (d) Mental health disorders
7. Identify chronic disease among the following:
   (a) Common cold
   (b) Diabetes
   (c) Obesity
   (d) Cholera
8. What is the primary cause for AIDS?
   (a) Bacteria
   (b) Protozoa
   (c) Virus
   (d) Fungus
9. An 8-year-old child is less energetic and complete blood count shows less of haemoglobin. What is the disease and its type, that the child is suffering from?
   (a) Diabetes, Infectious disease

(b) Diabetes, Deficiency disease
(c) Anaemia, Infectious disease
(d) Anaemia, Deficiency disease

10. Which of the following is not a pathogen?
(a) Virus
(b) Radiation
(c) Bacteria
(d) Protozoa

11. Match the following:

Column – A	Column – B
(i) Cholera	(a) Viral disease
(ii) Tuberculosis	(b) Vector borne disease
(iii) Sleeping sickness	(c) Air borne disease
(iv) Dengue	(d) Water borne disease
(v) Malaria	(e) Protozoal disease

B. Read the paragraph given below and answer the questions number 12 to 17:

Microorganisms can be both useful as well as harmful. When microorganisms are useful, they play very important roles in food industry. For example, they are used in the production of curd, alcohol and wine production as well as in the baking industry. They are also used for the production of antibiotics which protect us from pathogens and also to produce vaccines against specific diseases. Microorganisms also play an important role as decomposers and nitrogen fixers which increases the soil fertility. Microorganisms cause diseases, food spoilage and can also spoil clothes as well as leather.

12. The process which helps to convert sugar into alcohol with the help of microorganism is:
(a) Dehydrogenation
(b) Hydroxylation
(c) Fermentation
(d) Respiration

13. The microorganisms responsible for bread production
(a) *Lactobacillus*
(b) Yeast
(c) *Acetobacter malorum*
(d) *Penicillium* mold

14. Biological preparation that consists of dead or weakened germs
(a) Vaccine
(b) Antidote
(c) Antigen
(d) Antibody

15. Microorganisms found in the root nodules of leguminous plants
(a) Yeast
(b) *E.coli*
(c) Algae
(d) *Rhizobium*

16. Substance which is used for making jelly
(a) Linen
(b) Algin
(c) Leather
(d) Antibiotics

17. Match the following:

Column – A	Column – B
(i) Agar	(a) Measles
(ii) *Bordetella pertussis*	(b) Red algae
(iii) Rubeola virus	(c) Chicken pox
(iv) *Varicella zoster* virus	(d) Whooping cough
(v) *Acetobacter malorum*	(e) Vinegar production

ANSWER KEYS

Crossword

Across

2. Agar 5. Lymphocytes 6. Fungi 8. Virus 9. Genetic Diseases
13. *Lactobacillus* 14. Penicillin 16. Immunogen 17. Obesity 18. Antigens

Down

1. Immunity 2. Antibiotics 3. Chronic diseases 4. *Chlorella* 7. Fermentation
10. Algae 11. Vaccine 12. Pathogens 15. Algin

Classroom Wing

Very Short Answer Type Questions

1. *Lactobacillus* 2. Vaccine 3. *Rhizobium* 4. Immunogen 5. DNA 6. (c)
7. (c) 8. (c) 9. (b) 10. (c) 11. (a) 12. (c)

Competition Wing

Level 1: Apply your Concepts

1. Fermentation 2. Budding 3. Lactic acid 4. Decomposition 5. Acquired

NEET Special Wing

Multiple-Answer Type Questions

1. (a, b, c) 2. (a, c, d) 3. (a, c, d) 4. (a, c) 5. (a, b, c, d)

Comprehension-Based Questions

6. (a) 7. (b) 8. (c) 9. (d) 10. (b)

11. (i) → (d); (ii) → (c); (iii) → (b); (iv) → (a); (v) → (e)

12. (c) 13. (b) 14. (a) 15. (d) 16. (b)

17. (i) → (b); (ii) → (d); (iii) → (a); (iv) → (c); (v) → (e)

Hints and Explanations

CLASSROOM WING

Short Answer Type Questions

13. Microorganisms help to increase soil fertility in different ways. They act as decomposers in soil by decomposing the dead plant and animal wastes. Decomposition releases organic nutrients to the soil which can be again used up by plants. Microbes increase soil fertility also by fixing atmospheric nitrogen, for example, *Rhizobium*. *Rhizobium* lives in root nodules of leguminous plants and increases the nitrogen content in the soil.

14. Sir Alexander Fleming was the first to discover penicillin, a revolutionary antibiotic derived from the fungus Penicillium. Thousands of soldiers were saved from bacterial infections as a result of this discovery during World War II. His research paved the way for the development and widespread use of antibiotics, forever altering the landscape of medical treatments.

15. According to the duration, diseases can be classified into acute and chronic diseases. The main differences are given below.

Acute diseases	Chronic diseases
Lasts for a short period	Lasts for a long period of time, sometimes can be life-long
Sudden onset of symptoms that worsen rapidly	Develops gradually and worsens over time
Will not have time to cause major effects on human health if treated on time	Affects our normal health, for example, weight loss, tiredness, etc.
Can be cured	Require extended care or sometimes even hospitalization.
For example, common cold	For example, diabetes

16. Nitrogen-fixing bacteria, such as *Rhizobium*, form symbiotic relationships with the roots of certain plants, primarily legumes. These bacteria convert atmospheric nitrogen, which plants can't use directly, into compounds like nitrates and nitrites, which plants can absorb and use for growth. This symbiotic relationship not only aids the plants but also enriches the soil's nitrogen content, making it more fertile.

17. Foreign particles are called antigens because our body is not familiar with their structure and composition. Upon encountering a foreign body, our body generates molecules (antibody) to fight against them. Since antigens cause the generation of antibodies, they are called antigens.

Essay Type Questions

18. (a) Along with uses, microorganisms also cause some harmful effects on other living organisms. There are microorganisms that cause diseases in humans, animals and plants. The microorganisms that can cause disease are called pathogens, for example, viruses cause common cold. Microorganisms also cause food spoilage, and damage our clothes, leather, etc.

(b) In the medical field, the microorganisms can be used to make two important products, such as antibiotics and vaccines. Antibiotics are used to kill or stop the growth of other disease-causing microorganisms, for example, penicillin from *Penicillium*. Microorganisms can also be used in the production of vaccine. A vaccine is a biological preparation that consists of either dead or weakend microorganisms. Vaccines provide immunity to a particular disease, for example, rabies vaccine gives protection against the rabies virus.

19. (a) The ability of an individual to resist disease is called immunity. Any defect in the immune system makes the individual prone to disease. Immunity are of two types – Innate immunity and acquired immunity. The inborn immunity or immunity that is inherited from parent is called innate immunity (e.g., skin). Immunity

that is acquired after birth is called acquired immunity (e.g., immunity to chicken pox).

(b) Human immune system includes a network of cells, tissues, organs that work together to resist any attack by foreign invaders (bacteria, virus, etc.)

The various components are,

- **White blood cells:** Lymphocytes, monocytes, macrophages, neutrophils, eosinophils and basophils.
- **Organs:** Thymus, bone marrow, spleen and lymph nodes.

COMPETITION WING

Level 2: Review your Concepts

6. Yeast can convert sugar into alcohol through a process called fermentation. Fermentation is a metabolic process that takes place in the absence of oxygen, in which organic molecules are converted into acids, gases or alcohol by the action of certain microorganisms, such as yeast. Nivin's mother used yeast to perform fermentation and to convert grape sugar into wine (alcohol).

7. Environment plays a key role in maintaining proper health. Along with personal hygiene, environmental hygiene is also important. Cleanliness of water and air and proper waste disposal management are also necessary for a healthy life. There are many diseases that can be caused due to unhygienic environments, such as cholera, polio, etc., so it is advised to always keep the environment clean.

8. Vaccine is a biological preparation of microbes. However, the microbe is prepared in its weak state which is unable to cause harm to human body.

9. Immunity acquired after birth is called acquired immunity or adaptive immunity. When the causative agent for chicken pox attacks our body for the first time, we catch disease as our body is unable to fight against it. But, a subsequent attack of the same pathogen does not result in the same condition. Our body then fights against the antigen due to acquired immunity it has developed from the first attack.

Level 3: Assess Your Concepts

10. Outside the host cell, a virus is non-living as it is unable to function and reproduce. A virus gets the suitable and necessary environment only inside its host cell for reproduction.

11. No, not all microorganisms are harmful to human bodies. There are a number of microorganisms which help human beings either as food supplements or in medicinal industry or in production of food.

NEET SPECIAL WING

Multiple-Answer Type Questions

1. Microorganisms also cause some harmful effects on other living organisms. Microorganisms cause a number of diseases in humans, animals and plants. The microorganisms that cause diseases are called pathogens. For example, Rhinovirus causes common cold, ***Treponema pallidum*** causes Syphilis and *Varicella zoster* causes chicken pox.

2. Inborn immunity or immunity that is inherited from parents, for example, skin (prevents entry of foreign invaders), digestive enzymes in mouth, Mucus and chemical secretions and acid present in the stomach.

3. Thymus, bone marrow and tonsils are all part of the lymphatic system.

4. Genetic diseases are caused due to abnormalities in DNA, for example, cancer, cystic fibrosis, sickle cell anaemia etc.

5. Diseases spread by mosquitoes can be controlled by avoiding water stagnation, using mosquito nets, repellents, etc. Diseases spread by droplets from sneezing or cough can be prevented by using masks. Disease spread by flies can be prevented by keeping the eatables covered.

Comprehension-Based Questions

A.

6. Haemophilia and colour blindness are both caused due to defects in the genes and are thus called genetic diseases.

7. Chronic disease is the one which develops gradually and worsens over a long period of time, example, Diabetes

8. AIDS is caused by Human immunodeficiency virus and immune system of the body is destroyed by this virus.

9. Since the child has less energy and has haemoglobin deficiency, the child is anaemic and it is a deficiency disease. Increased intake or iron in the diet can alleviate the symptoms.

10. Harmful microorganisms which cause diseases are called pathogens, for example, bacteria, virus, protozoa, fungi, etc. Radiations are not pathogens but can cause genetic variations.

11. Match the following:

    Cholera is a water borne disease. It is a bacterial disease that is spread through water.
    (i) (d)

    Tuberculosis is a bacterial disease and is spread from diseased person to another healthy through air.
    (ii) (c)

    Sleeping sickness is a water borne disease and is spread through the vector Tsetse flies.
    (iii) (b)

    Dengue is a viral disease.
    (iv) (a)

    Malaria is a protozoal disease.
    (v) (e)

B.

12. (c) Yeast is used in the large-scale production of alcohol, wine, vinegar (acetic acid), etc. The basis of using yeast in wine production is fermentation. Fermentation is the process of converting sugar into alcohol.

13. Yeast is used in the baking industry for making breads, pastries, cakes, etc.

14. Vaccine is a biological preparation that consists of either dead or weakened microbes.

    When a vaccine is introduced into the body, the body produces antibodies against the vaccine, which remains in the body and protects the body from attack by the same microbe in the future.

15. Microbes increase soil fertility by fixing atmospheric nitrogen, for example, ***Rhizobium***. This microbe lives in root nodules of leguminous plants and increases the nitrogen content in the soil.

16. Red algae produces 'Algin' that is used for thickening cosmetics and food products like jelly.

17. Match the following:

    Red algae produces 'Agar' that is used as a solidifying agent in microbial research at a large scale.
    (i) (b)

Bordetella pertussis is a pathogen which causes whooping cough.
(ii) (d)

Rubeola virus causes measles in us.
(iii) (a)

Varicella zoster virus causes chicken pox.
(iv) (c)

Acetobacter malorum is used for vinegar production.
(v) (e)

CHAPTER

6

Ecosystem and Biodiversity

Remember

Before beginning this chapter, you should be able to:

- Recall the definition of ecosystem and its components
- Recall the basic concepts about the biotic and non biotic components
- Remember the different types of terrestrial and aquatic ecosystem
- Know the harmful effects of pollutants

Key Ideas

After completing this chapter, you should be able to:

- Describe the various components of ecosystem
- Understand the concept of food chain and food web
- Explain the various sources and control methods of different types of pollution
- Understand the concept of biodiversity
- Understand the concept of wildlife and its conservation

A Tribute to Alexander von Humboldt (1769-1859)

Alexander von Humboldt (1769–1859) is a well-known figure in ecology and biodiversity. His life's work as a German naturalist and explorer left an indelible mark on our understanding of the natural world. Humboldt travelled through South and Central America for five years, meticulously documenting plant and animal species, weather patterns, and geological features. His ground-breaking approach saw the Earth as a unified system, which was a radical concept at the time.

"Kosmos," Humboldt's magnum opus, encapsulated his ecological philosophy by depicting nature as an intricate web of interconnectedness. His insights into the effects of human activity on ecosystems and climate were astonishingly foresighted. Humboldt was awarded the Copley Medal and had numerous species and geographical features named after him.

His work established the foundation for modern ecology and environmental science, emphasising the importance of biodiversity preservation for ecological balance. As we face modern environmental challenges, Humboldt's legacy inspires scientists and conservationists around the world, reminding us of the profound interconnectedness of our planet's ecosystems.

FUN TIME

CROSSWORD

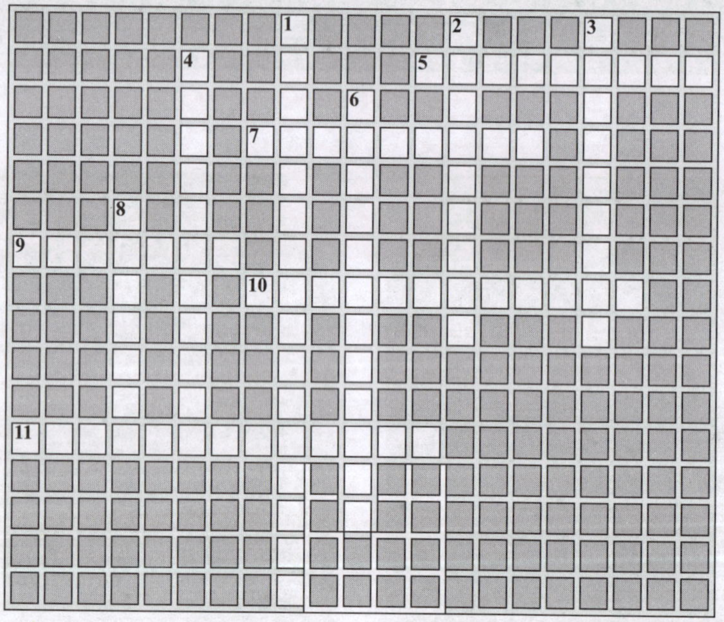

Across

5. The natural resources which can be replenished continuously
7. The category of consumers which can feed on both plants and animals
9. The species which are unique to a particular region
10. The execution of controlling the quality of forests for diverse needs
11. The practice of establishing a forest in an area which did not have any previous tree cover.

Down

1. The increased accumulation of contaminants across the food chain from lower trophic levels to higher trophic levels
2. The fossil fuel which derived its name from rock oil
3. The natural habitat in which the species are protected from hunting, predation or competition
4. The biological term given for each step in a food chain
6. The wide range of flora and fauna in the environment
8. The organism which can breakdown the dead and decaying plants and animals

INTRODUCTION

Ecosystem is the functional unit of nature comprising living organisms and non-living things. Living beings are known as biotic factors and non-living things are known as abiotic factors. Biotic factors include microbes, insects, plants, animals, etc. Abiotic factors include air, water, temperature, soil, humidity, sunlight, etc.

Components of an Ecosystem

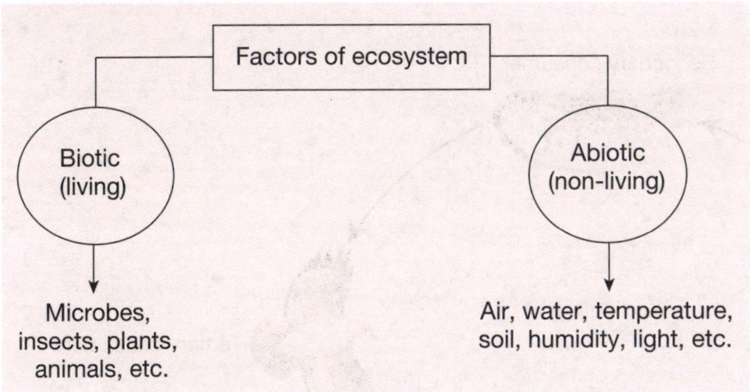

Figure 6.1 Factors affecting an ecosystem

> **Info Bytes!**
> The term "Ecosystem" was first coined by A.G.Tansley, an English botanist, in 1935.

In an ecosystem, biotic and abiotic factors interact with each other to meet their necessities. The components of ecosystem mainly consist of:

Producers → Consumers → Decomposers

Producers

Producers are the organisms that can synthesize their own food. These include green plants that utilize water and minerals absorbed from the soil, and sunlight trapped by chlorophyll (green-coloured pigment seen in plants) to synthesize their food. This energy in food is used by other organisms for their requirements. So green plants are called producers in an ecosystem.

Consumers

All animals that cannot synthesize their own food and depend on green plants directly or indirectly for their energy requirements are called consumers.

Consumers are of three types herbivores, carnivores and omnivores.

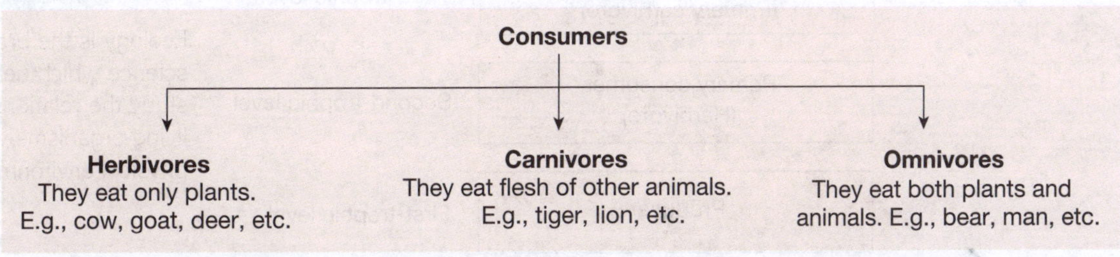

Figure 6.2 Types of consumers based on their feeding habits

Decomposers

Decomposers are organisms that can break down dead and decaying organisms. These organisms convert the decaying matter into organic matter and make it useful for the environment. The primary decomposers in many ecosystems are fungi. An earthworm is also a good example of a decomposer as it enhances soil fertility, improves soil porosity and hence it helps to improve the growth of a plant.

Food Chain and Food Web

The process of eating and being eaten up in a linear network, where the energy and the nutrients of food get transferred from one trophic level to another trophic level is called a **food chain**. In this, one organism eats other organism for its survival. Food chain results in flow of energy from one trophic level to another. The amount of energy decreases as it flows from lower trophic to higher trophic levels.

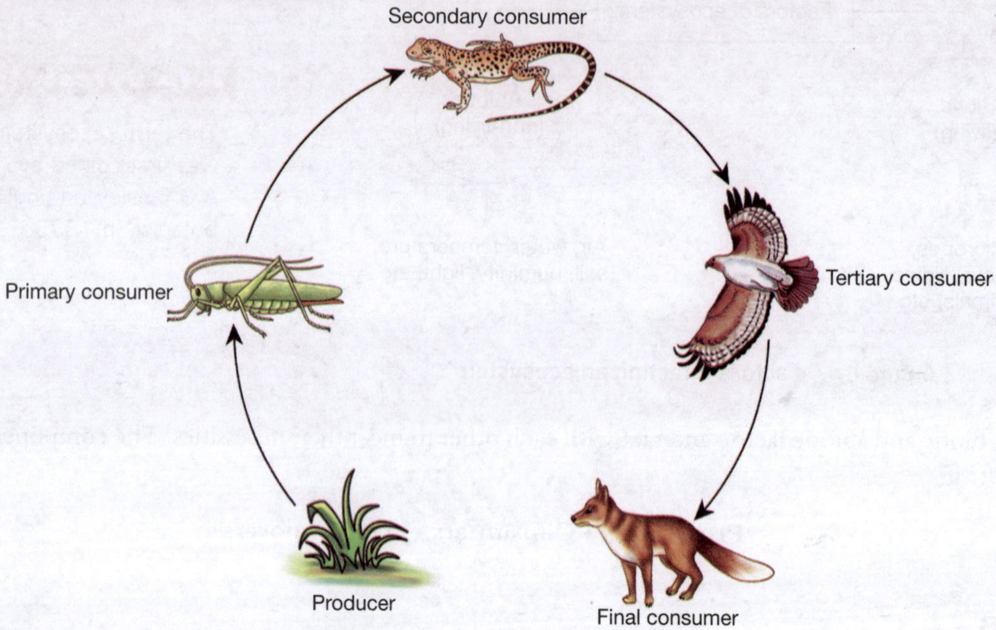

Figure 6.3 A simple grass-type food chain

Trophic Levels

It is a step or division of food chain. Number of trophic levels is equal to the number of steps in a food chain. Main fundamental units of trophic levels are producers (which produce energy in the ecosystem, for example, green plants) and consumers (which either depend directly on producers or on other animals that depend on producers).

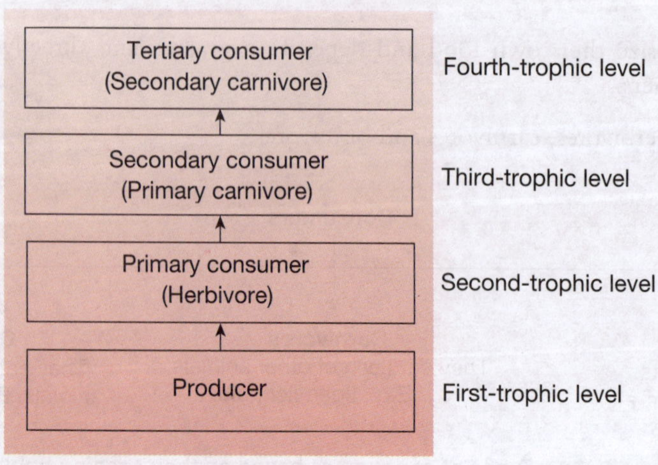

Figure 6.4 Flow diagram showing increasing trophic levels

Konnect

Ecology is the branch of science which help us to study the relationship of living organisms with their physical environment.

Interconnected food chain in an ecosystem is called **food web**. In a food web, many food chains are interconnected, for example, six food chains can connect with each other to form a food web. It is an important ecological concept. It represents the various feeding relationships within a community.

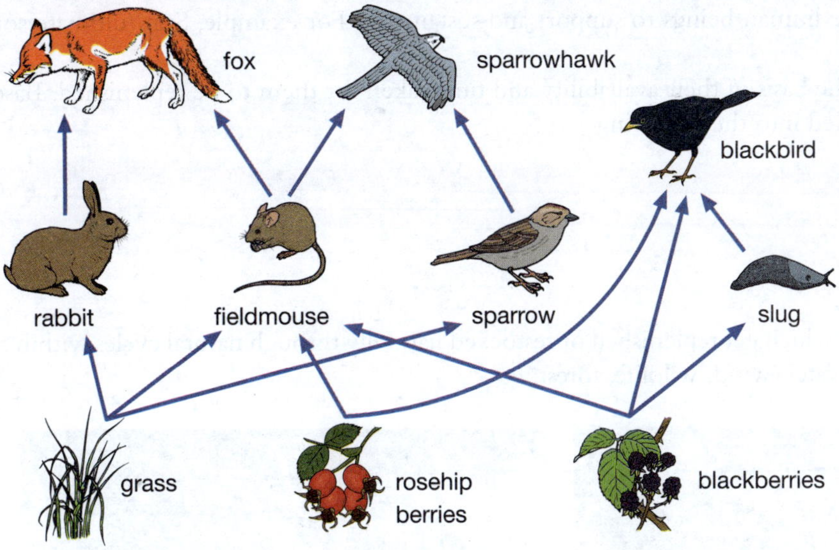

Figure 6.5 A food web showing interconnected food chains

Info Bytes!

A food chain is a linear sequence of organisms, whereas food webs consist of many interconnected food chains.

Biomagnification

Biomagnification is the increase or accumulation in concentration of toxic substances in the body of organisms at higher trophic levels. Biomagnification is also known as **bioamplification**, for example, an insecticide applied to a plant accumulates in a herbivore that feeds on it. This insecticide then enters different trophic levels through the food chain. The maximum amount of such toxic chemicals is seen in human beings, placed at the top of food chain. In an aquatic food chain, maximum DDT is found in fish-eating birds.

Figure 6.6 Biomagnification of pesticides in an aquatic food chain

Konnect

Full form of DDT is Dichlorodiphenyltrichloroethane

Info Bytes!

The species at the top of the trophic pyramid are most susceptible to toxic substances because of bioaccumulation and biomagnification.

Natural Resources

The term 'resource' refers to any source of supply that is kept in reserve. **Natural resources** are the resources that are found in nature and are used by the human beings to support and sustain life. For example, Sun (ultimate source of energy), water, soil, etc.

Natural resources are classified on the basis of their availability and time taken for them to be replenished. Based on these criteria, natural resources are classified into the following:

1. Renewable resources
2. Non-renewable resources

Renewable Resources

Renewable resources are the ones which get replenished or restocked naturally through natural cycles within an adequate timeframe. For example, sun, soil, water, wind, wildlife, forest, etc.

Figure 6.7 Renewable resources of energy

Renewable resources are also called perpetual resources or inexhaustible resources because of their continuous availability and ability to last billions of years. However, certain resources, such as water and forest, get exhausted if they are exploited too rapidly to be replenished in adequate time interval through natural cycles.

Non-renewable Resources

Non-renewable resources are the ones which cannot be replenished or restocked within an adequate timeframe. For example, coal, petroleum, natural gas, etc.

Figure 6.8 Non-renewable resources of energy

Non-renewable resources are called exhaustible resources because they cannot be easily replenished once they are lost.

Depletion of Natural Resources

Coal and petroleum are formed from the dead remains of plants and animals buried under the earth for millions of years. They are still being formed under the earth, however, the rate of their formation is significantly low.

As there have been immense technological advancements taking place in the world, a lot of it comes at the cost of exploiting our natural resources. Increase in population and hence, increase in demand for resources has put a tremendous pressure on the resources available to us. The rate at which they are being exploited has reached an alarming level that their restoration within adequate timeframe is threatened. Moreover, the ever-increasing demand for land has been leading to excessive deforestation which has further reduced their availability.

Figure 6.9 Deforestation of rainforest

Info Bytes!

Agriculture is the leading cause of deforestation.

Fossil Fuels

Fossil fuels are formed within the earth's crust from the buried plants and animals over a period of millions of years. Fossil fuels include coal, petroleum, natural gas, etc. All of them essentially contain carbon.

Coal

Coal is a fossil fuel formed from the remains of plants that lived and died about 100–400 million years ago. All living plants absorb light energy from the sun through photosynthesis. After the plants die, this energy is released as the plants decay. Under conditions favorable to coal formation, the decay process is disturbed, preventing the further release of the stored solar energy. Depending on the carbon content, coal is classified into following types.

- **Anthracite:** Contains about 95% carbon.
- **Bituminous:** Contains 65–80% carbon.
- **Sub-bituminous:** Contains 30–35% carbon
- **Lignite:** Contains 25–30% carbon

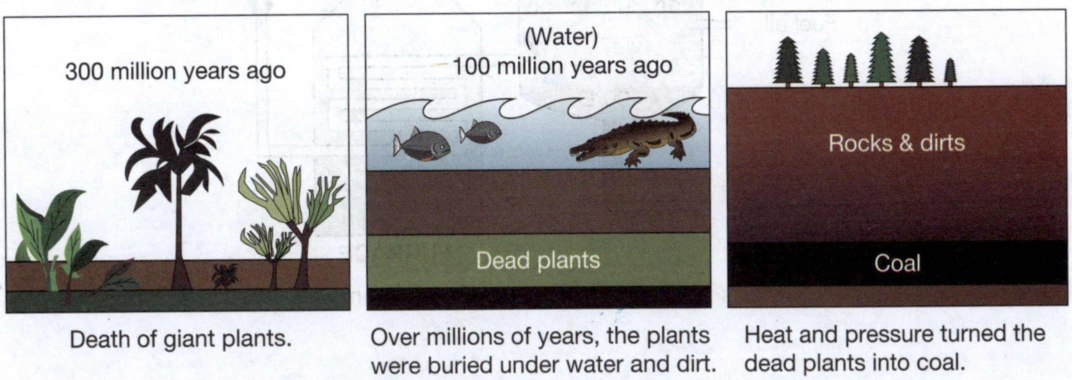

Figure 6.10 Formation of coal

Uses of Coal

Coal has a number of uses in the industry sector. It was used extensively during industrial revolution. It is used in steel production, power generation, as a source of steam energy, etc.

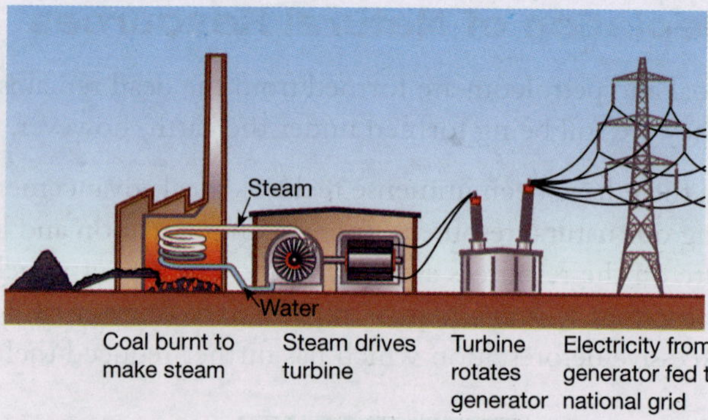

Figure 6.11 Coal-fired power station for electricity generation

Petroleum

The term 'petroleum' is derived from combination of two Latin terms: *petra* meaning rock and *oleum* meaning oil. **Petroleum** is a naturally occurring, yellow-to-black coloured liquid found beneath the Earth's surface. Crude oil is refined to give useful products as mentioned in table.

Table 6.1 Products obtained from petroleum refining

Products	Uses
Petroleum gas	Fuel for home and industries
Petrol	Automobile and aviation fuel
Kerosene	Fuel for stoves
Diesel	Heavy-motor vehicle and generator fuel
Lubricating oil	Lubrication
Paraffin wax	Candles, Vaseline, etc.
Bitumen	Paints and building roads

Info Bytes!

Crude oil is the Petroleum in its natural form when first collected.

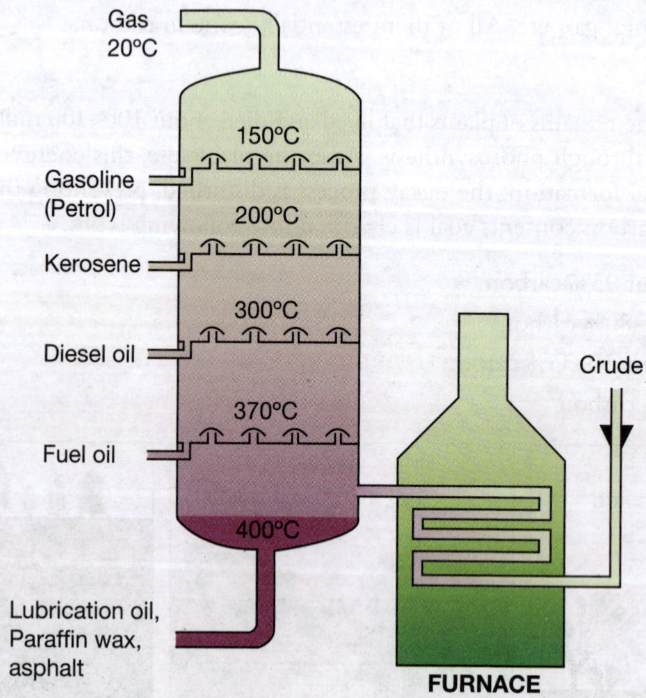

Figure 6.12 Refining of petroleum

Conservation of Fossil Fuels

Given the variety of ways in which fossil fuels are used by humans, they have become indispensable for our day-to-day life. However, as fossil fuels are non-renewable resources, their conservation is of urgent need. They can be conserved in the following ways:

Follow the rule of 3R's- reduce, recycle and reuse

- Using fuel-efficient vehicles like the ones that run on CNG
- Use of alternative sources of energy
- Use of biogas to generate electricity
- Judicial use of electricity

Info Bytes!

Fuels formed from the remains of ancient plants and animals buried millions of years ago.

Forests

Forest is a large area that is predominantly occupied by trees. Forests are the lungs of the earth and are essential for continuity of life. They are an important renewable resource. However, their status is threatened due to their depletion at a fast rate. In the section given below, we shall take a look at importance and conservation of forests. We daily make use of chairs to sit, paper to make notes, tissue to clean our hands after a meal, etc. In most of our activities, we depend on forests in an unthinkable number of ways. The importance of trees can be realized with the help of following points:

Importance of Trees

- The first and foremost need for having forests is the maintenance of oxygen–carbon dioxide balance. As we know that plants take in carbon dioxide and give us oxygen through the process of photosynthesis.
- Plants release water vapours into the atmosphere through the process of transpiration. This helps in continuous movement of water cycle which helps to maintain optimum level of water in nature.
- Trees give us fruits which are an important source of nutrition.
- Trees also provide us the vital things such as food, furniture, paper, medicines, etc.
- Forests are home/habitats to an abundant number of biodiversity of plants and animals
- Forests act as buffers during natural disasters like floods.

Info Bytes!

Forests are home to 80% of the world's terrestrial biodiversity.

Forests cover about 31% of the world's land area. That's around 4 billion hectares.

Figure 6.13 Forests are natural home to most of the wildlife

Deforestation

Deforestation is the cutting down of trees at a large scale over a short period of time. The over-exploitation of forests threatens the ecosystem and humanity as we heavily depend on forests for most of the ecological services. Following are the mains causes of deforestation.

- Small- and large-scale agriculture
- Mining
- Infrastructure
- Pulp plantations

Info Bytes!

Half of the world's tropical forests have been destroyed over the last century.

- Forest fires
- Illegal logging of wood
- Feeding animals on plants (livestock ranching)

Conservation of Forests

The following methods can be adopted to conserve forests.

- **Afforestation:** It is the practice of establishing a forest in an area which did not have any previous tree cover.
- **Sensible cutting of trees:** It is important that trees are cut down judiciously in order to fulfill human needs. New trees should be planted for the compensation of cut-down trees.
- **Silviculture:** It is the execution of controlling the establishment, growth, composition, health, and quality of forests to meet diverse needs.
- **Awareness:** Society should be made aware of the importance of forests and threats associated with their depletion. Society should be encouraged to make environment-friendly choices.

Figure 6.14 Restoring forests by silviculture

Pollution

Pollution is any undesirable change in the physical, chemical or biological characteristics of the environment that affects the living organisms negatively or may create a potential health hazard. It is the necessary evil arising due to reckless development and the ever-growing population. Substances that cause pollution are called **pollutants**, for example, human and animal wastes, garbage, dust, sewage waste, radiation, etc.

Pollution is mainly of three types:

1. Air pollution
2. Water pollution
3. Soil pollution

Air Pollution

Air pollution occurs when harmful substances, such as, smoke, dust, fumes, particulates, etc., are released into the atmosphere. Most of the air pollution occurs due to burning of coal, petrol, oil, exhaust from vehicles, fumes from factories, industries, brick kilns, etc. Ash from burning volcanoes, dust from storms and forest fires also contribute to air pollution but to a lesser extent.

Effects of Air pollution

Air pollution is a real problem regarding public health, environmental issues, health conditions of plants and animals, etc. The smoke released from various sources may combine with dust particles and fog in the atmosphere to form a deadly mixture called smog. Smog is very harmful to plants and causes asthma and other respiratory allergies in humans. It also causes global warming (increase in earth's temperature due to accumulation of CO_2 in the atmosphere), acid rain, etc.

Figure 6.15 Industrial emissions causing air pollution

Steps to Control Air Pollution

- Controlling emission from factories, vehicles, etc.
- Protecting forest that helps in increasing the amount of oxygen in the atmosphere.
- Using public transport and reducing usage of personal vehicles.
- Avoid burning of trash, wastes, etc.
- Using natural gas instead of coal, wood, kerosene oil for cooking and heating purposes.
- Installation of devices which reduce the release of pollutants, like filters, electrostatic precipitators, etc.

Konnect

Acid rain is caused by emissions of sulphur dioxide and nitrogen oxide. These gases react with water in the atmosphere and produce acids, such as sulphuric acid and nitric acid, resulting in acid rain.

Water Pollution

The contamination of water resources, such as lakes, rivers, oceans, ponds, etc., is called **water pollution**. This happens when pollutants are directly or indirectly discharged into the water sources. Sewages from houses, agriculture, industries, etc., are dumped directly into nearby water sources. People and animal bathing in water sources also make the water polluted. Fertilizers, pesticides, insecticides, etc., used in agriculture sometimes reach water sources due to rain which is again a pollutant.

Figure 6.16 Trash dumped near river causing water pollution

Info Bytes!

The Ganges river in India is considered one of the world's most polluted rivers, but efforts are being made to clean it up.

Effects of Water Pollution

- Drinking or using polluted water can be harmful to living things. Bathing in polluted water can cause skin irritation, rashes, etc.
- Diseases like cholera, diarrhoea, typhoid, etc., spread through contaminated water.
- Stagnant sewage water becomes breeding places for insects and pests, such as mosquitoes, fleas, cockroaches, etc., which cause diseases, like dengue, malaria, chikungunya, etc.

Steps to Control Water Pollution

- Industrial wastewater should be treated well before dumping into water sources.
- Waste, whether industrial or domestic, should not be directly thrown into water sources.
- Bathing in water sources should be avoided.
- Defecating in open places should not be allowed.

Soil Pollution

Dumping wastes in open area can cause soil pollution. It degrades the soil quality and also reduces its fertility. Wastes can be of any type, such as industrial wastes, domestic wastes, wastes from slaughter houses, agricultural wastes, etc. Chemical fertilizers and pesticides from agricultural field which reach the soil as run-off also contribute to soil pollution.

Figure 6.17 Soil pollution

Effects of Soil Pollution

- When wastes are dumped at a particular area, they start decaying and produce foul smell which destroys the natural beauty of the surroundings and makes living detrimental for the local people.
- They become breeding places for disease-causing germs, flies, insects, etc.
- The soil below also becomes infertile.
- Non-biodegredable substances like plastic never degrade and remain there for years. Disease carriers, such as flies, mosquitoes, cockroaches, etc., transfer disease causing pathogens from the waste to our food. Consuming such food can make a person sick.

Steps to Control Soil Pollution

- Dumping wastes in open should be avoided.
- Wastes should be categorized as biodegradable and non-biodegredable.
- Domestic wastes should be dumped in a compost pit.
- Necessary steps should be taken by municipality for waste treatment and disposal management of localities.
- Use of plastic bags must be banned and instead paper bags and cloth bags should be used.

Quick Recap

✔ What are the main components of an ecosystem and why are they called so?

Ecosystem includes living and non-living things that also have their inter-relationship with each other. The main components of an ecosystem are:

- **Producers:** These organisms can produce their own food mainly through photosynthesis, so they are called as producers. Other organisms depend either directly or indirectly on the producers.
- **Consumers:** These organisms cannot synthesize their own food and depend on producers for food, hence called consumers.
- **Decomposers:** These organisms are involved in the decomposition of dead and decaying matter in the ecosystem and are therefore referred to as decomposers.

✔ Define pollution. Name any three types of pollution.

The term 'pollution' refers to the undesirable changes in the environment due to the introduction of various contaminants. Substances that cause pollution are called pollutants, for example, industrial wastes, domestic wastes, etc. Soil, air and water are three types of pollution.

✔ What are the various control measures to prevent air pollution?

- Follow 3Rs-Reduce, Recycle and Reuse
- Say 'No to Plastics'
- Controlling emission from factories, vehicles, etc.
- Protecting forest that helps to increase the amount of oxygen in the atmosphere.
- Using public transport and reducing usage of personal vehicles.
- Avoiding burning of trash, waste, etc.

✔ What are the primary sources of soil pollution?

Soil pollution refers to the contamination of soil with harmful chemicals, often due to human activities. Major sources include:

- **Industrial waste:** Heavy metals and toxic chemicals from industries can leach into the soil.
- **Pesticides and fertilizers:** Overuse in agriculture can lead to harmful chemicals entering the soil.
- **Domestic waste:** Improper disposal of household waste can introduce non-biodegradable materials and toxins to the soil.
- **Oil spills:** These can contaminate large areas of land, making them unsuitable for cultivation.

✔ State the difference between food chain and food web.

Food chain is a linear sequence of organisms through which energy produced by producers flows from lower trophic to higher trophic levels. In food chain, each organism occupies different trophic levels. Food webs include interconnected food chains. The food webs are more realistic representation of energy transfer in an ecosystem.

Two examples of food chain are mentioned below:

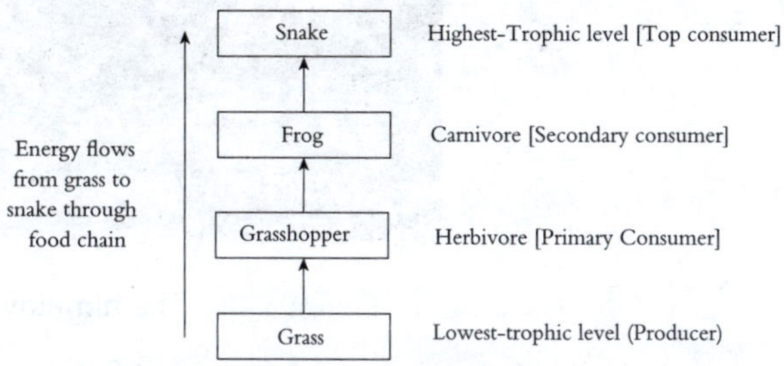

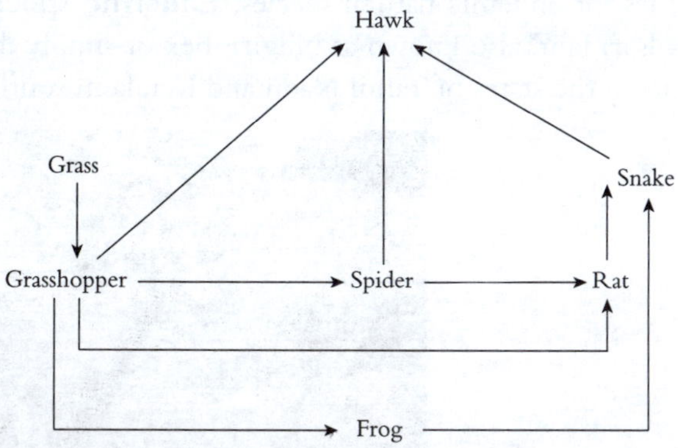

Biodiversity

The term 'bio' means 'life' and 'diversity' means 'forms'. The term, **biodiversity** implies the occurrence of different ecosystems, different species, organisms, their interaction with other living and nonliving forms, etc.
Biodiversity is of three types: Genetic diversity, species diversity and ecological diversity.

1. **Genetic diversity:** It is the diversity in number and types of gene and chromosomes present in different species or variation of genes within the same species, for example, India has many varieties of mangoes and rice.
2. **Species diversity:** It implies the variety in number and richness of a species in a particular region, for example, variety of amphibian species are present in Western Ghats.
3. **Ecological diversity:** It is the variation in ecosystems in a region. Variation can be in both terrestrial and aquatic ecosystems, for example, desert, tropical rainforests, etc.

Biodiversity Hotspot

A region with significant levels of biodiversity, which is threatened with destruction, for example, Western Ghats is called biodiversity hotspot. There are a total of 4 hotspots in India, namely the Western Ghats, the Himalayas, the Indo-Burma region and the Sundaland.

Figure 6.18 The himalayas—a biodiversity hotspot

Info Bytes!

Species is a group of organisms that have similarities in character and that can also inter-breed to produce a fertile offspring. It is the basic unit of classification and taxonomy.

They include areas with natural ecosystem that are intact and communities associated with hotspots are wild. Such regions are also homes for endemic natural species. **Endemic species** are those which are found only in a particular area. For example, Nilgiri tahr, also known as Nilgiri ibex or simply ibex, is endemic to the Nilgiri hills and the southern parts of western ghats in the states of Tamil Nadu and Kerala in southern India.

Figure 6.19 Nilgiri tahr—an endemic species

Threat to Biodiversity

Significant decrease in biodiversity has taken place within the last few decades. Many organisms that were once abundant have vanished from the earth's surface. Some of the reasons that could have caused such massive destruction are given below:

- **Habitat loss:** Ruthless cutting down of the trees and destruction of forest for human necessities have caused loss of habitat of many species.
- **Over-exploitation of species:** Whether a plant or an animal reduces its population.
- **Invasion of foreign species:** Invasion of some other species or introduction of some new species for economic use sometimes drives away the local communities.
- **Intensive agriculture:** Spread of agriculture to the grasslands, wetlands, etc., destroys the habitat of many species.
- **Forestry:** Growing economically important trees, such as teak, sandalwood, etc., at the cost of normal forest trees drives away the local forest inhabitants.
- **Co-extinction:** When two different species are dependent on each other, extinction of one would affect the other species, which results in the extinction of other species also. This is called co-extinction. For example, in host-parasite relationship, if host gets extinct it will eventually lead to the extinction of parasite also.
- **Natural calamities:** Calamities such as earthquakes and tsunamis wipe away many species at once.
- **Pollution:** Is again a major factor responsible for the extinction of many species from earth as these species are unable to survive in the polluted environment.

Wildlife and its Conservation

Traditionally, **wildlife** refers to undomesticated animal and plant species that occur in their natural habitat or are in a state of life in wild. Wildlife resources form an important link in the survival of human species and maintenance of the ecological balance of nature. It is also an area of much curiosity, research and interest among naturalists all over the world. Most of the wildlife habitats are under severe pressure and a large number of wildlife species have become extinct or are on the verge of extinction, due to the deleterious activities of humans. So finding and implementing effective means of conservation of wildlife animals is of utmost importance. **Wildlife conservation** is the practice of protecting and conserving plant and animal species in their natural habitat.

There are two main methods to conserve wildlife which are: *In situ* conservation and ex situ conservation

In Situ Conservation

It involves preserving wildlife in its natural habitat. A few examples are national parks, sanctuaries and biosphere reserves in wild regions with plentiful biodiversity which are explained separately in the following sections.

National Parks

A national park is a reserved area of land under governmental control which is preserved to protect its biodiversity from human exploitation. It provides special protection to single species of plants or animals that are rare.

For example:

(i) Silent Valley National Park in Kerala. This park protects lion-tailed macaques.

(ii) Gir National Park in Gujarat. This park protects Asiatic lions.

(iii) Kaziranga National Park in Assam. This park protects one-horned Rhinoceros.

(iv) Ranthambore National Park is in Rajasthan. This park protects tigers although many other animals like leopard, sloth bear, nilgai, etc., can be seen.

Figure 6.20 Kaziranga National Park in Assam protects one-horned rhino

Figure 6.21 Lion-tailed monkey is protected in **Silent Valley** National Park, Kerala

Sanctuary

A naturally occurring area such as an island that provides protection for species from hunting, predation or competition. It is a protected area, a geographic territory within which wildlife is protected. Limited human activities are allowed inside a sanctuary. Examples are Karakoram wildlife sanctuary, Bharatpur bird sanctuary (now known as Keoladeo Ghana National Park), etc.

Figure 6.22 Great Egret in Bharatpur Bird Sanctuary

Info Bytes!

The Nilgiri Biosphere Reserve was the first reserve in India which was established in 1986.

Biosphere Reserve

A biosphere reserve is a special ecosystem with flora and fauna that requires protection. They are managed and studied for conserving the biodiversity present in that region and is a biodiversity hotspot region. At present there are 18 biosphere reserves in India.

Figure 6.23 A herd of bisons in a biosphere reserve

Ex Situ Conservation

Ex situ conservation is conserving the components of an ecosystem outside its natural environment or in an artificially created environment. It involves conservation of not only wild and cultivated species but genetic species also, for example, gene banks, zoos, aquariums, botanical gardens, etc.

Some examples of *ex situ* conservation include:

Zoological Garden

In a zoological garden, animals are enclosed and bred in captivity. They are exhibited to public for recreational purposes, for example, zoological gardens in Kolkata.

Figure 6.24 Elephants eating hay in a zoo

Botanical Garden

It is meant for protecting endangered plant species under artificial conditions away from their natural environment. They are displayed for public for education, scientific and recreational purposes, for example, Indian Botanical Garden, Howrah, West Bengal.

Figure 6.25 Different plant species in a botanical garden

Quick Recap

✔ **What is endemism? Give one example.**

Endemism refers to species that are only found in a specific region or location and nowhere else in the world. For instance, the Kangaroo Island, Kangaroo is endemic to Kangaroo Island in Australia.

✔ **What does it mean by mutualism?**

Mutualism is a relationship in which two different species interact in a way that benefits both. For instance, bees get nectar from flowers for food, and in return, they help in pollinating the flowers.

✔ **Differentiate between bio-reserves and wildlife sanctuaries.**

Bio-reserves are large areas that preserve the biodiversity of an entire ecosystem and also cater to research, education, and local livelihood. Wildlife sanctuaries are protected areas where the wildlife is protected from hunting and habitat destruction. For example, the Sundarbans are a bio-reserve, while the Periyar Wildlife Sanctuary is specifically for the protection of certain species.

✔ **What is genetic diversity?**

Genetic diversity is a kind of biodiversity, which shows diversity in number and types of genes, chromosomes present in different species or variations of genes within the same species.

✔ **Write a brief note on national park with one example.**

National park is a reserved area of land under governmental control preserved to protect its biodiversity from human exploitation. It provides special protection to single species of plants or animals that are rare, for example, Silent Valley National Park, Kerala protects lion-tailed macaques.

Threatened Species and Red Data Book

IUCN, International Union for Conservation of Nature and Natural Resources took a lead in focusing our attention towards declining and disappearing species. The names of such organisms have been given in 'Red Data Book' maintained by IUCN. 'Red' indicates stop. It includes all flora and fauna that are on the verge of extinction. According to the IUCN red list, the species are categorized in terms of their relative risk of extinction.

Extinct: Species that have totally disappeared from the earth's surface, for example, Passenger pigeon, Western black rhinoceros, Pyrenean ibex, Tasmanian tiger, etc.

Figure 6.26 Passenger pigeon

Endangered: Species with low population numbers and that are in a state of extinction, for example, Indian tiger, snow leopard, asiatic lion, etc.

Figure 6.27 Endangered species—Snow leopard, Indian Tiger and Asiatic lion

Vulnerable: Species that are likely to move into the endangered category, for example, yak, olive ridley turtle, asiatic lion, etc.

Rare species: Species with a small population, thinly scattered which is not yet endangered or vulnerable but are at risk, for example, blackbuck, lion-tailed macaque, etc.

Figure 6.28 Blackbuck

Important Days in Nature Conservation

Important days in nature conservation are discussed below:

Table 6.2 List of important dates related to nature conservation

Date	Day
March 21	World Forest Day
March 22	World Water Day
April 22	World Earth Day
June 5	World Environment Day
Oct 4	World Animal Day
July 28	World Conservation Day
May 22	International Day for Biological Diversity

Main Organizations Related to Conservation

Main organization related to conservation are discussed below:

Greenpeace: It is an international non-governmental organization which provides international assistance for nature conservation.

IUCN: International Union for Conservation of Nature and Natural Resources

WWF: The Worldwide Fund for nature

MAB: Man and biosphere, under UNESCO helps in establishing and maintaining biosphere reserves.

Quick Recap

✔ **How does extinct species differ from endangered species?**

Extinct species are organisms that have been totally disappeared from the earth's surface, for example, passenger pigeons. Endangered species are organisms whose number is decreasing and who have low population numbers. They are in a state of extinction, for example, tigers.

✔ **How *ex situ* conservation differs from *in situ* conservation? Which method is suitable for the conservation of endangered species?**

Ex situ conservation involves conserving the organisms outside their natural habitat, for example, zoological and botanical gardens.

In situ conservation method involves, conservation of organisms in their natural habitat itself, for example, national parks, biosphere reserves, etc.

Ex situ conservation is most suitable for conservation of endangered species.

✔ **What is Red Data Book?**

The record that keeps the list of all endangered species is called Red Data Book and it is maintained by IUCN.

POINTS TO REMEMBER

- ✔ Ecosystem is the functional unit of nature which consists of organisms and their environment.
- ✔ The ecosystem is made of components, like producers, consumers and decomposers.
- ✔ Pollution is any undesirable change in the physical, chemical and biological component of environment. It is mainly of three types, i.e., air, water and soil.
- ✔ Biodiversity is the occurrence of different types of ecosystems, different species and their interaction with other living and non-living forms.
- ✔ Biodiversity is of three types, i.e., genetic, species and ecological diversity.
- ✔ There has been a significant loss to biodiversity in recent times due to various threats, like habitat loss, overexploitation, pollution, etc.
- ✔ Wildlife refers to undomesticated species of plants and animals that are found in their natural habitats. Wildlife conservation is the practice of protecting and conserving these species in their natural habitats.
- ✔ National parks, wildlife sanctuaries and biosphere reserves come under the in situ method of wildlife conservation.
- ✔ Zoological and botanical gardens come under ex situ method of wildlife conservation.
- ✔ The Red Data Book maintained by IUCN enlists all the threatened and declining species of the world.

DW

PRACTICE QUESTIONS CLASSROOM WING

Very Short Answer Type Questions

Directions for questions from 1 to 13:
Fill in the blanks in each question.

1. Organisms that feed on both plant and animals are ________.
2. Organisms that feed on dead and decaying matter are ________.
3. Biomagnification is also known as ________.
4. Substances that cause pollution are ________.
5. Animals that carry disease-causing microbes are called ________.
6. Kaziranga National Park protects ________.
7. Bharatpur Bird Sanctuary is an example for ________ conservation.
8. Organisms that are found only in a particular area are called ________.
9. Extinction of a parasite along with extinction of its specific host is an example of ________
10. Full form of IUCN is ________.
11. World environment day is ________.
12. Species that are likely to move into endangered category are ________.
13. Passenger pigeon is an example of ________.

Directions for questions from 14 to 20:
For each of the following questions, four choices have been provided. Select the correct alternative.

14. Which of the following is NOT a type of consumer?
(a) Carnivore (b) Herbivore
(c) Omnivore (d) Synthesizer
15. The primary decomposers in many ecosystems are:
(a) Bacteria (b) Earthworms
(c) Fungi (d) Plants
16. Which of the following terms describes the interconnected food chain in an ecosystem?
(a) Trophic Level (b) Food Chain
(c) Food Web (d) Biomagnification
17. Based on the chapter, which of the following would likely be the final consumer in a simple grass-type food chain?
(a) Tiger (b) Grass
(c) Goat (d) Fungi
18. Why is coal classified into different types like Anthracite and Lignite?
(a) Based on the region where it is found
(b) Based on its carbon content
(c) Based on its use in industries
(d) Based on its age
19. Match the following

A. Gaseous emission	i Water pollution
B. Agricultural wastes	ii Mosquito
C. Cholera	iii Air pollution
D. Carriers	iv Soil pollution

	A	B	C	D
(a)	i	iv	iii	ii
(b)	iii	iv	ii	i
(c)	iv	iii	i	ii
(d)	iii	iv	i	ii

20. Which one of the following is a wrong statement?
(a) Accumulation of toxic substances increases from lower trophic to higher trophic levels.
(b) Energy reduces as it flows from producer to consumer.
(c) Energy reduces as it moves from lower trophic to higher trophic levels.
(d) Energy content will be high in carnivores than herbivores in a food chain.

Short Answer Type Questions

21. Given the importance of decomposers in recycling nutrients, predict the impact on an ecosystem if decomposers were to be removed.
22. What is the difference between species diversity and genetic diversity?
23. How carnivores differ from herbivores?
24. How do national parks differ from sanctuaries in their conservation objectives?
25. What are trophic levels and how energy transfer occurs from one trophic level to other?
26. Define species.
27. Write a note on the significance of wildlife sanctuary.
28. Make a comparison between zoological and botanical garden
29. What are rare species?
30. How national park differs from a zoological garden?

Essay Type Questions

31. Discuss the major threats to biodiversity and the importance of its conservation.
22. (a) What are the various control methods for soil pollution?
    (b) How deforestation causes species extinction?
33. What does it mean by *ex situ* conservation methods? Give two examples.

PRACTICE QUESTIONS COMPETITION WING

Level 1: Apply your Concepts

Directions for questions from 1 to 5:
Fill in the blanks in each question.

1. An organism that breaks down decaying matter and simultaneously improves soil fertility is ________.
2. ________ is the science that studies the relationship of living organisms with their physical environment.
3. The principle of 3R's in conservation of fossil fuels includes 'reduce', 'recycle' and ________.
4. Deforestation, apart from being caused by mining and infrastructure, is also accelerated due to the creation of ________ plantations.
5. Among air, water, and soil pollution, the contamination that results from the excessive use and mismanagement of chemical fertilizers and pesticides primarily affects the ________.

Level 2: Review your Concepts

6. Producers are important for the proper functioning of an ecosystem. Justify the statement.
7. Analyze the food chain given below and answer the following questions.

   Grass → Grasshopper → Small bird → Snake → Owl

   (a) Which is the primary carnivore?
   (b) Which is the top consumer?
   (c) Which organism has the highest energy and the lowest energy content in body?
8. How various species are classified according to their risk for existence?
9. Is humidity in atmosphere related to the functioning of biotic factors in an ecosystem?
10. In a grass-type food chain, what would be the level of a fish?
11. Why in an aquatic food chain, maximum DDT is found in fish-eating birds?
12. How can gases present in the atmosphere cause acid rain?
13. Describe the various threats to biodiversity.

Level 3: Assess Your Concepts

14. Write a note on various *in situ* conservation methods.
15. Does a group of organisms that are similar to each other but unable to reproduce form species?

AT

PRACTICE QUESTIONS NEET SPECIAL WING

Multiple-Answer Type Questions

Questions number 1 to 5 are multiple-choice questions. Each question has FOUR options (a), (b), (c), and (d). ONE OR MORE THAN ONE of these four option(s) is/are the correct answer(s).

1. Which of the following are products of crude oil?
   (a) Lubricating oil
   (b) Bitumen
   (c) Paraffin wax
   (d) Anthracite
2. Identify the consumers out of the following:
   (a) Herbivores
   (b) Producers
   (c) Carnivores
   (d) Omnivores
3. Identify the causes of deforestation.
   (a) livestock ranching
   (b) Infrastructure
   (c) Mining
   (d) Pulp plantations
4. Examples of National Park are:
   (a) Ranthambore in Rajasthan
   (b) Karakoram
   (c) Gir in Gujarat
   (d) Kaziranga in Assam
5. Identify the extinct species:
   (a) Passenger pigeon
   (b) Lion tailed macaque
   (c) Tasmanian tiger
   (d) Western black rhinoceros

Comprehension-Based Questions

A. Read the paragraph given below and answer the questions number 6 to 11:

Biodiversity means the richness of the different species of organisms existing around us. A region which has a very high level of biodiversity is called biodiversity hotspot. For example, the western ghats of India are considered to be biodiversity hotspot. Significant decrease in biodiversity has taken place due to the following reasons-Habitat loss, over exploitation of species, invasion of foreign species, intensive agriculture, forestry, co- extinction, natural calamities, pollution, etc. Wildlife conservation is the practice of protecting and conserving plant and animal species in their natural habitat. There are two main methods to conserve wildlife which are: *In situ* conservation and *ex situ* conservation. *In situ* conservation method includes National parks, Sanctuary, biosphere reserve. *Ex situ* conservation methods include zoological garden, botanical garden, etc. IUCN maintains a 'Red Data Book' which includes names of all the species which are categorized in terms of their relative risk of extinction.

6. Identify the species which is not included in the list of IUCN.
   (a) Endangered species
   (b) Endemic species
   (c) Vulnerable species
   (d) Extinct species
7. What is the full form of WWF?
   (a) World Wide Foundation
   (b) World Web Foundation
   (c) World Wide Fund
   (d) World Wide Federation
8. On which of the following date is World environment day celebrated?
   (a) June 5
   (b) May 22
   (c) October 4
   (d) March 21
9. The type of conservation wherein wildlife is conserved outside its natural environment.
   (a) *In situ* hybridization
   (b) *Ex situ* hybridization
   (c) *In situ* conservation
   (d) *Ex situ* conservation

10. Sanctuary is:
(a) an island
(b) a protected territory
(c) a natural area where wildlife is protected
(d) reserved area under governmental control

11. Match the following:

Column – A	Column – B
(i) Endangered species	(a) Blackbuck
(ii) Vulnerable species	(b) Olive ridley turtle
(iii) Rare species	(c) Tasmanian tiger
(iv) Extinct species	(d) Nilgiri tahr
(v) Endemic species	(e) Snow leopard

B. Read the paragraph given below and answer the questions number 12 to 17:

The continuous interaction occurring between the living as well as the non-living components of the biosphere is called an ecosystem. Ecosystem consists of three main components that is producers, consumers and decomposers. The producers are the green plants which can synthesize their own food in the presence of sunlight and water. Consumers are the group of organisms which depend directly or indirectly on the green plants for their food. Consumers are further classified into herbivores, carnivores and omnivores. Decomposers are responsible for the decomposition of the dead and decaying organisms. The continuous cycle of eating and being eaten is called the food chain and when the complexity in the food chain increases it becomes a food web. It is this system of food web which results in accumulation of toxic substances in the body or organisms at different trophic levels by the process of biomagnification.

12. The organism on the fourth trophic level is:
(a) Herbivore
(b) Producer
(c) Primary carnivore
(d) Secondary carnivore

13. Organisms that eat both plants and animals are called:
(a) Herbivore
(b) Carnivore
(c) Omnivore
(d) Both a and b

14. Example of Abiotic component is:
(a) Insects
(b) Microbes
(c) Pathogens
(d) Light

15. In a food chain consisting of green grass, grass hopper and lizard, the role of grass hopper is:
(a) Producer
(b) Primary consumer
(c) Secondary consumer
(d) Tertiary consumer

16. The branch of science that studies relationship between living organisms and physical environment.
(a) Ecology
(b) Ecosystem
(c) Biosphere
(d) Cytology

17. Match the following:

Column – A	Column – B
(i) DDT in fish eating birds	(a) Food chain
(ii) Linear sequence of organisms for cycle of nutrition	(b) Carnivore
(iii) Bear	(c) Herbivore
(iv) Lion	(d) Omnivore
(v) Sparrow	(e) Bioamplification

ANSWER KEYS

Crossword

Across

5. Renewable **7.** Omnivores **9.** Endemic **10.** Silviculture **11.** Afforestation

Down

1. Biomagnification **2.** Petroleum **3.** Sanctuary **4.** Trophic levels **6.** Biodiversity **8.** Decomposers

Classroom Wing

Very Short Answer Type Questions

1. Omnivores **2.** Decomposers **3.** Bioamplification **4.** Pollutants **5.** Carriers **6.** One-horned rhinoceros **7.** *In situ* **8.** Endemic species **9.** Co-extinction **10.** International Union for Conservation of Nature and Natural Resources **11.** June 5 **12.** Vulnerable **13.** Extinct species **14.** (d) **15.** (c) **16.** (c) **17.** (a) **18.** (b) **19.** (d) **20.** (d)

Competition Wing

Level 1: Apply your Concepts

1. Earthworm **2.** Ecology **3.** Reuse **4.** Pulp **5.** Soil

NEET Special Wing

Multiple-Answer Type Questions

1. (a, c) **2.** (a, c, d) **3.** (a, b, c, d) **4.** (a, c, d) **5.** (a, c, d)

Comprehension-Based Questions

6. (b) **7.** (c) **8.** (a) **9.** (d) **10.** (c)

11. (i) → (e); (ii) → (b); (iii) → (a); (iv) → (c); (v) → (d)

12. (d) **13.** (c) **14.** (d) **15.** (b) **16.** (a)

17. (i) → (e); (ii) → (a); (iii) → (d); (iv) → (b); (v) → (c)

Hints and Explanations

CLASSROOM WING

Short Answer Type Questions

21. If decomposers were removed from an ecosystem, dead and decaying organic matter would accumulate, leading to a build-up of waste. Nutrients would not be returned to the soil, making it less fertile over time. This would disrupt nutrient cycles, potentially harming plant growth and the entire food chain dependent on them.

22. Species diversity refers to the variety in the number and richness of species in a particular region, while genetic diversity pertains to the diversity in genes and chromosomes present in different species or variations within the same species. While species diversity looks at the broader categorization of living organisms based on types and numbers, genetic diversity digs deeper into the genetic makeup, ensuring resilience and adaptability of species over time.

23. Herbivores feed directly on plants for energy requirements. They are present in the second trophic level of a food chain, where plants or producers constitute the first trophic level, for example, cows. Carnivores are organisms that feed on herbivores. They eat flesh of other animals. for example, tigers.

24. National parks are reserved areas aimed primarily at the protection of biodiversity, providing special protection to specific rare species. In contrast, sanctuaries are natural areas that protect species from hunting, predation, or competition and might allow limited human activities. The primary distinction lies in the degree of protection and human intervention allowed. While both are conservation tools, national parks often have stricter regulations.

25. The trophic level refers to the 'various steps in a food chain'. The plants or producers of an ecosystem constitute the lowest or first trophic level.

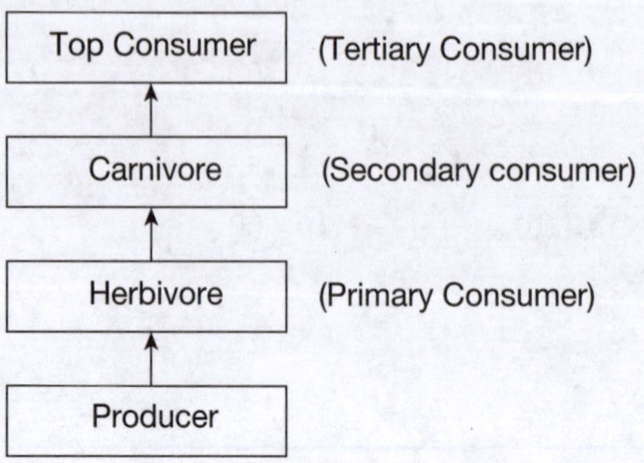

The energy synthesized by producers reaches organisms in the next trophic level or herbivores when they feed on plants. Similarly energy reaches each trophic level when organisms in one trophic level are eaten up by organisms in the next trophic level. Amount of energy decreases as it flows from lower to higher trophic levels, in other words, from producer to consumer.

26. A group of organisms that have similarities in character and that can also interbreed to produce a fertile offspring.

27. Wildlife sanctuaries are a type of *in-situ* conservation methods where organisms are protected in their natural habitat. They provide protection of species from major threats, such as hunting, poaching, killing, etc. These conservation methods prevent the extinction of various species of organisms, thereby maintaining their number on earth.

28. Botanical and zoological gardens are examples for *ex situ* conservation methods where wildlife is protected outside their natural habitat.

In zoological gardens, animals are enclosed and bred in captivity. They are exhibited to public for recreational purposes, for example, Zoological Gardens in Kolkata. Botanical gardens are meant for protecting endangered plant species under artificial conditions away from their natural habitat. They are displayed for public education, recreational and scientific purposes, for example, Indian Botanical Garden, Howrah, West Bengal.

29. Species with a small population and that are thinly scattered around the world are called rare species. They are not yet endangered or vulnerable but are at risk.

30.

National park	Zoological park
In situ conservation method	*Ex situ* conservation method
Conservation in their natural habitat	Conservation outside their natural habitat
Animals (wildlife) are protected from public exploitation	Animals are exhibited to public for recreational purposes
For example, Silent Valley National Park	For example, Zoological Gardens in Kolkata

Essay Type Questions

31. Biodiversity, or the variety of life on Earth, is under threat in the modern era. Many species lose their homes as a result of habitat loss, which is primarily caused by deforestation and urbanisation. Another major issue is over-exploitation, in which certain species are harvested at rates faster than their natural reproduction. Foreign species invasion frequently disrupts local ecosystems and, in some cases, drives native species to extinction. Practices such as intensive agriculture and prioritised forestry frequently put natural flora and fauna at risk. The concept of co-extinction, in which two interdependent species become extinct after the loss of one, is becoming more common. Furthermore, natural disasters and pollution exacerbate the decline in biodiversity.

Biodiversity conservation is critical for a variety of reasons. For starters, it ensures survival; diverse ecosystems are more resilient to change and recover from adversity faster. Many species are essential for medicines, food, and industry, so biodiversity has direct economic value. It also has aesthetic and cultural values that shape human experiences, beliefs, and practices. Conservation ensures the health of ecosystems, which in turn ensures clean air, water, and fertile soils, all of which are necessary for human survival.

32. (a)
- Dumping wastes in open should be avoided.
- Wastes should be categorized as bio-degradable and non-biodegradable.
- Domestic waste should be dumped in a compost pit.
- Necessary steps should be taken by municipality for waste treatment and disposal management of localities.

(b) Deforestation or ruthless cutting of trees results in loss of natural habitat of many organisms. Habitat loss is the major reason for extinction of species.

33. *Ex situ* conservation is conserving the components of an ecosystem outside its natural environment or in an artificially created environment.

Ex situ conservation includes:

Zoological garden: Here animals are enclosed and bred in captivity. They are exhibited to public for recreational purposes, for example, Zoological Gardens in Kolkata.

Botanical garden: It is meant for protecting endangered plant species under artificial conditions away from their natural environment. They are displayed to the public for educational, scientific and recreational purposes, for example, Indian Botanical Garden, Howrah, West Bengal.

COMPETITION WING

Level 2: Review your Concepts

6. Producers are the organisms that have the unique ability to produce food or energy. They produce their own food mainly through photosynthesis. Other organisms that cannot synthesize their own food depend on producers (green plants) either directly or indirectly for their energy requirements. Thus producers are the ones that make energy required by all organisms in an ecosystem.

7. (a) Primary carnivore – Small birds

   (b) Top consumer – Owl

   (c) Grass will have the highest energy as it is the producer and owl will have the lowest energy because energy level decreases as it flows from the lower trophic level to the higher trophic level.

8. **Extinct:** Species that have totally disappeared from the earth's surface, for example, passenger pigeon.

   Endangered: Species with low population numbers and are in a state of extinction, for example, Indian tigers.

   Vulnerable: Species that are likely to move into endangered category.

   Rare species: Species with a small population, thinly scattered and which are not yet endangered or vulnerable but are at risk.

9. Yes, humidity is an integral part of the functioning of the ecosystem. Humidity forms the abiotic component of an ecosystem. It is directly involved in shaping the type of vegetation in an ecosystem.

10. In a grass-type food chain, fish have no trophic level as the energy is transferred from grass to primary consumer (grasshopper), secondary consumer (frog) to tertiary consumer (snake). Fish forms part of aquatic ecosystem. Hence, they are not involved in this type of food chain.

11. DDT sprayed in fields enters the soil. From soil, it reaches the ground water and when the agriculture waste is dumped into water bodies, DDT enters water resources. DDT (dichlorodiphenyltrichloroethane) cannot get degraded biologically because of its composition and hence, it enters food chain. It is absorbed by aquatic organisms like fish. Fish, in turn, pass on DDT to the birds that prey on them. Eventually, the organisms which occupy the highest trophic level suffer the most (fish-eating birds in this case).

12. When it rains, the water reacts with the gases present in the atmosphere. This reaction of water with sulphur and nitrogen oxides results in the formation of acids viz., sulphuric and nitric acids.

13. The main reasons for the loss of biodiversity have been given below:
    - **Habitat loss:** Ruthless cutting down of the trees and destruction of forest for human necessities have caused loss of habitat of many species.
    - Overexploitation of species, whether it is a plant or an animal, reduces its population.
    - **Invasion of foreign species:** Invasion of some other species or introduction of some new species for economic use sometimes drives away the local communities.
    - **Intensive agriculture:** Spread of agriculture to most of the grasslands, wetlands, etc., destroys the habitat of many species.
    - **Forestry:** Growing economically important trees, such as teak, sandalwood, etc., at the cost of normal forest trees drives away the local forest inhabitants.
    - **Co-extinction:** When two different species are dependent on each other, extinction of one would affect the other species which results in its extinction. This is called co-extinction. For example, in host–parasite relationship, if host gets extinct it will eventually lead to extinction of parasite also.
    - Natural calamities, such as earthquake and tsunami wipe away many species.
    - **Pollution:** Is again a major factor responsible for the removal of many species from earth as these species are unable to survive in the polluted environment.

Level 3: Assess Your Concepts

14. *In situ* conservation includes conservation of wildlife in its natural habitat, for example, national parks, wildlife sanctuaries and biosphere reserves.

    National park: Is a reserved area of land under governmental control preserved to protect its biodiversity from human exploitation. It provides special protection to single species of plants or animals that are rare. For example, Silent Valley National Park in Kerala protects lion-tailed macaques and Kaziranga National Park in Assam protects one-horned rhinoceros.

    Sanctuary: It is a naturally occurring area such as an island that provides protection for species from hunting, predation or competition. It is a protected area, a geographic territory within which wildlife is protected. Limited human activities are allowed inside a sanctuary. For example, Bharatpur Bird Sanctuary.

Biosphere reserve: A biosphere reserve is a special ecosystem with flora and fauna that requires protection. They are managed and studied for conserving the biodiversity present in that region and is a biodiversity hotspot region.

15. For a group of organisms to be able to be called species, they must interbreed with each other to form fertile offspring.

NEET SPECIAL WING

Multiple-Answer Type Questions

1. Petroleum or crude oil is a naturally occurring, yellow-to-black coloured liquid found beneath the Earth's surface. Crude oil is refined to give useful products. Lubricating oil is used for lubrication and paraffin wax is used to make candles, Vaseline, etc.

2. All animals that cannot synthesize their own food and depend on green plants directly or indirectly for their energy requirements are called consumers. Consumers are of three types herbivores, carnivores and omnivores.

3. Deforestation is the cutting down of trees at a large scale over a short period of time. The overexploitation of forests threatens the ecosystem and humanity as we heavily depend on forests for most of the ecological services. The mains causes of deforestation include small- and large-scale agriculture, mining, infrastructure, pulp plantations, forest fires, illegal logging of wood, feeding animals on plants or livestock ranching.

4. Ranthambore National Park is in Rajasthan. This park protects tigers although many other animals like leopard, sloth bear, nilgai, etc., can be seen. Gir National Park in Gujarat. This park protects Asiatic lions. Kaziranga National Park in Assam. This park protects one-horned Rhinoceros. Karakoram wild life sanctuary established in 1987, located in Ladakh.

5. Species that have totally disappeared from the earth's surface, for example, Passenger pigeon, Western black rhinoceros, Pyrenean ibex, Tasmanian tiger, etc. Lion tailed macaque is an endangered species under red list category of IUCN.

Comprehension-Based Questions

A.

6. IUCN has a list of species that are either extinct, endangered, vulnerable or rare species, but it does not include names of species that are only found in a particular are or endemic.

7. WWF is an organization related to conservation and its full form is World Wide Fund for nature.

8. June 5 is celebrated as World environment day which is among many important dates related to nature conservation.

9. *Ex situ* conservation is conserving the components of an ecosystem outside its natural environment or in an artificially created environment. It involves conservation of not only wild and cultivated species but genetic species also, for example, gene banks, zoos, aquariums, botanical gardens, etc.

10. Sanctuary is a naturally occurring area such as an island that provides protection for species from hunting, predation or competition. It is a protected area, a geographic territory within which wildlife is protected. Limited human activities are allowed inside a sanctuary.

11. Match the following:

Species with low population numbers and that are in a state of extinction, for example, snow leopard, etc.
(i) (e)

Species that are likely to move into the endangered category, for example, olive ridley turtle, etc.
(ii) (b)

Species with a small population, thinly scattered which is not yet endangered or vulnerable but are at risk, for example, blackbuck, etc.
(iii) (a)

Species that have totally disappeared from the earth's surface, for example, Tasmanian tiger, etc.
(iv) (c)

Endemic species are those which are found only in a particular area. For example, Nilgiri tahr, also known as Nilgiri ibex or simply ibex, is endemic to the Nilgiri hills and the southern parts of western ghats in the states of Tamil Nadu and Kerala in southern India.
(v) (d)

B.

12. Fourth trophic level consists of secondary carnivore organisms in the food chain.

13. Omnivores are organisms which consume both plants and animals.

14. The abiotic components are the non-living components which consists of light, air, water, temperature, humidity, etc.

15. Grass hopper consumes the green grass or the producer and hence it is a herbivore or a primary consumer.

16. Ecology is a branch of science which studies the relationship between the living as well as non-living components of the ecosystem.

17. Match the following:
Bioamplification is the increase or accumulation in concentration of toxic substances in the body of organisms at higher trophic levels. For example, increased levels of DDT used as an insecticide in fields is found in fish eating birds, as it is passed down in the food chain. DDT reaches the water bodies due to leaching, is absorbed by planktons and then passed onto the fishes and ultimately is found in the body of fish-eating birds.
(i) (e)

The process of eating and being eaten up in a linear network, where the energy and the nutrients of food get transferred from one trophic level to another trophic level is called a food chain.
(ii) (a)

Omnivores are organisms which consume both plants and animals. E.g., human, bears, etc.
(iii) (d)

Carnivores are organisms which consume other animals. E.g., Lion.
(iv) (b)

Organisms which depend on plants directly for food are called herbivores. E.g., Sparrow.
(v) (c)

CHAPTER 7

Food—Production and Management

Remember

Before beginning this chapter, you should be able to:

- Understand the importance of food in our life
- Remember the basics of agricultural practices
- Recall the concept of animal husbandry

Key Ideas

After completing this chapter, you should be able to:

- Describe crop improvement
- Classify crops
- Explain various agricultural practices
- Understand hybridization and genetic engineering
- Understand and describe animal husbandry

A Tribute to Norman Borlaug (1914-2009)

During his remarkable life from 1914 to 2009, Norman Borlaug, a towering figure in the realms of food production and management, left an indelible mark on our world. His unwavering commitment to agricultural advancements not only elevated him to legendary status, but also had a significant impact on global food security.

Borlaug's contributions to science were nothing short of revolutionary. He is best known for developing high-yielding, disease-resistant wheat varieties, which sparked the Green Revolution in the mid-20th century. This game-changing discovery resulted in a dramatic increase in crop yields, preventing widespread famine and saving countless lives.

Borlaug received the Nobel Peace Prize in 1970 for his extraordinary contributions to humanity. His work not only prevented widespread hunger, but it also boosted international cooperation in dealing with global food crises.

Borlaug's accolades and accomplishments attest to his unwavering dedication. Along with the Nobel Peace Prize, he was awarded the Presidential Medal of Freedom and the Congressional Gold Medal, among many other honours.

Norman Borlaug's legacy is an everlasting reminder of the profound impact that one person's dedication and scientific ingenuity can have on mitigating global food insecurity, leaving a legacy of hope for future generations. His work continues to inspire scientists, policymakers, and humanitarian organisations all over the world.

FUN TIME

CROSSWORD

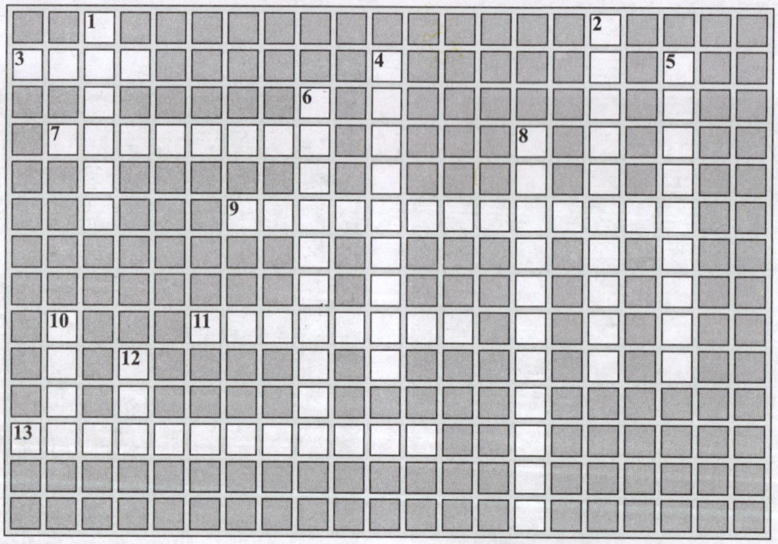

Across

3. The jelly like substance obtained from red algae used for growing microorganisms in laboratory
7. The plants grown for the purpose of silkworm rearing
9. Father of green revolution
11. The chicken grown in poultry for the purpose of meat production
13. Method of sowing involving scattering of seeds by hand in the field

Down

1. The organic matter added to soil for increasing the fertility
2. Artificial supply of water to the crops at regular intervals
4. The areas where the grains from the crop are stored
5. First step of agriculture for cultivation of any crop
6. The process of crossing of two dissimilar plants
8. Rearing of silkworms for the purpose of making silk fibre
10. Variety of algae which are rich in vitamin B_{12} and Beta-carotene
12. Term given for monsoon crops harvested in October

INTRODUCTION

Food is the third most basic need for life, after oxygen and water. Everyone requires food to perform normal activities of daily living. Agriculture is the practice of production of food, fibres, and other useful items by the cultivation of plants and animals. The primary objective of agriculture is the production of food. As human population has been constantly increasing, there is an increased need for food production. Rearing of animals on a large scale for fulfilling our needs for food and other products comes under animal husbandry while development of existing crop varieties to produce new varieties that are much more advanced in terms of food production and disease resistance, etc., falls under crop improvement. Animal husbandry and crop improvement programmes play a major role in increasing food production.

Crops

Plants grown at a large scale on a piece of land are called **crops**. Few examples of crops are wheat, cereals, pulses and fruit crops, etc. Crops are usually grown to produce food at a large scale that could be sold for money in the market. Some crops are also grown as fodder crops that are used to feed the animals.

Crops can be classified into three groups according to the season in which they are cultivated.

Classification of crops (Based on season)

Kharif
- Monsoon crops
- Grown in rainy season
- Planted in July
- Harvested in October

For example, Rice, Maize, Soybean, etc.

Rabi
- Winter crops
- Grown in winter season
- Planted in October
- Harvested in March

For example, Wheat, Linseed, Mustard, etc.

Zaid
- Summer crops
- Grown in summer season
- Planted in March
- Harvested in June

For example, Watermelon, musk melon, pumpkin, etc.

Figure 7.1 Classification of crops on the basis of season

Agricultural Practices

Various steps involved in agriculture are collectively known as agricultural practices, which include:

- Ploughing
- Sowing
- Addition of manure and fertilizer
- Irrigation
- Weeding
- Harvesting
- Storage

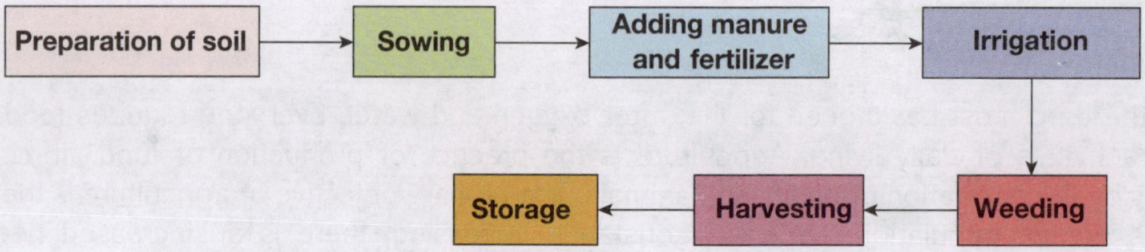

Figure 7.2 An overview of the steps involved in cultivation of a crop

Ploughing

This is the first step in agricultural practices, which includes preparation of soil before sowing. Ploughing is done to turn or loosen the soil. The soil crumbs formed after ploughing can be broken with the help of a tool called plank. The three important tools of ploughing are plough, hoe and cultivator (shown in fig - 7.4). Levelling is also done after ploughing to make a uniform soil bed for sowing and irrigation. Levelling also prevents soil erosion.

Konnect

The method of turning or loosening of soil is called tilling.

Figure 7.3 Tractor ploughing field for planting crops

Info Bytes!

The word 'sow' in 'sowing seeds' comes from the Old English word 'sawan' which means to scatter seed on the ground.

Advantages of Ploughing

- It helps in bringing nutrient-rich soil to the top layer.
- It helps in removing weeds.
- It increases the growth of decomposers (microbes) and earthworms which in turn help in decomposition of plant and animal wastes.
- It helps the root to penetrate deep into the soil and allows it to breathe easily.

Tools Used for Ploughing the Field

Plough Hoe Cultivator

Figure 7.4 Different types of tools used in ploughing

Sowing

The act of planting seeds is known as sowing. Before sowing, it has to be ensured that the seeds are of good quality. Sowing bad quality seeds or damaged seeds reduces the yield. Planting the seeds at uniform distances is also important to avoid overcrowding. The seeds should not be grown too deep also as it will not germinate due to lack of oxygen. This allows plants to get enough sunlight, nutrients and water.

Different methods of sowing are:

1. **Broadcasting:** It is scattering of seeds by hand.
2. **Drilling:** It is the dropping of seeds into the soil with the help of tools like seed drill and covering with soil. It can be done either by manually or with the help of machines..
3. **Transplanting:** In this method, seeds are grown in the nursery first and then planted into the field at seedling stage.
4. **Use of traditional tool:** In this the seeds are sowed manually by the help of funnel shaped tools.

Drilling

Transplanting

Use of traditional tool

Figure 7.5 Different methods of sowing seeds

Addition of Manure and Fertilizers

Plants absorb nutrients from the soil. Continuous cultivation of crops at a particular piece of land reduces the soil fertility, which needs to be supplied artificially. The major nutrient-supplying sources are manures and fertilizers.

Manure: Manure is the organic matter formed by the decomposition of plant and animal wastes. Manure adds humus to the soil and helps to retain water in the soil.

Fertilizers: Fertilizers are industrially produced chemicals that contain nutrients required by plants, for example, Nitrogen, Phosphorus, and Potassium (NPK), Urea, etc.

Table 7.1 Points of differences between manure and fertilizers

Manures	Fertilizers
Plant or animal origin	Chemically synthesized
Organic in nature	Inorganic in nature
Natural product	Artificial product
Supply all primary nutrients	Supply specific type of nutrients
Improve soil properties	Have negative effect on soil, reduce soil fertility on prolonged use
For example - Cowdung	For example - nitrogen, phosphorus and potassium fertilizers

Manures and fertilizers are added to the soil to increase its fertility. However there are some natural methods to increase soil fertility. Some of them are discussed below:

Crop rotation: Growing different crops alternatively on a piece of land is called crop rotation. For example, wheat and leguminous plants could be cultivated alternatively for higher yield. Wheat requires more nitrogen from the soil. Nitrogen can be replenished naturally by cultivating legume in the next season. Leguminous plants contain a bacterium called *Rhizobium* which is located in the root nodules. These bacteria are capable of fixing atmospheric nitrogen into the soil thereby increasing the nitrogen content of the soil.

Mixed cropping: Planting two or more crops simultaneously on the same piece of land is called mixed cropping. Mixed cropping allows the crops to work together, for example, cotton and groundnut can be grown together for better yield.

Field fallowing: Leaving the land uncultivated for one or more seasons is called field fallowing. This helps the soil to replenish the nutrients on its own and helps to regain the fertility of the soil.

Irrigation

The artificial supply of water to the crops at regular intervals is called irrigation. Irrigation is mainly used in areas where rainfall is irregular or droughts are expected. The sources of irrigated water are numerous, like groundwater, water from springs or wells, rivers, lakes or even treated wastewater. All living organisms require water for their normal growth and functioning. Plants contain nearly 90% water. For a healthy crop, field needs to be watered regularly.

Types of Irrigation

There are different types of irrigation to supply water to the plant. It is important to water the plants as uniformly as possible, which allows the plants to get the amount of water it needs. The three different types of irrigation are:

1. **Surface irrigation:** Water moves across the surface of an agricultural field.
2. **Drip irrigation:** Water falls drop by drop at the position of roots. This can be the most efficient method of irrigation in regions with water scarcity. Water wastage is minimized by utilizing this method.

Figure 7.6 Drip irrigation in a crop field

3. **Sprinkler irrigation:** It consists of a main pipe to which many pipes with rotating nozzles on top are attached. The nozzles rotate at regular intervals. When pressurized water flows through the main pipe, it escapes through the nozzles. Due to this, the water sprinkles on the crops and it seems as if it is raining. Sprinkled irrigation is helpful on uneven land and sandy soil.

Figure 7.7 Sprinkler irrigation in a crop field

Info Bytes!

Subsurface irrigation is a type of irrigation in which the water is supplied directly to soil under the surface of the plant

Weeding

The unwanted plants that grow along with crops naturally are called weeds. It is important to remove weeds as they will compete with the main crops for nutrients, water, sunlight and space. The removal of weeds is called weeding. Weeding is usually done before the flowering of weeds.

Following processes are done for carrying out weeding:

- **Manual removal:** Uprooting or cutting the weeds close to the ground manually. It is done with the help of a tool called *khurpi* or seed drill.

Figure 7.8 Manual removal of weeds

- **Use of weedicides:** Chemicals used for weed control are known as weedicides, for example, 2, 4–D. They do not damage the crops.
- **Ploughing:** Ploughing helps to uproot the weeds, causing them to die.
- **Animal grazing:** Allowing animals (goats, cows) to feed on weeds.

Figure 7.9 Weedicide being sprayed on a field

Harvesting

The process of gathering the crops after they mature to separate the useful products, such as grains is called harvesting. Separation of grains from crops includes two steps:

1. **Threshing:** Separation of grain seeds from harvested crop is called threshing. There is a machine called combine that can be used for both harvesting and threshing.
2. **Winnowing**: Separation of grains from chaff is called winnowing. It is done with the help of wind, the lighter particles of the chaff are blown away leaving the heavier grain particles falling down.

Winnowing

Figure 7.10 Methods used in harvesting

Storage

Storage of grains after harvesting is of great importance as it will affect the yield. If they are not stored properly, there is a chance of loss of grains due to attack by insects, pests, rats or microorganisms.

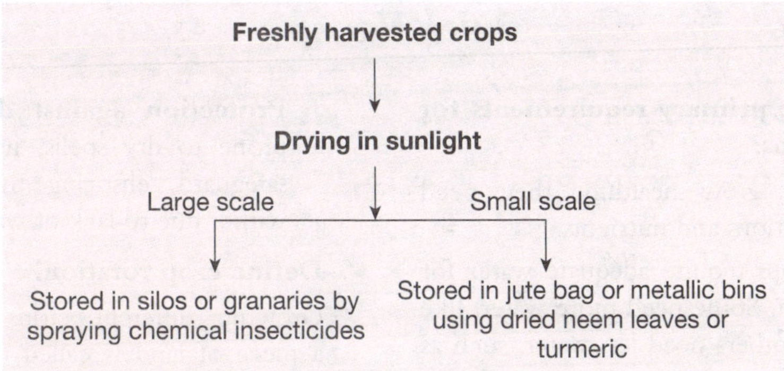

Figure 7.11 Steps involved in storage of harvested crops

Different methods to store grains are given below:

- Before storing, grains should be dried properly in sunlight to reduce moisture content. If freshly harvested grains are stored without drying, they may get spoilt or attacked by microorganisms losing their germination capacity.
- Grains can be stored at a large scale in silos or granaries, by spraying chemical insecticides.
- On small-scale production, grains can be stored in jute bags or metallic bins. Instead of chemical insecticides, dried neem leaves or turmeric can be used to repel insects, pests, etc.

Granaries Silos

Figure 7.12 Large scale storage of grains

Quick Recap

What are the primary requirements for growing crops?

For crops to grow healthily, they need essential conditions and nutrients.

- **Water:** Crops require adequate water for their growth. Some need more water, like rice, while others need less water, such as millets.
- **Soil:** Different crops prefer different types of soil. For instance, sandy soil is suitable for crops like peanuts, while clayey soil is preferred for paddy.
- **Sunlight:** Sunlight plays a crucial role in photosynthesis, a process vital for the growth of crops. While some crops, like sunflowers, thrive in direct sunlight, others, such as lettuce, can tolerate some shade.

How is irrigation essential for crop cultivation?

Irrigation is the method of providing water to crops to aid in their growth. Its importance can be understood from three key perspectives:

1. **Regular Supply**: Ensures that crops get a consistent and adequate amount of water, especially in regions with irregular rainfall.
2. **Improved Yield**: Proper irrigation can lead to better crop growth and, consequently, increase yields.
3. **Protection against drought**: In areas prone to dry spells, irrigation acts as a safeguard, ensuring that crops do not wither due to lack of water.

Define crop rotation.

Growing different crops alternatively on a piece of land is called crop rotation. For example, wheat and leguminous plants can be cultivated alternatively for higher yield. Wheat requires more nitrogen from the soil. Nitrogen can be replenished naturally by cultivating legume in the next season. Leguminous plants contain a bacterium called *Rhizobium* in the root nodules. These bacteria are capable of fixing atmospheric nitrogen into the soil thereby increasing the soil nitrogen content.

Define field fallowing.

Leaving the land uncultivated for one or more seasons is called field fallowing. This helps the soil to replenish the nutrients on its own.

Write the difference between threshing and winnowing.

Threshing is done to separate grain seeds from harvested crop whereas winnowing is done to separate grains from chaff.

Plant Improvement Programmes

Plant improvement or crop improvement programmes include production of desired plant variety that gives better yield, and possesses qualities, such as disease resistance, resistance to climatic conditions, etc.

Crop variety that has desired quality can be produced by various methods such as:

Hybridization

It is the process of crossing of two dissimilar plants. Hybridization helps to bring qualities of two parent plants together in the daughter plant. For example, Jaya and Ratna are two rice varieties that have been developed through hybridization.

Figure 7.13 Hybrid cocoa trees

Info Bytes!

India's first genetically modified crop was Bt Cotton, which helped to fight against harmful pests.

Genetic Engineering

Development of plant varieties expressing the desired agronomic characteristic is the ultimate goal of a plant breeder. Since traditional methods of plant breeding were not reliable enough and did not give satisfactory results, a new technology called genetic engineering was introduced in plant breeding. Genetic engineering is that technique which involves introduction of a gene (or DNA) that would impart the desired quality to the crop. It does not always involve inserting DNA from other organisms, plants can also be modified by switching off their own genes, to produce a particular trait.

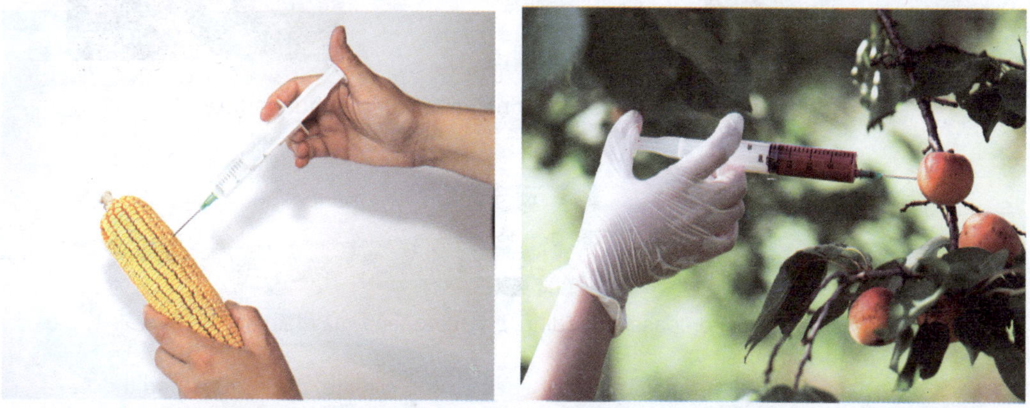

Figure 7.14 Developing plants through genetic engineering

Animal Husbandry

A branch of agriculture dealing with rearing of animals for their products is called animal husbandry. It includes dairy farming, poultry, pisciculture, etc. Domesticated animals for commercial purposes are called livestock, for example, cow, sheep, etc.

Animals are domesticated mainly for:

- **Dairy products:** Cow and goat
- **Meat:** Cattle and chicken
- **Land management:** Animal grazing to control weed growth
- **Wool:** Sheep
- **Labour:** Horse and donkey

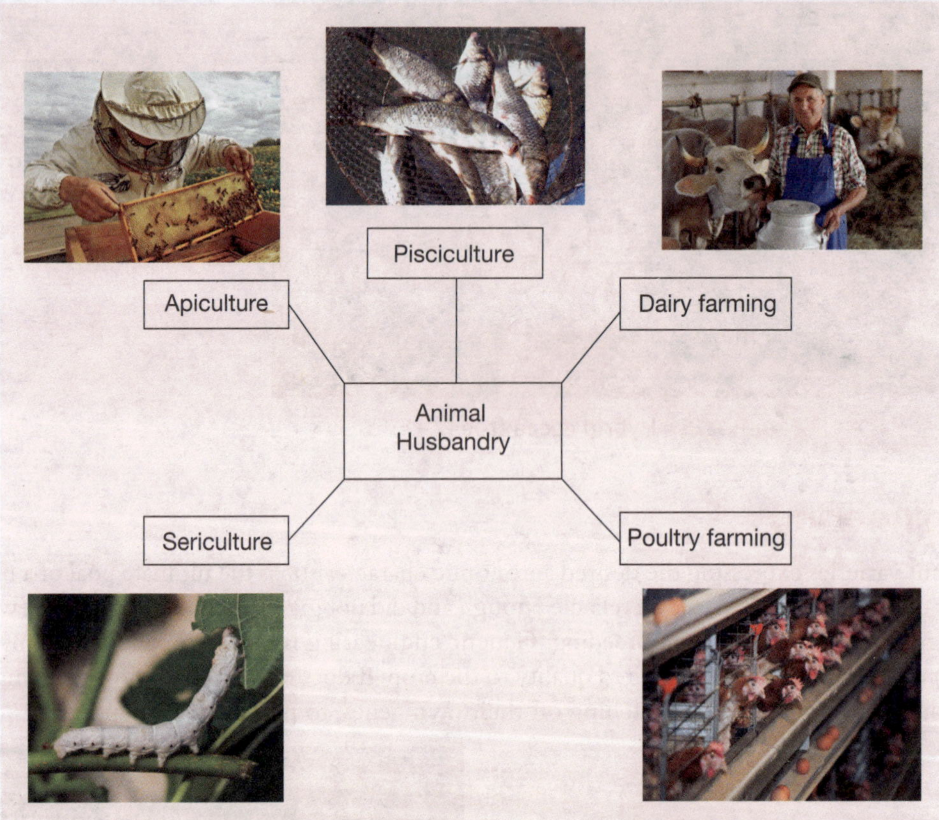

Figure 7.15 Various divisions under animal husbandry

Konnect

- Animal husbandry encompasses feeding, breeding, and maintaining the overall health of the animals.
- It differs depending on the varieties of species, the climate, the culture, and the tools available to the farmers.

Dairy Farming

Management of animals for milk and milk products is called dairy farming. The main domesticated animals for dairy farming are cows, sheeps, buffaloes and goats. The yield of milk mainly depends upon the breed quality. So it is important to select breed of good quality and also breeds with disease resistance.

Figure 7.16 Cows in a dairy farm

Info Bytes!

India is the largest milk producer in the world, thanks to dairy farming.

Following are some of the measures that can be taken to increase milk yield:

- Select good quality breed.
- Select breed with disease resistance.
- Take good care of the farm animals by maintaining proper hygiene and by providing them with good feeds.
- Maintain proper hygiene while milking, storage and transport of the milk and its products.
- Regular visits by veterinary doctor.

Poultry Farming

Domesticating birds for their products is called poultry farming, for example, domesticating chicken for their meat and eggs. Other birds that are domesticated include duck, turkey, geese, etc. Factors that affect yield in poultry farming are:

- Selection of disease-free breeds
- Proper and safe farm conditions
- Proper feed and water
- Maintenance of proper hygiene and health of farm birds

Figure 7.17 Chickens in a poultry farm

Types of Chickens

Depending on the utility, poultry chicken are classified into two types as follows.

1. **Broilers:** Chickens that are reared for their meat are called broilers. They are given a protein-rich diet. They are reared in groups are raised in well-maintained conditions of surroundings. Once the batch is reared, the whole area is sterilized and made ready for a new batch/group.
2. **Egg-layers:** Chickens that are reared for their eggs are called egg-layers. They are bred in individual cages. They are fed on wheat and other mashed cereals. They are bred on a sloping floor such that when an egg is laid, it rolls down and easily comes out of the cage and get collected.

Sericulture

The rearing of silkworm for the production of silk is called sericulture. Sericulture is also called silk farming. Most widely used silkworm for sericulture is mulberry silkworm *Bombyx mori*.

Figure 7.18 Silkworms feeding on mulberry leaves

Life Cycle of Bombyx mori

Bombyx mori has a short life cycle consisting of four stages described as below.

Egg stage: The female silk moth lays eggs (thousands in number). These eggs are grown under suitable environment for growth. It takes about 14 days to hatch.

Larval stage: After hatching, larva comes out of the eggs. These larvae are then placed on the mulberry leaves which are specifically cultivated for this purpose. The larvae feed on mulberry leaves.

Pupal stage: After five weeks of eating mulberry leaves, larva climbs a twig of the tree and starts spinning cocoon. Larvae secrete saliva that contains liquid form of the fibre. Larvae spins large amount of fibre around themselves forming cocoons. Inside cocoons, larvae undergo changes to form pupa.

Adult stage: Pupa grows inside the cocoon and undergoes changes. It breaks open the cocoon and emerges as an adult moth. The adult silk moths mate, lay eggs and die within a few days.

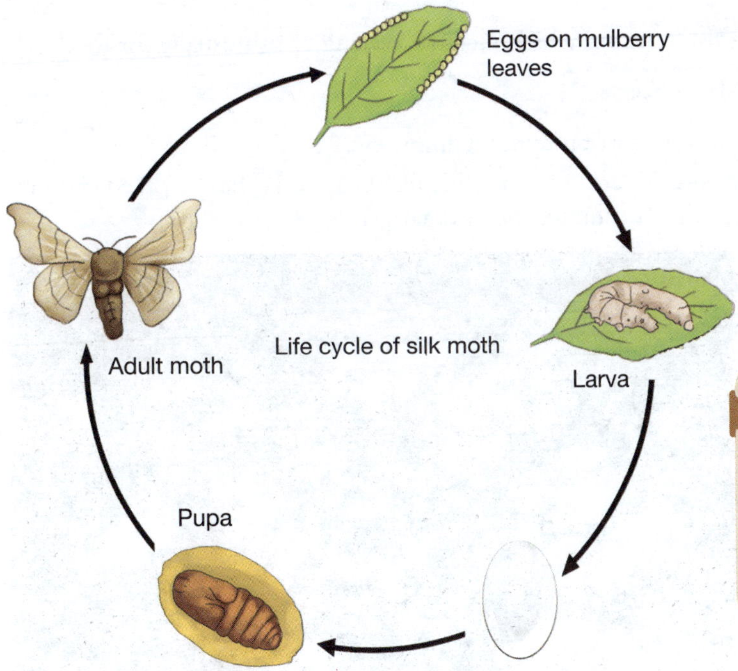

Figure 7.19 Life cycle of silk moth

Info Bytes!

Even though they're so tiny, silkworms can get sick. Some silkworm diseases can reduce silk production by up to 50%.

Production of Silk

Cocoons are harvested within 10 days from pupal stage before the pupa emerges. Cocoons are then put in boiling water. Pupa are killed by boiling water and the silk fibres are loosened. These fibres are then spun into silk threads. Each silk fibre processed from one cocoon produces a filament.

Apiculture

Rearing of honey bees for the production of honey and bee wax is called apiculture. Honey is a sweet, edible fluid that has important medicinal values. It contains sugars, minerals, viamins, etc. Similarly, bee wax is of great industrial importance. It has been used in many cosmetics, ointments, furniture, polishes, etc.

Figure 7.20 Working bees on a honeycomb

Pisciculture

Pisciculture is also known as fish farming which includes rearing of fish usually for food.

There are many uses of fish such as:

- **Food:** It is an excellent source of protein, vitamins, etc.
- **For controlling diseases:** There are some fish like Gambusia that can feed on mosquito larvae, thereby help in controlling disease spread by mosquito, such as malaria.

Figure 7.21 Fishes underwater in a fish farm

Animal Breeding

The term 'breed' refers to a group of animals that are similar in most characters, such as appearance, features, size, etc. Producing improved breeds of domesticated animals is called animal breeding. The factors that are mainly considered for animal breeding are:

- Increased yield of products, such as milk, meat, egg, wool, etc.
- Increased quality of products.
- Increased resistance of animals to diseases.

Animal breeding involves artificially selecting animals of superior quality and allowing them to mate to produce progeny with improved quality.

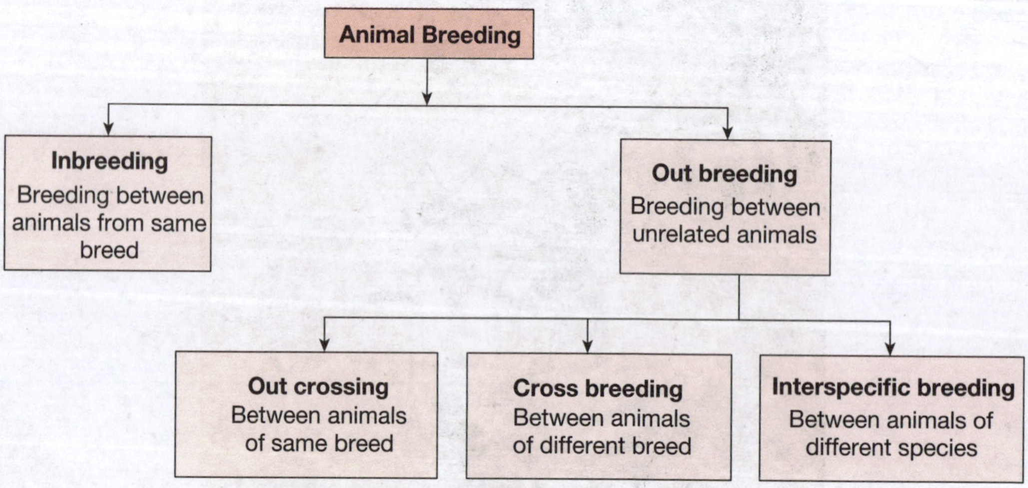

Figure 7.22 Branches under animal breeding

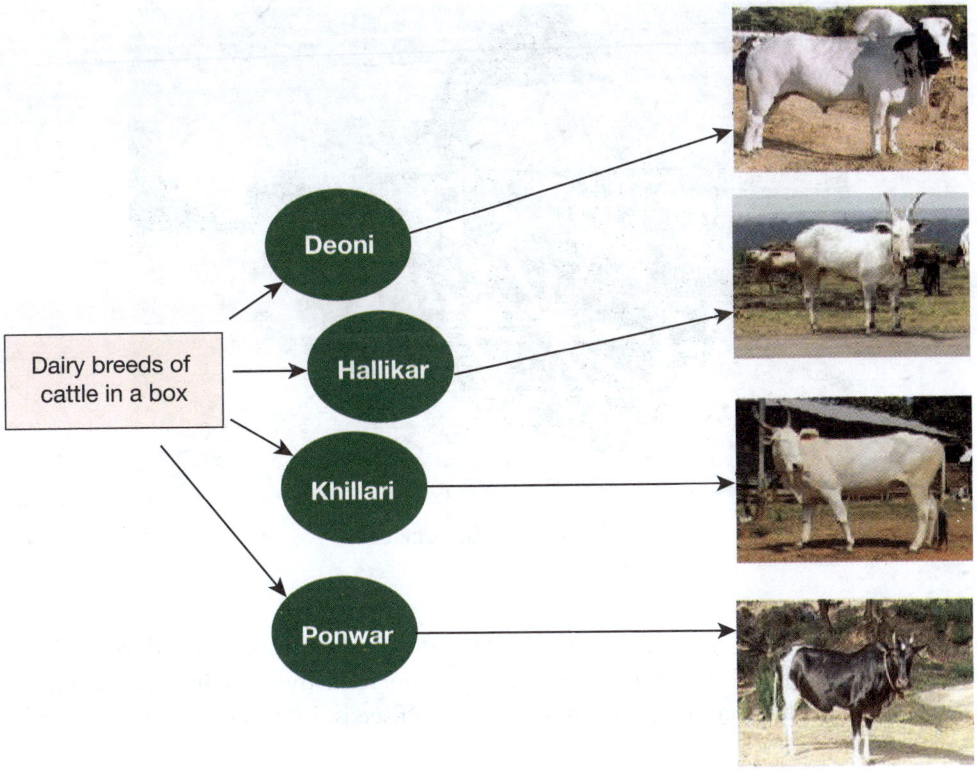

Figure 7.23 Indigenous dairy breeds of cattle

Animal breeding can be done in various ways:

- **Inbreeding:** Involves mating of superior animals that are from the same breed, for example, in case of cattle, superior female that can yield more milk can be mated with superior male from the same breed to get progeny that has qualities of both parents.
- **Outbreeding:** Outbreeding involves breeding between unrelated animals.

Outbreeding is of three types:

1. **Outcrossing:** Breeding between unrelated animals of the same breed.
2. **Crossbreeding:** Breeding between animals of different breeds.
3. **Interspecific breeding:** Breeding between animals of different species.

Draught Animals

Draught animals are the ones that are used to carry heavy burden or pull vehicles. For example, horses, bullock, donkeys, camels, etc. These animals carry and transport people/goods from one place to another.

- Elephants are used to transport heavy items like logs of wood.
- Donkeys and camels are used for pulling carts.
- Bullocks are also used for ploughing in agricultural field.
- Horses are also used for riding for recreational purposes

Figure 7.24 Bullock cart

Green Revolution

Green revolution refers to increased agricultural production worldwide through the development of technologies, beginning most markedly in the late 1960's. Norman Borlaug, who took the initiative, is known as 'Father of Green Revolution.' It involved the introduction of high yielding varieties of seeds, increased use of fertilizers, etc.

Animal Diseases

As humans, animals are also prone to illness and diseases caused by a number of reasons. Some of the major diseases are discussed below.

Livestock Diseases

There are various common diseases which cattle suffer from. Some of them are given below.

Disease	Symptom
Anthrax	High fever, swelling of body parts; this disease is highly infectious
Cowpox	Appearance of nodules on skin
Rinderpest	Discharge from eyes and nostrils
Foot-and-mouth disease	Blisters on mouth and feet
Black quarter	Fever, loss of appetite, difficult breathing

Poultry Diseases

The most common diseases that birds suffer from are Fowl pox and Ranikhet disease. Virus H5N1 causes avian flu and sometimes the infection passes to humans.

Silkworm Diseases

The most common disease affecting silkworms is Pebrine disease (also called pepper disease). It is caused by *Nosema bombycis* (a protozoan). Affected larvae have dots on their body and are unable to produce silk fibre. This disease mainly occurs during rainy and winter season.

Honeybee Diseases

Common diseases affecting honeybees are:

- **American Foulbrood:** It is caused by bacterium *Paenibacillus* larvae. The bacteria infects the larvae which die before becoming adults.
- **European Foulbrood:** It is caused by the bacterium *Melissococcusplutonius*.
- **Chalk Brood:** It is caused by fungus, *Ascosphaeraapis*. This disease is most prevalent in spring during which brood area is expanding

Fish Diseases

Poor quality of water and low oxygen content cause diseases in fish. For example, Whirling disease of salmons caused by *Myxobolus cerebralis*.

Info Bytes!

Run-offs of fertilizers deplete oxygen dissolved in water thereby increasing the ammonia content. As a result, fish do not get enough oxygen and their gills turn purplish. This is called ammonia poisoning.

Useful Microorganisms

There are certain microorganisms which are used for manufacture or processing of different food items. There are many species of algae, bacteria and fungi which are commonly used in food industry. We shall take a look at how food production and management is done with the help of these organisms.

Algae

There are certain genera of algae which are used in cultivation and production of different food products.

Algae are a rich source of vitamins and minerals, which makes them suitable as nutritional supplements. Some species of genus *Chlorella* have more vitamins than many cultivated plants. Members of the genus *Spirulina* are rich in β-carotene vitamin B12. Hence, these genrera are used as nutritive supplements. Algae are also used as a source of natural colours. Pigments, such as chlorophylls, carotenoids and phycobiliproteins, found in algae are used as natural colourant in food industry.

Agar, obtained from red algae, is a jelly-like substance used as a medium of growth in laboratories to grow a number of microorganisms.

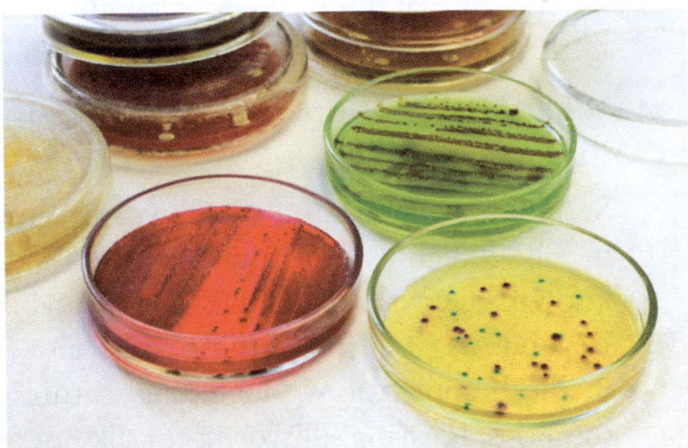

Figure 7.25 Bacteria grown on agar medium in laboratory

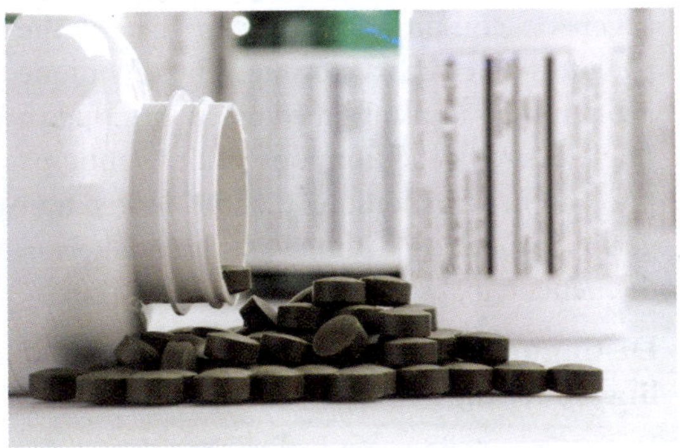

Figure 7.26 *Chlorella* tablets

Fungi

Various species of fungi are used in processing of food products. The most commonly used fungus is Baker's yeast, a unicellular fungus, that is used to make wheat-based products like bread. Yeasts are also used in making wine and beer by the process of fermentation. Different varieties of cheese are produced using different species of fungi. Members of the genus *Aspergillus niger* are used in production of citric acid. Fungi like mushrooms are eaten as food as they are rich in nutrients.

Figure 7.27 Bakers' yeast is used in production of bread

Figure 7.28 *Armillaria mellea*—edible mushroom

Bacteria

There are many bacteria that are used to process cheese, coffee and tobacco. *Acetobacter aceti* is used in production of vinegar. Members of the genus *Lactobacillus* are used in production of milk and yogurt.

Info Bytes!

The oldest known bread, discovered in Jordan, was made with wild yeast about 14,400 years ago.

Quick Recap

✔ **Explain the importance of back-crossing in hybridization.**

The process of crossing a hybrid plant with one of its parents or an organism genetically similar to the parent, to achieve offspring with a genetic constitution closer to that of the parent, is called back-crossing. This technique is often used in plant breeding to introduce a single desired gene from one plant's genotype into another. This ensures that the desired trait gets incorporated without drastically altering the genetic makeup of the desired cultivar.

✔ **Distinguish between inbreeding and line-breeding.**

Both inbreeding and line-breeding are methods used in animal breeding to increase homogeneity in genetic makeup. Inbreeding refers to the mating of closely-related animals, often siblings or parent-offspring. While this can help in solidifying certain desired traits, it also risks amplifying genetic defects. Line-breeding, on the other hand, is a milder form of inbreeding, often involving distant relatives. It aims to maintain a high genetic relationship to an outstanding ancestor without the immediate mating of close relatives.

✔ **What is sericulture and why is it important?**

Sericulture (cultivation of silkworms) results in silk which is a natural protein fibre, is known for its shine, softness, and durability. Beyond its use in clothing, silk also has medical applications, including sutures in surgeries. Rearing silkworms for silk not only contribute to the textile industry but also provides employment opportunities in rural areas, supporting livelihoods and boosting economies.

POINTS TO REMEMBER

- ✔ Agriculture is the practice of production of food, fibre and other commercial crops.
- ✔ There are three types of crops based on the type of season they are grown in, viz., Kharif, Rabi and Zaid.
- ✔ There are a number of steps involved in agricultural practice starting from ploughing, sowing, addition of manure and fertilizer, irrigation, weeding to harvesting and storage of cultivated crops.
- ✔ Techniques like hybridization and genetic engineering have increased the crop yield manifolds and made some varieties disease resistant.
- ✔ Animal husbandry is the branch of agriculture dealing with rearing and maintenance of animals for their products.
- ✔ Animal husbandry includes sericulture, apiculture, pisciculture, poultry farming and dairy farming.
- ✔ Animal breeding involves artificial selection of animals of superior characters and their mating for increasing yield and quality of products obtained from them.
- ✔ Inbreeding and outbreeding are the two types of animal breeding.

PRACTICE QUESTIONS CLASSROOM WING

Very Short Answer Type Questions

Directions for questions from 1 to 10:
Fill in the blanks in each question.

1. Zaid crops are grown in ________ season.
2. The bacterium that is capable of performing nitrogen fixation is ________.
3. One of the advantages of ploughing is that it promotes the growth of decomposers like ________ and ________, which assist in the decomposition of organic wastes.
4. Animal husbandry encompasses dairy farming, poultry, and ________ which deals with rearing of fish.
5. The rearing of silkworm primarily for the production of silk is termed as ________.
6. The process by which two different plant varieties are crossed to obtain a progeny with the desired traits is called ________.
7. Livestock, which includes animals like cows and sheep, are domesticated mainly for products like milk, meat, and ________.
8. Sericulture is also called ________.
9. Breeding between animals of same breed is called ________.
10. Domesticated animals for commercial purposes are called ________.

Directions for questions from 11 to 23:
For each of the following questions, four choices have been provided. Select the correct alternative.

11. Which of the following is NOT an advantage of ploughing?
 (a) Helps in removing weeds
 (b) Allows crops to grow without sunlight
 (c) Brings nutrient-rich soil to the top layer
 (d) Enhances the growth of beneficial soil organisms like earthworms

12. Which among these methods involves growing seeds in a nursery first before transplanting them to the main field?
 (a) Broadcasting (b) Drilling
 (c) Transplanting (d) Use of traditional tool

13. The main difference between manures and fertilizers is
 (a) Manures are always chemically synthesized while fertilizers are organic.
 (b) Manures supply specific types of nutrients while fertilizers supply all primary nutrients.
 (c) Manures have a positive effect on soil fertility, while prolonged use of fertilizers can reduce soil fertility.
 (d) Manures and fertilizers have the same impact on soil fertility.

14. What advantage does hybridization serve in plant improvement?
 (a) It ensures plants are similar to their parents.
 (b) It combines qualities of two parent plants.
 (c) It reduces the growth rate of plants.
 (d) It ensures only one parent's quality is passed on.

15. Match the following

(A) 2,4, D	(i) Organic matter
(B) Manure	(ii) Transplantation
(C) NPK	(iii) Fertilizer
(D) Sowing	(iv) Weedicide

	A	B	C	D
(a)	i	ii	iii	iv
(b)	iv	ii	i	iii
(c)	i	iv	ii	iii
(d)	iv	i	iii	ii

16. Which one of the following is not a rabi crop?
 (a) Maize (b) Wheat
 (c) Linseed (d) Mustard

17. Identify the wrong statement.
 (a) Fertilizers add humus to the soil.
 (b) Manure provides all primary nutrients.
 (c) Long-term use of fertilizer reduces soil fertility.
 (d) Crop rotation avoids depletion of a particular nutrient from the soil.

18. In ________ irrigation water falls drops by drop at the position of roots.
 (a) Surface (b) Drip
 (c) Sprinkler (d) Manual

19. NPK is an example of
    (a) Weedicide (b) Manure
    (c) Fertilizer (d) Insecticide

20. Leaving the land uncultivated for one or more seasons is called
    (a) Crop rotation (b) Inter cropping
    (c) Field fallowing (d) Both (a) and (b)

21. **Assertion (A):** Maize is a kharif crop
    Reason (R): Maize is grown in rainy season
    (a) Both A and R are true and R is the correct explanation for A.
    (b) Both A and R are true and R is the not the correct explanation for A.
    (c) A is true and R is false
    (d) A is false and R is true

22. **Assertion (A):** Legumes revive the soil fertility.
    Reason (R): Microbes in the root nodules of legumes fix the atmospheric nitrogen.
    (a) Both A and R are true and R is the correct explanation for A.
    (b) Both A and R are true and R is the not the correct explanation for A.
    (c) A is true and R is false
    (d) A is false and R is true

23. **Assertion (A):** Grains should be dried properly before storing.
    Reason (R): Moisture content increases the chances of spoilage due to micro-organisms.
    (a) Both A and R are true and R is the correct explanation for A.
    (b) Both A and R are true and R is the not the correct explanation for A.
    (c) A is true and R is false
    (d) A is false and R is true

Short Answer Type Questions

24. What is the significance of practicing crop rotation and how does it benefit soil health?
25. How do the roles of broilers and egg-layers differ in poultry farming?
26. Differentiate between rabi and zaid crops with one example.
27. What does it mean by mixed cropping?
28. Differentiate between manures and fertilizers.
29. Write a note on sprinkler irrigation.
30. What are the main factors that affect the yield in poultry farming?
31. Compare between the various outbreeding methods.
32. Write about the significance of pisciculture.

Essay Type Questions

33. Write which one is the best method for sowing and give reason.
    (a) Broadcasting (b) Drilling
34. Growing different crops alternatively can increase the yield. Justify the statement.
35. Discuss the various agricultural practices mentioned in the chapter and explain their significance in ensuring a successful harvest.
36. (a) Describe the various methods to increase the yield in dairy farming.
    (b) What is animal breeding and what is its importance?

PRACTICE QUESTIONS COMPETITION WING

Level 1: Apply your Concepts

Directions for questions from 1 to 5:
Fill in the blanks in each question.

1. Mustard is a ________ crop.

2. Scattering the seeds by hand is called ________.

3. Organic matter formed by the decomposition of plant wastes is called ________.

4. The most efficient method of irrigation is ________.

5. The tool used to break soil crumbs is ________.

Level 2: Review your Concepts

6. Describe any one method that can increase the crop yield.

7. What kind of precautions should be taken to avoid loss during storage of grains?

8. Maintenance of proper hygiene and health can increase the yield in animal husbandry. Justify the statement.

9. Why are broilers fed protein-rich diet?

10. Generally, wheat and leguminous plants could be cultivated alternatively. Why?

11. How can water waste be minimized during irrigating the field?

Level 3: Assess Your Concepts

12. Why our dried neem leaves or turmeric added to grains stored in jute bags?

13. Why is rice grown in the period from July to October?

AT

PRACTICE QUESTIONS NEET SPECIAL WING

Multiple-Answer Type Questions

Questions number 1 to 5 are multiple-choice questions. Each question has FOUR options (a), (b), (c), and (d). ONE OR MORE THAN ONE of these four option(s) is/are the correct answer(s).

1. The process of ploughing:
   (a) helps in removing unwanted herbs and weeds
   (b) helps in bringing nutritious soil to the top
   (c) helps to decrease the growth of microbes and earthworms
   (d) helps the roots to penetrate deeper into the soil

2. Which of the following are not methods of sowing?
   (a) Manual removal
   (b) Drilling
   (c) Field fallowing
   (d) Transplanting

3. Methods which can be employed to increase milk yield in cows are:
   (a) Selection of good quality breed
   (b) Selection of breed with disease resistance
   (c) Breeds are given feed rich in lactation inducing nutrients
   (d) Maintenance of proper hygiene and disease resistance

4. Which of the following are types of outbreeding?
   (a) Outcrossing
   (b) Crossbreeding
   (c) Testcrossing
   (d) Interspecific breeding

5. The diseases which affect honeybees include:
   (a) Pebrine disease
   (b) Ranikhet disease
   (c) American Foulbrood
   (d) Chalk Brood

Comprehension-Based Questions

A. Read the paragraph given below and answer the questions number 6 to 11:

Animal husbandry involves rearing of animals to reap economic benefits. This includes domesticated animals like cow, sheep, etc. and they are called as livestock. Products that are usually obtained include dairy products, meat, wool, etc. These animals can also be used to control weed growth or can be used as labour on fields. Rearing of animals like cows, sheep, buffaloes and goats for milk and milk products is called dairy farming. Domestication of birds for their products is called poultry farming. Animal husbandry also includes rearing of silkworms for silk and rearing of honey bees for honey and bees wax. Pisciculture involves rearing of fishes for food production. Animal breeding is carried out to get better quality of animals to get better yield as well as disease resistant varieties. Livestock need to be protected from diseases just like humans.

6. Gambusia fish help control disease spread by mosquitoes by:
   (a) feeding on mosquito eggs
   (b) feeding on mulberry leaves
   (c) feeding on pupa
   (d) feeding on mosquito larvae

7. Larvae of silkworms spin large amounts of fibre around themselves to form:
   (a) Coccyx
   (b) Cochlea
   (c) Cocoon
   (d) Choroid

8. Indigenous breeds of cattle include:
   (a) Deoni
   (b) Jersey
   (c) Catla
   (d) Roha

9. Increased agricultural production lead to:
   (a) White revolution
   (b) Green revolution
   (c) Red revolution
   (d) Yellow revolution

10. Ascosphaeraapis is a:
   (a) Protozoa
   (b) Algae
   (c) Bacteria
   (d) Fungus

11. Match the following:

Column – A	Column – B
(i) Avian flu	(a) Causes a bacterial disease in honey bees
(ii) Black quarter	(b) Disease in Salmons
(iii) *Nosema bombycis*	(c) Virus H5N1
(iv) European Foulbrood	(d) Causes disease in silkworm
(v) Whirling disease	(e) Livestock disease

B. Read the paragraph given below and answer the questions number 12 to 17:

Various agricultural practices are carried out to ensure optimum yield and better variety of crops. The first step is the preparation of soil. The soil is loosened and overturned with the help of ploughing. The second step is sowing of seeds which can be done manually or with the help of some tools. Further for better growth of crops manure or fertilisers rich in the NPK minerals are added to the soil depending on the requirement of the crops. Water is supplied to the growing crops at regular intervals is called irrigation. For better growth of crops unwanted plants need to be removed by the process known as weeding. After the crops are matured, they are harvested and separation of grains is done by threshing and winnowing. After these processes, grains are stored in large granaries, there they are protected from insects, pests, rats as well as microorganisms.

12. The most efficient method of providing crops with water during scarcity.
   (a) Surface irrigation
   (b) Drip irrigation
   (c) Sprinkler irrigation
   (d) Both a and b

13. Keeping the land uncultivated for a season or two to replenish the nutrients is called:
   (a) Crop rotation
   (b) Mixed cropping
   (c) Field fallowing
   (d) Hybridisation

14. The minerals found in cow dung include:
   (a) Nitrogen, phosphorus, Sulphur
   (b) Nitrogen, Sulphur, Phosphorous
   (c) Natrium, phosphorus, potassium
   (d) Nitrogen, Phosphorous, Potassium

15. Cultivator is a tool for:
   (a) Ploughing
   (b) Sowing
   (c) Weeding
   (d) Threshing

16. Addition of fertilizers and manure comes after which step for cultivation of crop?
   (a) Storage
   (b) Weeding
   (c) Irrigation
   (d) Sowing

17. Match the following:

Column – A	Column – B
(i) Turmeric	(a) Small scale storage of crops
(ii) Silos	(b) Separation of chaff from grains
(iii) Winnowing	(c) Large scale storage of crops
(iv) 2, 4 - D	(d) Natural insect repellent
(v) Metallic bins	(e) Weedicide

ANSWER KEYS

Crossword

Across

3. Agar **7.** Mulberry **9.** Norman Borlaug **11.** Broilers **13.** Broadcasting

Down

1. Manure **2.** Irrigation **4.** Granaries **5.** Ploughing **6.** Hybridization
8. Sericulture **10.** *Spirulina* **12.** Kharif

Classroom Wing

Very Short Answer Type Questions

1. Summer season **2.** Rhizobium **3.** Microbes, earthworms **4.** Aquaculture
5. Sericulture **6.** Hybridization **7.** Wool **8.** Silk farming **9.** Inbreeding
10. Livestock **11.** (b) **12.** (c) **13.** (c) **14.** (b) **15.** (d)
16. (a) **17.** (a) **18.** (b) **19.** (c) **20.** (c) **21.** (a)
22. (b) **23.** (a)

Competition Wing

Level 1: Apply your Concepts

1. Rabi **2.** Broadcasting **3.** Manure **4.** Drip irrigation **5.** Plank

NEET Special Wing

Multiple-Answer Type Questions

1. (b, d) **2.** (a, c) **3.** (a, b, c, d) **4.** (a, b, d) **5.** (c, d)

Comprehension-Based Questions

6. (d) **7.** (c) **8.** (a) **9.** (b) **10.** (d)
11. (i) → (c); (ii) → (e); (iii) → (d); (iv) → (a); (v) → (b)
12. (b) **13.** (c) **14.** (d) **15.** (a) **16.** (d)
17. (i) → (d); (ii) → (c); (iii) → (b); (iv) → (e); (v) → (a)

Hints and Explanations

CLASSROOM WING

Short Answer Type Questions

24. Crop rotation involves alternating different crops on the same piece of land. This practice benefits soil health by preventing the depletion of specific nutrients. For instance, wheat requires more nitrogen, which can be naturally replenished by growing leguminous plants, like beans, in the subsequent season. These leguminous plants harbor bacteria like *Rhizobium* in their root nodules, which fix atmospheric nitrogen into the soil, enhancing its nitrogen content.

25. In poultry farming, broilers are chickens raised specifically for their meat. They are provided with a protein-rich diet and reared in well-maintained conditions. Egg-layers, on the other hand, are chickens raised for their eggs, bred in individual cages, and are fed primarily on wheat and other mashed cereals.

26.

Rabi crops	Zaid crops
Winter crops	Summer crops
Grown in winter season	Grown in summer season
Planted in October	Planted in March
Harvested in March	Harvested in June
For example, wheat, linseed, mustard, etc.	For example, watermelon, musk melon, etc.

27. Planting two or more crops simultaneously on the same piece of land is called mixed cropping. Mixed cropping allows the crops to work together, for example, cotton and groundnut can be grown together for better yield.

28. Manure is the organic matter formed by the decomposition of plants and animal wastes whereas fertilizers are industrially produced chemicals. The main differences are given below:

Manures	Fertilizers
Plant or animal origin	Chemically synthesized
Organic in nature	Inorganic in nature
Natural product	Artificial product
Supply all primary nutrients	Supply specific types of nutrients
Improve soil properties	Have negative effect on soil and reduce soil fertility

29. It consists of a main pipe to which many pipes with rotating nozzles on top are attached. The nozzles rotate at regular intervals. When pressurized water flows through the main pipe, it escapes through the nozzles. Due to this, the water sprinkles on the crops and it seems as if it is raining. Sprinkled irrigation is helpful on uneven land and sandy soil.

30. Factors that affect yield in poultry farming are:
    - Selection of disease-free breeds
    - Proper and safe farm conditions
    - Proper feed and water
    - Maintenance of proper hygiene and health of farm birds

31. Breeding between unrelated animals is called outbreeding. It can be done in three ways: Outcrossing, crossbreeding and interspecific breeding.

Outcrossing	Crossbreeding	Interspecific breeding
Breeding between animals of same breed	Breeding between animals of different breeds	Breeding between animals of different species

32. Rearing of fish or fish farming is called pisciculture. It is mainly done for two purposes:
    - Food – as they are excellent source of protein, vitamin, etc.
    - Farming of fish such as Gambusia is also done as it can feed on mosquito larva and thus can control diseases spread by mosquitoes.

Essay Type Questions

33. Sowing using seed drill is more appropriate as it helps in planting the seeds in uniform depth and distance. Sowing seeds at uniform distance prevents overcrowding and sowing seeds at appropriate depth reduces the damage caused by birds.

34. Growing different crops alternatively on a piece of land is called crop rotation. For example, wheat and leguminous plants could be cultivated alternatively for higher yield. Wheat requires more nitrogen from the soil. Nitrogen can be replenished naturally by cultivating legume in the next season. Leguminous plants contain a bacterium called '*Rhizobium*' which is located in the root nodules. These bacteria are capable of fixing atmospheric nitrogen into the soil thereby increasing the nitrogen content of the soil.

35. Agricultural practices are the systematic steps taken to successfully cultivate and harvest crops. They begin with ploughing, which loosens the soil to make it more conducive to plant growth and improve nutrient absorption. It also makes weed removal easier and promotes the growth of beneficial organisms. Sowing is the act of planting seeds, and it is critical to use high-quality seeds and plant them at the proper depths and distances for maximum yield. Manures and fertilisers are used to supplement the nutrients in the soil. Manures are organic and improve soil properties, whereas fertilisers provide specific nutrients but can harm the soil if used excessively. Irrigation practices such as surface irrigation, drip irrigation, and sprinkler irrigation are used to ensure that plants receive adequate water. Weeding is necessary to remove unwanted plants that compete for nutrients with crops. Harvesting marks the end of the growing season by collecting mature crops and separating useful parts such as grains. After harvest, proper storage practices protect the grains from pests and environmental factors. Each of these practises is critical to a successful harvest, and their combined application results in optimal crop yield and quality.

36. (a) Management of animals for milk and milk products is called dairy farming. The animals that are mainly domesticated are—cows, sheeps, buffaloes and goats.

The yield can be increased by the following methods:

- Select good quality breed.
- Select breed with disease resistance.
- Take good care of the farm animals by maintaining proper hygiene and by providing them with good feed.
- Maintain proper hygiene while milking, storage and transport of the milk and its products.
- Regular visits by veterinary doctor.

(b) Producing improved breeds of domesticated animals are called animal breeding. Animal breeding is done to develop improved animal varieties that have superior qualities, such as disease resistance, improved yield, improved product quality, etc.

COMPETITION WING

Level 2: Review your Concepts

6. Crop rotation is a method for naturally replenishing nutrients in the soil. It involves growing different crops alternatively.

   For example, wheat and leguminous plants could be cultivated alternatively for higher yield. Wheat requires more nitrogen from the soil. Nitrogen can be replenished naturally by cultivating legume in the next season. Leguminous plants contain a bacterium called *Rhizobium* which is located in the root nodules. These bacteria are capable of fixing atmospheric nitrogen into the soil thereby increasing the nitrogen content of the soil.

7. Storage of grains after harvesting is of great importance as it will affect the yield. If the grains are not stored properly, there is a chance of their loss due to attack by insects, pests, rats or microorganisms. Before storing, grains should be dried properly in the sunlight to reduce moisture content. If freshly harvested grains are stored without drying, they may get spoilt or attacked by microorganisms losing their germination capacity. Insecticides are also utilized to repel insects while storing. Chemical insecticides are used while storing grains in silos or granaries. Insecticides of biological origin such as turmeric or neem leaves can be used in small-scale storages, such as storage in jute bags or metallic bins. Suitable temperature and hygienic conditions are also maintained in storage areas.

8. Maintenance of proper hygiene will help to keep the animals healthy and disease free. It will help to reduce mortality rate. Proper hygiene in the housing, product transport facilities, etc. will in turn increase the quality of products.

9. Broilers are raised for meat production. Hence, they are given protein-rich diet so that they are grown healthy. They are grown to suitable health and size to produce a quality product for the consumers.

10. Wheat and leguminous plants could be cultivated alternatively for higher yield. Wheat requires more nitrogen from the soil. Nitrogen can be replenished naturally by cultivating legume in the next season. Leguminous plants contain a bacterium called *Rhizobium* which is located in the root nodules. These bacteria are capable of fixing atmospheric nitrogen into the soil thereby increasing the nitrogen content of the soil.

11. Water waste can be minimized during irrigating the field by drip irrigation. Water falls drop-by-drop at the position of roots. This can be the most efficient method of irrigation in regions with water scarcity. Water wastage is minimized by utilizing this method.

Level 3: Assess Your Concepts

12. Dried neem leaves or turmeric can be used to repel insects, pests, etc., which could harm the stored grains.

13. To grow under optimal condition, rice requires rainy season. As it is a Kharif crop, it is rice grown in the period from July to October.

NEET SPECIAL WING

Multiple-Answer Type Questions

1. This is the first step in agricultural practices, which includes preparation of soil before sowing. Ploughing is done to turn or loosen the soil and bring nutritious soil to the top. It also helps the roots to penetrate deeper into the soil
2. There are various methods of sowing seeds like broadcasting, drilling, transplanting and using funnel shaped tools. Manual removal is a method of weeding and field fallowing is a natural method to increase fertility of the soil.
3. Various methods can be employed to increase milk yield such as-Selection of good quality breed, selection of breed with disease resistance, breeds are given feed rich in lactation inducing nutrients and maintenance of proper hygiene and disease resistance
4. Outbreeding is of three types- Outcrossing is breeding between unrelated animals of the same breed; Crossbreeding is breeding between animals of different breeds and Interspecific breeding is breeding between animals of different species.
5. Common diseases that affect honey bees include American Foulbrood which is a bacterial disease that affects the larvae. Chalk Brood is a fungal disease.

Comprehension-Based Questions

A.

6. Pisciculture is also carried out for disease control. Some fish like Gambusia that can feed on mosquito larvae, thereby help in controlling disease spread by mosquito, such as malaria.
7. After five weeks of eating mulberry leaves, larva climbs a twig of the tree. Larvae secrete saliva that contains liquid form of the fibre. Larvae spins large amount of fibre around themselves forming cocoons.
8. The indigenous breeds of cattle include Deoni, Hallikar, Khillari, Ponwar, etc.
9. Green revolution refers to increased agricultural production worldwide through the development of technologies, beginning most markedly in the late 1960's. Norman Borlaug, who took the initiative, is known as 'Father of Green Revolution.' It involved the introduction of high yielding varieties of seeds, increased use of fertilizers, etc.
10. ***Ascosphaeraapis*** is a fungus which causes the disease Chalk brood in honey bees.
11. Match the following:
    Avian flu is caused by the virus H5N1 and is a common poultry disease.
    (i) (c)

    Black quarter is a livestock disease which causes fever, loss of appetite and difficulty in breathing.
    (ii) (e)

    Pebrine or pepper disease is a common disease affecting silk worms. It is caused by Nosema
    Bombycis -a protozoan.
    (iii) (d)

    European Foulbrood is a disease usually seen in honey bees and is caused by the bacterium ***Melissococcusplutonius***
    (iv) (a)

    Poor quality of water and low oxygen content cause diseases in fish. For example, Whirling disease of salmons caused by ***Myxobolus cerebralis.***
    (v) (b)

B.

12. Drip irrigation is the method in which water falls drop by drop at the position of roots. This can be the most efficient method of irrigation in regions with water scarcity. Water wastage is minimized by utilizing this method.
13. Leaving the land uncultivated for one or more seasons is called field fallowing. This helps the soil to replenish the nutrients on its own and helps to regain the fertility of the soil.
14. Cow dung consists of minerals like Nitrogen, Phosphorous, Potassium, etc. These are the macronutrients required by plants for their growth.
15. Cultivator is one of the instruments used for the process of ploughing which helps to loosen up the soil.
16. Addition of manure and fertilisers to the soil is done post sowing of the seeds.

17. Match the following:

Turmeric is used as a natural insect repellent during storage of grains.

(i) (d)

Silos are used for large scale storage of grains.

(ii) (c)

Separation of grains from chaff is called winnowing. It is done with the help of wind, the lighter particles of the chaff are blown away leaving the heavier grain particles falling down.

(iii) (b)

2,4-D is a chemical which is used as a weedicide.

(iv) (e)

Metallic bins are used to store grains on a small scale.

(v) (a)

Photo Credits

CHAPTER 1: CELL—THE BASIC UNIT OF LIFE

Page 1.3—Martin Shields/Alamy Stock Photo; **Page 1.3**—World History Archive/Alamy Stock Photo; **Page 1.4**—blickwinkel/Alamy Stock Photo; **Page 1.4**—WaterFrame/Alamy Stock Photo; **Page 1.4**—Melba Photo Agency/Alamy Stock Photo; **Page 1.4**—blickwinkel/Alamy Stock Photo; **Page 1.5**—Jose Luis Calvo. Shutterstock; **Page 1.5**—Friedrichsmeier/Alamy Stock Photo; **Page 1.6**—Sashkin. Shutterstock; **Page 1.6**—Science Photo Library/Alamy Stock Photo; **Page 1.6**—Jose Luis Calvo. Shutterstock; **Page 1.6**—BSIP SA/Alamy Stock Photo; **Page 1.7**—123rf.com **Page 1.7**—Sakurra. Shutterstock; **Page 1.8**—Kateryna Kon; **Page 1.9**—designua. 123rf.com; **Page 1.9**—blueringmedia. 123rf.com; **Page 1.10**—alila. 123rf.com; **Page 1.11**—alxhar (c) Shutterstock; **Page 1.12**—Tefi. Shutterstock; **Page 1.12**—mikrostoker. 123rf.com; **Page 1.13**—snapgalleria. 123rf.com; **Page 1.14**—designua. 123rf.com; **Page 1.15**—Tefi. Shutterstock; **Page 1.15**—Designua. Shutterstock; **Page 1.16**—snapgalleria. Shutterstock; **Page 1.17**—Alila Medical Media. Shutterstock; **Page 1.19**—Amit John. Pearson India Education Services Pvt. Ltd; **Page 1.20**—Oxford Designers & Illustrators Ltd. Pearson Education Ltd

CHAPTER 2: TISSUES AND BODY MOVEMENTS

Page 2.5—Honeyeyed. Shutterstock; **Page 2.6**—Power and Syred/Science Photo Library; **Page 2.6**—Mohd Suhail. Pearson India Education Services Pvt. Ltd; **Page 2.6**—Mohd Suhail. Pearson India Education Services Pvt. Ltd; **Page 2.7**—Valentina Moraru. Shutterstock; **Page 2.7**—Science History Images/Alamy Stock Photo; **Page 2.8**—Blamb; **Page 2.9**—Christopher Meade. Shutterstock; **Page 2.9**—Jose Luis Calvo. Shutterstock; **Page 2.9**—Oxford Designers & Illustrators Ltd. Pearson Education Ltd; **Page 2.10**—RomanenkoAlexey. Shutterstock; **Page 2.10**—Kateryna Kon. Shutterstock; **Page 2.10**—Anna Jurkovska. Shutterstock; **Page 2.11**—Designua. Shutterstock; **Page 2.11**—tonaquatic19. 123rf.com; **Page 2.11**—Designua. Shutterstock; **Page 2.11**—Jose Luis Calvo. Shutterstock; **Page 2.11**—Designua. Shutterstock; **Page 2.11**—Jose Luis Calvo. Shutterstock; **Page 2.12**—848740. Shutterstock; **Page 2.13**—Yurchanka Siarhei. Shutterstock; **Page 2.13**—Jubal Harshaw. Shutterstock; **Page 2.13**—royaltystockphoto.com. Shutterstock; **Page 2.14**—blickwinkel/Alamy Stock Photo; **Page 2.14**—Arvind Singh Negi/Red Reef Design Studio. Pearson India Education Services Pvt. Ltd; **Page 2.15**—elenabsl. Shutterstock; **Page 2.15**—Potapov Alexander. Shutterstock

CHAPTER 3: CLASSIFICATION OF LIVING ORGANISMS

Page 3.4—Maggy Meyer. Shutterstock; **Page 3.4**—Tatiana Frank. Shutterstock; **Page 3.8**—blueringmedia. 123rf.com; **Page 3.9**—Lebendkulturen.de. Shutterstock; **Page 3.9**—Lebendkulturen.de. Shutterstock; **Page 3.9**—Science Photo Library/Alamy Stock Photo; **Page 3.9**—Simon Baylis. Shutterstock; **Page 3.11**—Lebendkulturen.de. Shutterstock; **Page 3.11**—phs2121. 123rf.com; **Page**

3.11—John Foxx Collection. Imagestate; **Page 3.11**—Dancestrokes. Shutterstock; **Page 3.11**—Smile Fight. Shutterstock; **Page 3.12**—mychadre77. 123rf.com; **Page 3.12**—vapi. 123rf.com; **Page 3.12**—Kondratuk Aleksei. Shutterstock; **Page 3.12**—D. Kucharski K. Kucharska. Shutterstock; **Page 3.12**—Rattiya Thongdumhyu. Shutterstock; **Page 3.12**—123rf.com; **Page 3.13**—Aleksey Stemmer. Shutterstock; **Page 3.13**—Masalski Maksim. Shutterstock; **Page 3.13**—Juniors Bildarchiv GmbH/ Alamy Stock Photo; **Page 3.13**—Maximilian Weinzierl/Alamy Stock Photo; **Page 3.13**—brulove. Shutterstock; **Page 3.13**—Beth Swanson. Shutterstock; **Page 3.14**—Vlada Photo. Shutterstock; **Page 3.14**—Dirk Ercken. Shutterstock; **Page 3.14**—Jerry Lin. Shutterstock; **Page 3.14**—Cultura Creative (RF)/Alamy Stock Photo

CHAPTER 4: REPRODUCTION IN ANIMALS AND PLANTS

Page 4.5—Alila Medical Media. Shutterstock; **Page 4.6**—Macrovector. Shutterstock; **Page 4.6**—Double brain.Shutterstock; **Page 4.7**—587245. Shutterstock; **Page 4.8**—rendix_alextian. Shutterstock; **Page 4.10**—Sue McDonald. Shutterstock; **Page 4.10**—Vaida. Shutterstock; **Page 4.11**—HL Studios / Pearson Education Ltd; **Page 4.12**—HL Studios / Pearson Education Ltd; **Page 4.15**—My Life Graphic. Shutterstock; **Page 4.16**—Anne Kitzman. Shutterstock; **Page 4.16**—Madlen. Shutterstock; **Page 4.16**—123rf.com; **Page 4.17**—Mohd Suhail. Pearson India Education Services Pvt. Ltd; **Page 4.18**—123rf.com; **Page 4.18**—KentaStudio. Shutterstock; **Page 4.19**—Russell Kightley/Science Photo Library; **Page 4.21**—Brian A Jackson. Shutterstock; **Page 4.21**—Mohd Suhail. Pearson India Education Services Pvt. Ltd; **Page 4.22**—Bogdan Wankowicz. Shutterstock; **Page 4.22**—Bogdan Wankowicz. Shutterstock;

CHAPTER 5: MICROORGANISMS AND HUMAN HEALTH

Page 5.3—BSIP SA/Alamy Stock Photo; **Page 5.3**—Lightspring. Shutterstock; **Page 5.3**—Lightspring. Shutterstock; **Page 5.3**—age fotostock/Alamy Stock Photo; **Page 5.3**—blickwinkel/Alamy Stock Photo; **Page 5.5**—zigzagmtart. 123rf.com; **Page 5.5**—serezniy. 123rf.com; **Page 5.6**—Kelly Marken. Shutterstock; **Page 5.6**—Victoria 1. Shutterstock; **Page 5.8**—Designua. Shutterstock; **Page 5.8**—rob3000. 123rf.com; **Page 5.10**—Blaj Gabriel. Shutterstock; **Page 5.11**—ifong. Shutterstock

CHAPTER 6: ECOSYSTEM AND BIODIVERSITY

Page 6.4—Shivani Anshuk. Pearson India Education Services Pvt. Ltd; **Page 6.5**—Oxford Designers & Illustrators Ltd. Pearson Education Ltd; **Page 6.5**—HL Studios. Pearson Education Ltd; **Page 6.6**—426. Shutterstock; **Page 6.6**—majeczka. Shutterstock; **Page 6.6**—xtrekx. 123rf.com; **Page 6.6**—noomcpkstic. Shutterstock; **Page 6.7**—Rich Carey. Shutterstock; **Page 6.8**—HL Studios. Pearson Education Ltd; **Page 6.9**—Erik Mandre. Shutterstock; **Page 6.10**—Gunter Marx/Alamy Stock Photo; **Page 6.11**—lexaarts. Shutterstock; **Page 6.11**—Tupungato. Shutterstock; **Page 6.14**—Anna Kompanieitseva. Shutterstock; **Page 6.14**—Emjay Smith. Shutterstock; **Page 6.16**—123rf.com; **Page 6.16**—silentwings. Shutterstock; **Page 6.17**—anmbph. Shutterstock; **Page 6.17**—123rf.com; **Page 6.17**—YuryZap. Shutterstock; **Page 6.18**—blickwinkel/Alamy Stock Photo; **Page 6.19**—Aleksandr Denisyuk. Shutterstock; **Page 6.19**—Paul Goldstein. Imagestate; **Page 6.19**—123rf.com; **Page 6.19**—dnivrab. 123rf.com

CHAPTER 7: FOOD PRODUCTION AND MANAGEMENT

Page 7.3—123rf.com; **Page 7.3**—nata-lunata. Shutterstock; **Page 7.3**—ve_ro_sa. Shutterstock; **Page 7.5**—arogant. Shutterstock; **Page 7.5**—Sergey Galushko/Alamy Stock Photo; **Page 7.5**—Alexander Perepelitsyn/Alamy Stock Photo; **Page 7.5**—handsomepictures. Shutterstock; **Page 7.5**—Showcake. Shutterstock; **Page 7.5**—Muellek Josef. Shutterstockv; **Page 7.6**—Tish1. Shutterstock; **Page 7.7**—Tish1. Shutterstock; **Page 7.7**—Cornelia Pithart. Shutterstock; **Page 7.8**—123rf.com; **Page 7.8**—stigmatize. Shutterstock; **Page 7.9**—MattLphotography; **Page 7.6**—Andrea Izzotti. 123rf.com; **Page 7.11**—Dr. Morley Read. Shutterstock; **Page 7.11**—jovanjaric. 123rf.com; **Page 7.11**—macor. 123rf.com; **Page 7.12**—123rf.com; **Page 7.12**—YanLev. Shutterstock; **Page 7.12**—Visionsi. Shutterstock; **Page 7.12**—fuyu liu. Shutterstock; **Page 7.12**—Alexander Sayenko. Shutterstock; **Page 7.15**—Mohd Suhail. Pearson India Education Services Pvt. Ltd; **Page 7.15**—StudioSmart. Shutterstock; **Page 7.16**—Dr. Morley Read. Shutterstock; **Page 7.18**—123rf.com; **Page 7.19**—Fotofermer. Shutterstock; **Page 7.19**—monticello. Shutterstock; **Page 7.20**— Marie C Fields. Shutterstock; **Page 7.20**— dusanzidar. 123rf.com

SUPPLEMENT READING: SCOPE OF SCIENCE

Page xxii— Olivier Le Queinec. Shutterstock; **Page xxiii**— Tassh. Shutterstock;

